D0818905

Date Due

MAY 8 1973		
NOV 12 1973		
FEB 1975		
4:05		
8:15		
9:00		
10:30		
DEC 7 1984		
DEC 1 0 1988		
MAY 2 1991		
MAY 28 1991		
MAY 2 1993		
OCT 1 4 1993		
NOV 11		
DEC 2 0 1993		
JAN -2 1995		
JAN 2 1996		
APR 1 0 1996		
DEC 4 1996		

Environmental Qua

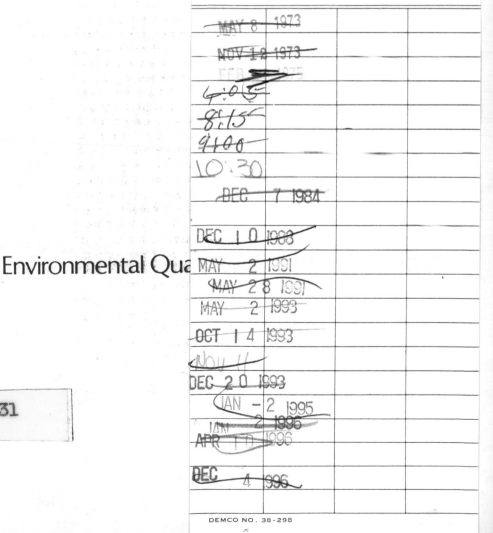

DEMCO NO. 38-298

Environmental Quality And Social Responsibility

Edited by
Ravindra S. Khare
James W. Kolka
Carol A. Pollis

University of Wisconsin–Green Bay
Green Bay, Wisconsin

Library of Congress Catalog Card Number: 79-185314.

© 1972, Regents of The University of Wisconsin

Cover design by Linda Chen.

Portions of this book may be reprinted and used in environmental workshops, seminars, and conferences with permission of the editors.

Preface

These proceedings are essentially a close transcription of the presentations and discussions that took place during the symposium, "Environmental Quality and Social Responsibility," held on April 22-23, 1971, at the Downtowner Motel, Green Bay, Wisconsin. Editing has been limited to improving the continuity and readability of the material; some portions of the panel discussions that were either less clear or colloquially phrased have been rewritten to go along with more formal presentations. Most of the panel speakers have availed themselves of the opportunity for revising their presentation for inclusion in this volume; they have added appropriate footnotes and references. The editors have undertaken the responsibility of arranging, collating, and listing the reference and bibliographic material in the text and at the end of the volume. A consistent style of citation and an alphabetical listing of all the references are provided to further facilitate the reading of the text.

The editors have also provided "overviews" at the end of each panel discussion and the banquet speech. Each such contribution is initialed by the editor writing it and he or she alone is responsible for any specific evaluations expressed in it. However, since the editors generally shared major approach and viewpoints, any divergency in their evaluations is academically fruitful. No attempt has been made to systematically present the overall conclusions that such a symposium might have reached because it is the assessment of the editors that the subject matter, at this stage of discussion, is best dealt with in an "open-ended" fashion. Much more spadework and preliminary analysis needs to be done across the field of study of natural and social environments before some more precise relationships can be hypothesized between them for pulling together the nebulous complexities represented by such a phrase as "environmental quality and social responsibility." Any *ad hoc* conceptual improvisation for such a diversity is bound to remain either too simplistic (hence an approximation of some cliche already in currency) or too remote to offer any accurate frame of reference to the problems implied by the topic.

If this issue indicates the necessity for generating some discussion that is beyond the symptomatic facets of the "environmental problem" which is so much in the air, and if the proceedings lead us to ask some more searching questions that now need to be asked, the purpose behind the effort will have been amply met.

Finally, on behalf of the faculty of the Modernization Processes Concentration of The University of Wisconsin—Green Bay, the editors would like to thank the co-sponsors for their financial suport and interest in this symposium: the Office of Communiversity Projects of this University, the Kimberly-Clark Corporation, and the Dow Chemical Company.

R.S.K.
J.W.K.
C.A.P.

Table of Contents

Introduction and Welcome

John R. Beaton

It is a pleasure to welcome our speakers, our discussants and our audience to this symposium, "Environmental Quality and Social Responsibility." As you will know from the program, the symposium is sponsored jointly by the Concentration in Modernization Processes of The University of Wisconsin—Green Bay, by Kimberly—Clark Corporation and by Dow Chemical Company. We are indebted to our co-sponsors not only for their financial support but also for their demonstrated concern with the problems to be discussed here during the next two days. We thank you.

This is the fifth major symposium or conference held at The University of Wisconsin—Green Bay in this academic year. As with previous symposia, this one is concerned with a major problem area and recognizes the environmental focus of our university. At UWGB we are concerned with the environment in all its broad aspects—physical, biological, social, economic and aesthetic; indeed, our academic plan, developed in a three-year period by many people and implemented since fall, 1969, was built upon environmental concerns. In this implementation we have followed the concept of an interdisciplinary approach to education in recognition of the observation that societal problems are neither caused nor solved by single disciplines working in isolation. If one reviews the program of this symposium, for example, it is apparent that a number of academic disciplines are required to look at a problem from the several required viewpoints.

I hope you will find the next two days to be enjoyable, instructive, and productive. I know that we will, and that your deliberations will benefit us greatly as we develop our programs of instruction, research, and community outreach at The University of Wisconsin—Green Bay. To our visitors from out of town, I extend an invitation to visit our campus while you are in Green Bay. To all of you, I say welcome to our university, to the symposium, and I thank you for joining us in this endeavor.

I will now call upon Dr. Ravindra Khare, Chairman of the Concentration in Modernization Processes, to introduce the subject matter of this symposium.

Purpose of the Conference

R. S. Khare

The purpose of this symposium on "Environmental Quality and Social Responsibility" is to focus our attention on some of those dimensions of society that somehow have been taken for granted in the context of science and technology and their impact on the environment. Normally, when we talk about the problem of "environmental quality," the industrial misuse of air, water, and land immediately comes to our attention. However, there is more to the problem than first meets the eye. The question that probably will run through all the presentations that follow will be: When we talk about the environmental problems of such a highly industrialized society as the United States, can we find complete answers to the problem at physical and technological levels alone? Or is it that the norms and values of the society are an equally important aspect of the problem? If machines change the society and the individual, it is the individual and the society that invent and employ machines according to certain systems of values and priorities.

Major points and aims of the conference are:

(a) It is to draw attention towards the social counterpart of the problem of environmental deterioration.

(b) It is to indicate that man, technology, and environment are mutually interdependent variables, and technology alone cannot resolve the problems to which it has given rise. Society, with its norms and values, provides us with a fundamental dimension that should be considered essential to any lasting solution devised at the levels of biological, physical, and technological sciences.

(c) Norms and values of such a society as the U. S. get profusely interconnected with technology at different levels (whether it is a car or a computer) and any enduring change in technology and the environment must involve a basic change in people's behavioral norms and values. Reordering of priorities must be achieved at different levels—whether it is within a family by a housewife, or by a governing board of a business corporation, or by a legislative group of a state or the federal government.

(d) The first lesson from the environmental crisis for such an industrialized nation as the U. S. is that technology and science cannot be considered independent of the human social context and, if the change of pace in one sector does not keep pace with the other one, distorted priorities and perspectives will always emerge.

(e) The second most important lesson is that science and technology produce effects which can be assessed either on a short-term or long-term basis. What we have learned is that since good short-term effects can turn out to be bad in the long run, we cannot any more afford to go only on the short-term basis. We cannot consider science-and-technology simply to be our handy "delivery boy," although it has been both efficient and effective in the short run. This "delivery boy" cannot be endlessly employed without appropriate forethought.

It is from the preceding that the themes and purposes emerge for the four panels of this conference. Each panel picks up a problem area in relation to the question of environmental quality, and examines a system of norms and values that may need to be changed.

PANEL I The panel picks up the familiar theme of production and consumption of goods and services—but with a change, by asking what is the aftermath of Mass Production and Mass Consumption? One answer familiar to us will be: more uniform availability of goods and services, or to put it in a nutshell, assured affluence. However, the other answer is: mass waste. Thus the contention here is that the priorities for and attitudes about "mass waste" have to be suitably changed. Waste is not necessarily useless, as we are rapidly finding out, provided that we have made appropriate adjustments in our attitudes toward waste and waste disposal practices. Industrial wastes, under this changed focus, can again become a high-priority raw material.

Our panelists, predominantly economists, will present a variety of perspectives bearing on the above theme.

PANEL II The panel on "Man vs. Nature" brings to our attention the points made above, but in a much wider context. The panel is organized on the issue that the man versus nature approach is opposed to man's biosocial survival and hence its continuation may result in many problems, one of which is environmental pollution. Thus, the question of imputing appropriate values to nature in relation to man and other living creatures immediately comes up. To view either nature against man or man against nature is to set a basically incorrect relationship because the two are inseparable except in a superficial, short-range perspective. We cannot afford to make such a mistake anymore, unless we would like to minimize the chances of human survival.

Our panelists include an engineer, a physician, a biologist, and an economist. The diversity of know-how is there and I am sure the topic of the panel demands such a wide ambient of inquiry and discussion.

PANEL III The panel on "Institutional Response to Technological Change" is aimed to draw our attention to the fact that when a highly industrialized society like the U. S. continues its journey towards technological advancement, the complexity of changes going on in its social institutions and organizations requires very careful attention. Again, environmental problems that seem to emerge in industries, factories, and cities do not appear independent of the shared systems of values and priorities that the families, neighborhoods, and communities hold. The economic notion of affluence, the environmental notion of the optimum, and the social scales of class and individual status, interrelate with one another, and they have to be so understood by those who intend to improve environmental quality. The simple premise for discussion is that unless the values and views developed within different institutions and organizations of the society are simultaneously changed in a coordinated manner, the drive to maintain or improve the quality of the environment will not be fully effective. It will not become a way of life. What families habitually do and communities daily aspire for, actually crucially count in a drive for environmental quality. While some specialists may study the ecological movement and dismiss it as a momentary social fad, others may see the birth of a silent but profound social revolution in modern man's civilization. Whatever the perspective, the individual and the collective, the part and the whole, must be attended to in relation to one another in this effort against environmental deterioration. Technology, society, and nature cannot anymore be considered independent of each other.

The panelists, again drawn from different disciplines like sociology, economics, political science, and anthropology, will discuss the above themes as they see them.

PANEL IV The last panel, like the first, focuses on a more specific issue, particularly on the politics and law of pollution. When the government, the court, the industry, and the community organization intersect the domain of environmental quality, the question of preserving individual rights as well as the collective good becomes a most challenging but difficult task in a free society. Again, like man versus nature, the proposition, individual rights versus collective good, is wrongly conceived. No more can individual rights be disproportionately sacrificed for the collective, the corporate, the industrial, while the reverse also remains equally true. Accordingly, the industry, the government, the community, the law, and the individual must mutually dovetail their separate rights and collective responsibilities. Again here, the relationships of responsible balance are required, and they should neither be of confrontation nor of one sector unduly dominating the other. As is becoming increasingly evident in our current efforts against environmental deterioration, this now is a demand on us, and not merely an idealistic slogan. Technology will probably force us to accomplish those very social and political aims that we have orally espoused but have only half-heartedly practiced. The individual and the collective, with mutual responsibilities towards each other, will have to reach an arrangement which will, on a long-range basis, attend to the question of environmental quality.

The four panels of the symposium, therefore, represent four major constellations of social, economic, political and ecological values and activities. This symposium should help generate some discussion and thinking along the above, very simple but repeatedly proven, tendencies of change. Environmental problems, let me repeat, challenge the family, neighborhood, community, and nation to rearrange their priorities of day-to-day living and thinking. The task cannot be accomplished in any lesser way.

Finally, let me add a word on the program planned for you in our evening session when Professor Lee Rainwater of Harvard University will be speaking at the banquet. His topic, "The Urban Social Environment: Problems of Affluence, Membership and Security," converges many of the crucial issues discussed and implied during the four panel sessions of the symposium.

PART 1

Mass Production,
Mass Consumption,
Mass Waste

Breakdowns in Society's Metabolism

Michael F. Brewer

I feel not only welcome, but also at home here, although this is my first trip to Green Bay. When a symposium is initiated by the type of comments Dean Beaton has just made, I view those convened here as something of an extended family.

The title of our morning session suggests an array of problems and associated challenges which must be understood and elicit a response from us as individual citizens, as students, and as practitioners of whatever professional or quasi-professional role happens to be "our bag." Dr. Khare's elaboration on this title has employed several metaphors which suggest that a new type of personal and corporate involvement is required in environmental processes if we are to solve the critical problems they pose to our society. I am delighted to be here with you and participate in a dialogue on this important topic. The Green Bay campus is a most appropriate locus for such a symposium, for it has itself evolved a response to the challenges posed by its immediate environment. From the looks of the river it has not yet achieved complete solution to the problems posed, but there is evident concern about them and constructive dialogue is underway.

I have chosen to title my comments this morning, "Breakdowns in Society's Metabolism," and hope they will provide a frame of reference for several substantive areas that I am sure will be discussed in greater depth later in this symposium.

At the outset I would invite your attention to the single living cell, because we can illustrate some of our environmental problems quite clearly in this context. The processes by which the cell functions include: the intake of food, the production of protoplasm, and its conversion into simpler compounds. These processes entail the release of energy which serves the organism in many different ways. The metabolic system is necessary to sustain life. Its processes serve a variety of needs in a flexible fashion; but on occasion, they break down. At such time the status of the organism must change: either the metabolic processes must be supplemented by chemical or physical manipulation, or the systemic processes that occur within the cell become modified, or life terminates.

There are stresses in society resembling the metabolic stresses that occur when cells are subjected to inhospitable environments or are made to fulfill functions for which they were not originally designed. If continued, these stresses will result in consequences similar to those experienced by the single cell. I have sketched out a very simple diagram depicting several of society's metabolic processes. We can start out with the box in the diagram representing production activities. These require (or "use") a number of resources originating in the natural environment. Emerging from this box are produced goods and certain types of services (those requiring resource inputs) which are consumed or used by the society's citizenry. The same citizenry contributes to the production processes by providing labor. Consumption occurs, resulting in some sort of final "net gain" to the society. Just as energy is released from the physical and chemical processes of cell metabolism, an economic surplus is generated by these social processes. Production activities also yield wastes or leftover materials, as is true also with consumption, which have to be disposed of in one form or another.

Society's production-consumption processes have been placed under stress, or at least we believed it to be so subject at three points. One involves the relationship between production activities and consumer welfare. The desirability of the collection of goods and services produced by society has been extensively debated. Economists, along with other social scientists, have examined market structures, monopolistic power, and poorly distributed

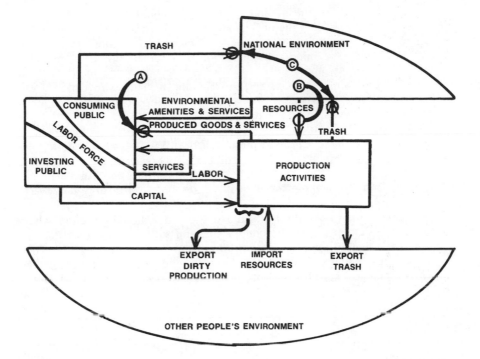

political power, questioning whether or not they resulted in a mix of goods and services that were fully congruent with the needs and desires of consumers. Point "A" on our diagram represents what long has been alleged as an important social stress point.

Another stress area has occurred at Point "B." Much concern has focused upon the flow of resources into the production processes of society. Indeed, concern over the adequacy of this resource flow was a rallying issue of the conservation movement in this country. The question raised was whether we would run out of nonrenewable resources, and as a result experience a slowdown, or even cessation, of economic growth. More recently, public concern has centered on the possibilities of breakdown at Point "C," where the waste materials resulting from production and consumption activities impact upon the environment. We're finding that many of these wastes, instead of just unobtrusively disappearing into the ambient environment, boomerang back on us in uncomfortable ways. They interfere directly with the welfare of society derived from its production and consumption activities and, through effects on human health, may reduce the size of society itself.

What conclusions can be drawn from the attention and study that have been accorded these three points of potential breakdown in society's metabolism? The question of whether our market system and political power structure yields the socially desirable mix of goods and services remains open. Its answer requires, among other things, careful examination of the incentives, ground rules, and reward-and-punishment arrangements under which we operate. Does this complex array of signals and guides for a production emphasis and allocation of resources elicit the final goods and services the country wants? The notion of social desirability, of course, itself evolves in response to changing social conditions. An important question is whether we have operable mechanisms that sense those shifts and transmit new guides for production so that the resulting array of goods and services are in phase with what society desires. All of these matters constitute an active and important domain of social science concern, albeit a traditional one.

The focus of attention on resource scarcity has been a more recent phenomenon. It came to a peak in the post-World War II years and during the early 1950's. The questions raised then still are highly relevant, although studies indicate that, generally, rapid technological development has permitted materials substitution and the use of "lower quality" resources, offsetting the adverse economic consequences of physical scarcity.

We come now to the third pressure point in our diagram, the one which today's symposium really is all about. Achieving and retaining a satisfactory environmental quality poses a spectrum of extremely difficult questions. They will require new patterns of thought and new kinds of social institutions if they are to be effectively coped with. Not only must we ascertain ways in which the environment can provide an adequate supply of resources for our production activities, but also we must figure out how the environment can contain the waste materials consumption and production activities generate.

Let's touch briefly on some of the challenges posed. At the outset one should not overidentify environmental quality problems with pollution, although both topics are closely related. Environments come in different sized packages. We have our own internal environments, which can be thrown out of kilter when body metabolism is disrupted by undernourishment, fatigue, drugs, or anything else. There is also the social environment of the home, usually dominated by the personal relationships among those who live there. Then there is the environment of the local community and the more aggregate communities of state, nation, and the world. Qualitative problems exist in each one of these systems. Pollution, congestion, or other stresses threaten them with degradation.

Let's take a closer look at the phenomenon of pollution, for it is more than meets the eye. Initially we may think that pollution involves dirty things, cluttered landscapes, water with a low level of dissolved oxygen, or other such indicators. Common sense suggests that if we keep things from getting into the water or the air, they will remain clean. Accordingly, many believe the route to a high level of environmental quality simply entails removing pollutants or potential pollutants from the air, the water, and the land. Yet, if we recall the law of conservation of matter, we will realize there is no way of making the leftovers from production and consumption disappear. We can, however, change the form in which they occur. We also can change the time and place at which we introduce them into the environment, and we may even be able to increase the capacity of the environment to receive those materials. We do the latter, for example, when we build off-stem water storage reservoirs for the purpose of augmenting river flow during periods of natural low flow. These considerations suggest the essential pollution problem is not how to prevent pollutants from entering the environment, but, rather, how to manage the waste materials with which we necessarily must cope. Instead of managing things with positive values—as implied by the term "resource management"—we are doing it for wastes which have mostly negative values to society.

As in any management problem, we may begin examining environmental quality problems by identifying options available. One of these clearly is to cut down on the physical quantity of waste materials that we put through our economy and society. This might be done in several ways. One would be to simply prolong the period of useful life of material—for example, building automobiles which last longer than 18 months. Another option is to change the mix of goods and services which society produces and uses. If the waste materials from production of a good places an increasing burden on society because of its pollution effects on the natural environment, the real cost of continued production of that good is correspondingly increasing. Were some mechanism to exist that sends this message back to the production box in our diagram, alternative goods and services which are less damaging to the environment would become increasingly competitive. This is the logic behind present trends toward policies that provide economic incentives for effecting this kind of substitution or for accelerating the development of clean production technologies. The proposed tax on the sulphur content of fuels would be an example.

In addition to these conceptual challenges, environmental quality also poses a formidable challenge for acquiring empirical information. The United States is today on the threshold of embarking upon a broad array of national policies dealing with materials scarcity, environmental pollution, and the quality of life. It is precisely at such times that hard information is most valuable, but also frequently least available. An illustration of this shortcoming is our recent attempt to develop a federal program for water pollution control. Initiated in the early 1960's with a structure that was thought to be sensible at the time, the programs provided for were never tested against a hard body of empirical data. The information simply wasn't available to the federal agencies who were given responsibility for establishing the national program. Nor was this information available to members of the Congress who were deciding the ground rules for organizing federal water pollution abatement activities. You will recall what happened. An agency to look after water quality was established in the Department of the Interior, quite separate from another agency in another department that was assigned responsibility for air quality, both of which were separate from a third office created several years later to provide guides for managing the disposal of solid wastes.

Trying to manage environmental quality through three separate, autonomous groups was doomed to failure. Each of them was trying to keep wastes out of their domain of concern. Collectively, this is a bit like poking a half-inflated balloon: you make progress here only by creating pressure in some other part of the environment. A river free from wastes is not an environment free of waste materials. Under the arrangement we created, the obtainment of clean water only increased the solid waste stresses or airborne waste stresses of the common environment.

The basic point is that we had neither sufficient experience nor knowledge about the waste systems and production activities that produce these wastes to frame an intelligent and sensible public policy. Too often this is the case with government agencies which have an understandable tendency to focus their energy on problems that are present and pressing, rather than acquiring a sound basis of knowledge for future policy guidance. It is precisely here where universities and other research organizations can make a major contribution to the national effort to achieve and sustain a high quality natural environment.

I want to come to another challenge posed by our environmental problems. This is a challenge to our public institutions, which must play an integral role in resolving these problems, which will require them to assume quite different functions than they have in the past when they were used to solve problems of natural resource scarcity. These earlier problems were amenable to analysis, diagnosis, and prescription by experts—whether they were economists, engineers, geologists, or whatever. They could intelligently prescribe physical management systems which would assure reasonably efficient use of our natural resource endowments. Public organizations and other types of institutions were used as vehicles through which these plans were implemented.

For matters of environmental quality, public institutions must provide forums within which public participation in diagnosing and prescribing solutions can be achieved. The very term "environmental quality" rings with ambiguity— an ambiguity which must be removed in particular instances by the relevant publics who are affected. For example, what constitutes a polluted river? When swimming is no longer possible; when dissolved oxygen drops to a level at which fish die; or when septic conditions are reached? Different members of the affected public will answer the question differently. If the community is to redress problems of deteriorating water quality, it must find the mechanism through which public choice can be reached with respect to both management targets and strategies. These institutions also must permit the political process to function. An interplay of values held by members of the community must be possible, and there must be some feasible means for compensating those who are mildly against pursuing a particular management course by those who are very much for following that course of action. In short, we will have to acquire institutions which permit debate, education, and political interaction. Our traditional natural resource institutions have been designed to efficiently execute programs. We now need them to help the public identify objectives and tolerance limits, and to facilitate public participation in formulating programs which can respond to local environmental circumstances. One might add this is true not only in the environmental domain, but also in such crucial areas as civil rights, the elimination of poverty, and other places where the quality of national life needs enhancement.

Thoughts similar to these undoubtedly were in the minds of those who helped create the Green Bay campus of The University of Wisconsin. It provides for a splendid mixture of education and debate, for dialogue and direct involvement in the local community. It is precisely this mixture of training and experience which we will desperately need if we are to solve our pressing environmental problems, and it is toward this end that the present symposium is being held.

Toward an Environmentally Oriented System of Social Accounts

James M. Murray

Measurement Matters—The people who are concerned about our environment today tend to be action-oriented rather than passively involved. For this reason they may question the relevance of a dialogue on the measurement of our economy's product as a means to effect an improvement in our environment. Therefore, it is appropriate to discuss the role which measurement plays in policy determination to justify a concern with the way we count things.

The market process continues to play a commanding role in the direction of our economy, but the federal government has clearly assumed the function of navigator. In setting the course for the economy, the administration and its economic advisers use the National Income Accounts as a measure of the market's performance. The objectives of full employment and price stability are pursued by attempting to maximize the level of the real Gross National Product within the confines of existing technology.

If national economic policy is established with the use of these accounts as norms, it is important to know what they measure and the effect of their use on our total life experience. In his recent book entitled *The Pursuit of Loneliness,* Philip Slater expressed it this way:

"The problem is that technology, industrialism, and capitalism have always been evaluated in their own terms. But it is absurd to evaluate capitalism in terms of the wealth it produces, or technology in terms of the inventions it generates, just as it would be absurd for a subway system to evaluate its service in terms of the number of tokens it manufactured. We need to find ways of appraising these systems in terms of criteria that are truly independent of the systems themselves. We need to develop a human-value index—a criterion that assesses the ultimate worth of an invention or a system or a product in terms of its total impact on human life, in terms of ends rather than means. We would then evaluate the achievements of medicine not in terms of man-hours of prolonged (and often comatose) life, or the volume of drugs sold, but in terms of the overall increase (or decrease) in human beings feeling healthy. We would evaluate city planning and housing programs not in terms of the number of bodies incarcerated in a given location, or the number of millions given to contractors, but in terms of the extent to which people take joy in their surroundings. We would evaluate the worth of an industrial firm not in terms of the money made or the number of widgets manufactured or sold, or how distended the organization has become, but in terms of how much pleasure or satisfaction has been given to people. It is not without significance that we tend to appraise a nation today in terms of its gross national product—a phrase whose connotations speak for themselves." (1970:129)

Slater's pursuit of an index of happiness is a noble but idealistic endeavor. Nevertheless it does seem possible to improve on the measures which we do have. A quick description of our present system of social accounts can demonstrate their inadequacy in reflecting the effect of economic activity on the environment.

Basically, the Gross National Product is an aggregation of all the newly produced goods and services for a given year. The goods and services in the private sector are measured at cost. The Gross National Product measures the flow of activity in our economy. It is a time rate measurement expressed in dollars per year. As a consequence, it does not reflect the changes in the total stock of goods, or the nation's wealth, which result from the year's economic activity. Another expression, namely, the Net National Product, is used to describe the result of subtracting the value of assets exhausted in the course of producing the total product from the Gross National Product. However, the subtraction involves only the depreciable assets as prescribed by tax laws and is not a meaningful reflection of the destruction which might accompany production. It does not, for example, reflect the water or air which was used or destroyed in the course of generating the GNP. Therefore, the Net National Product is little better than the GNP as a measure of the effect upon the nation's true wealth of a year's economic activity.

The relationships of this system of measurement to our natural environment can be easily observed by considering the impact of a natural disaster on the level of GNP. A massive flood, tornado, or earthquake may temporarily reduce the flow of activity because of physical disruption. However, the process of rebuilding begins very rapidly and the reconstruction generates an increased level of income. The massive destruction has little direct effect upon the Gross National Product, but the reconstruction activity, including both materials and labor costs, becomes a part of the total income for the current year. The result is that most national disasters actually increase our Gross National Product when resources are not fully employed. In periods of full employment, such disasters tend to be inflationary.

The analogy between this observation and the economic effect of a war have frequently been made, especially by those who contended that a capitalist economy cannot prosper without the high levels of spending associated with conflict. The incredible destruction of men and resources associated with a war is not reflected in the present system of measuring our national product, but the income generated in the course of producing our war machines is counted.

The inadequacy of these social accounts would not be of great concern if they were not such an important part of the policy-making process. The federal government agencies which are principally responsible for advising the administration on fiscal policy or for establishing monetary policy, namely, the Council of Economic Advisers and the Board of Governors of the Federal Reserve System, use these accounts as the signals for needed action, and their goal is clearly to achieve the maximum rate of growth in total output as measured by the social accounts, which is compatible with price stability. The environmental consequences of national economic policy are in no way reflected in the data used in these deliberations. A higher real GNP is simply considered better than a lower real GNP even if it destroys proportionately more of our natural resources than would a lower level of output. The basic policy goal is full employment, which can only be accomplished by increasingly higher levels of production.

The necessity to continuously produce goods and services to sustain full employment in itself creates a problem for the environment because it involves the using up of resources at a faster rate than nature can replace them. However, if we engaged in production only to generate employment with less concern for the usefulness of that output, the environmental consequences might be less serious. To illustrate my point, let me quote from the principal author of the present system of social accounts, John M. Keynes:

"Ancient Egypt was doubly fortunate, and doubtless owed to this its fabled wealth, in that it possessed two activities, namely, pyramid-building as well as the search for precious metals, the fruits of which, since they could not serve the needs of man by being consumed, did not stale with abundance. The Middle Ages built cathedrals and sang dirges. Two pyramids, two Masses for the dead, are twice as good as one; but not so two railways from

London to York. Thus we are so sensible, have schooled ourselves to so close a semblance of prudent financiers, taking careful thought before we add to the 'financial' burdens of posterity by building them houses to live in, that we have no easy escape from the sufferings of unemployment." (1964:131)

Keynes was making the point that our utilitarian traditions make it more difficult for us to generate full employment because we insist on producing "useful" things. The problem is further complicated by the fact that we insist on using the useful things we produce, which means that we must generate additional income this year to absorb the output of the increased quantity of useful things we produced last year. Thus, if we do not generate increases in income and output we will suffer unemployment, and we can only increase income by increasing output, which means more useful goods.

This seemingly vicious cycle, properly supervised, results in prosperity. It also results in massive problems for the environment. The required rate of growth to maintain full employment is so high that large quantities of useful goods must be destroyed and replaced each year. Durability takes a clear back seat to obsolescence in this situation.

In contrast, two pyramids, or two Gothic, nonlit cathedrals, neither require extensive use nor does their use involve a great threat to the environment. While either might conceivably last a century or more, this would not be a factor in the present technique of measuring their contribution to the economy. The present system gives the same value to 100 billion dollars in automobiles, half of which will be discarded in five years, as it would to 100 billion dollars in school buildings which would last 50 years. Indeed, the autos are given a priority over more durable assets because the process of junking them also employs people and resources and adds to our GNP.

As long as we measure economic activity as we presently do, and aim our policies at maximizing the rate of growth in this activity, any given product with a certain value and a short life span will have a higher priority because it will add more to GNP than a product with the same initial value which is more durable. Planned obsolescence is not just a product of modern advertising, it is inherent in our present method of measuring and regulating this nation's economy.

Recycling products, especially those which are fabricated from our scarcest natural resources, is obviously desirable from the environmental perspective. But recycling cans and bottles is not the same as recycling automobiles or wash machines. One involves nearly complete recovery while the other continues to demand more inputs of scarce minerals. Nevertheless, the problem remains, goods which are recycled are preferable to those which are not because the former generate more income and employment. The problem lies in not giving value to durability. As mentioned earlier, durability does not generate employment, only production generates employment. It is clear that an emphasis upon durability will require substantial changes in our system of distributing income, but there is no time for that discussion in this paper.

Improving the Measurement of Progress—As a first step, however, it should be possible to modify our present measurement system to make it possible for those concerned with the environment to give our economy the same degree of scrutiny as those concerned with income and employment. One possible method of doing this would be to measure the effect of economic activity upon wealth as well as upon income.

Economists have long recognized two measures of economic activity, namely, wealth and income. Income, as described above, is a measure of the flow of activity over a period of time and is the basis of the social accounts which are currently so widely used and discussed. Wealth is a measure of the stock of usable assets at a given moment in time but this measure has received little attention in recent decades. This was not always the case, however. Indeed, Adam Smith, who has been called the "father of economics" entitled his principal work, "An Inquiry into the Sources and Causes of the Wealth of Nations." It was the major Depression of the 1930's that generated the increasing emphasis upon Keynes' "General Theory of Employment, Interest, and Money," in which the emphasis is upon income, and wealth is both deliberately neglected and cynically dismissed as a misdirected concern. This may have been appropriate, and even necessary, in remedying the human misery afforded by the Depression. However, it is clearly unfortunate that we were forced to remedy that circumstance by our involvement in a war. The expenditures on war machines were so successful in generating income that in spite of devoting over half of the nation's resources to the war effort the per capita real income of the average American was higher in 1944 than it was before our entry into the war in 1940. Think what such an effort might have accomplished if it had been directed toward the development and preservation of our natural and human resources.

Now that we better understand the process of generating a full employment level of income, it is time to take a second look at the effect of our activities on the total stock of wealth in our country, indeed, in our world. The wealth of a nation, as the economist defines it, includes all of the assets possessed by a sovereign state and all of its citizens. The measurement of wealth is not as well developed nor refined as the measurement of income, primarily because of a lack of effort in this direction. Most citizens who read a newspaper are aware that we will have a trillion dollar GNP this year, but how many know the total value of our reproducible and nonreproducible assets? According to the best estimates provided largely by the work of John W. Kendrick, the value of wealth in the U. S. today is over three trillion dollars. The problem with this measure is that it values reproducible assets at their market value, which causes us to credit too much worth to the conversion of natural resources into "useful" products. Thus, a standing redwood tree is valued at less than if it were converted into a house. Nevertheless, our income measures treat both the production and destruction of products as positive activities while our wealth measure would subtract those destroyed from those produced. Durability is given value in our wealth measure because a product with a longer life remains in the stock of wealth for a longer period.

If the measurement of wealth is refined, it would be possible to scrutinize economic policy proposals not only in terms of their effect upon income but upon total wealth. The advantage here would be that we would be able to observe at least some of the environmental consequences of production. Those activities which require vast quantities of scarce natural resources, or those which generate income by creating goods which will rapidly be disposed of, would be identified by their impact upon the stock of both reproducible and nonreproducible assets.

Until we are able to resolve the problem of placing a value on air and water, we could measure the reduction in wealth associated with their use by the cost of restoring them to their original state. In cases where restoration is impossible under present technology, we would consider the cost as infinite and never permit economic activity which threatens irreparable damage to our natural assets. If this results in unemployment, as in the case of the SST, I would prefer to pay those persons involved until they could find alternatives rather than to allow the project to proceed. In reflecting upon the employment effects of environmentally oriented restrictions on production, we can again find an appropriate comment in Philip Slater's *Pursuit of Loneliness:*

"Yet I personally would far rather pay people not to make nerve gas than pay them to make it; pay them not to pollute the environment than pay them to do it; pay them not to inundate us with instant junk than pay them to do it." (1970:138)

Perhaps the environmentalist's greatest concern would be with those assets categorized as nonreproducible. It is here that our measurement is least adequate. The only nonreproducible asset that finds its way into the measurement of wealth is land. Water and air have been treated as noneconomic goods in the past, on the assumption that they have not been scarce relative to the need for them. In any case, it is interesting to note that in spite of rapidly rising land values, the percentage of our total wealth represented by nonreproducible assets has slipped from 25.8% in 1929 to 16.0% in 1967. This change is to be expected, of course, from the very fact that we are dealing with reproducible assets which can be increased, and nonreproducible assets which are static in quantity. However, the valuation of these assets is also a factor in this change. The market process may be putting a value on nonreproducible assets which reflects a very short time horizon. A consideration of the collective welfare of humanity over a very long period of time (i.e., forever) would undoubtedly increase the value of these nonreproducible assets. An analogy can be cited from our recent experience. The large multiple purpose dams constructed in the U. S. largely in the 1930's and 1950's would not have been constructed by private enterprise. The reasons for this are (1) the return on the investment would take too long to recover and (2) the only revenue-producing activity would be the sale of hydroelectric power. Preventing loss of life and property damage from floods has never been a paying proposition. As a result of these and other considerations, only the government which best represents the collective interest of all citizens over all time was in a position to construct the large dams. Because all of their benefits cannot be quantified, it often proved difficult to justify them to Congress, and they are probably undervalued in the measurement of our total wealth. This is an example of the difference between the time horizon of society as a group and that of individual participants in the market place. If we continue to allow our nonreproducible assets to be counted at their current market value, we risk a serious misallocation of these resources over the very long run.

Any reference to the long run in economics usually prompts a reference to a remark attributed to John M. Keynes. In responding to a concern frequently expressed by his predecessors, he once made the facetious remark that "in the long run we'll all be dead." His point was that we must be concerned with the welfare of each generation, and the misery of the Depression could not be justified by the prospect that the market would someday recover. However, we now know that we can prevent such a breakdown in our system within the framework of our present institutions, and economists no longer advocate leaving the state of our national economy to the vagaries of the market process. However, we must now assure ourselves that in the process of generating full employment in the short run with incredible volumes of output and the consequent destruction of our environment, we don't change Keynes' remark to the statement that "in the short run we'll all be dead." As a start in this direction we might borrow an expression from the recent work of Thomas D. Crocker and A. J. Rogers entitled "Environmental Economics" and measure our annual activity as follows: Gross National Product minus Gross National Crud equals Net Useful Income.

To Live Is to Pollute

Larry J. Smith

In a physical sense, the title of this paper is a tautological restatement of the title of this panel, "Mass Production, Mass Consumption, Mass Waste." The tautology is based upon the Law of Conservation of Mass combined with the biological

*The title for this paper was borrowed (initially unwittingly) from Chapter I in J. H. Dales, "Pollution, Property and Prices." (1968)

requirement of environmental inputs to sustain life. Thus, living, at whatever level, implies consumption and consumption implies waste in identical physical quantities. The mass dimension does not modify the basic identity between production and waste, although it is the source of the sense of urgency surrounding discussions of environmental quality. But all wastes are not equally damaging to man's environment and thus to his future capacity to enjoy life. The environment itself is capable of converting certain wastes, in limited quantities, into productive resources. The life cycle on earth which is based upon photosynthetic conversion of waste organic matter into life supporting organic matter is an example. There are, however, certain wastes which are inconvertible, at least over reasonable periods of time, given the present state of the environment, including man's own technology. These are the wastes with which we are most concerned: the ones which are potentially most damaging to our life support system called the environment.

Table I presents some summary data on the rate of production, and thus waste, generated by the U. S. economy for a few of these more harmful pollutants. These data frighten me, and suggest that given the present structure of individual and social values in this economy the only way of solving "the environmental crisis" would entail a major economic depression.

The key to this dismal prediction is the column of Table I labeled, "Estimated Elasticity." This summary statistic relates the percentage change in production, and thus consumption and waste, for the specified time periods to changes in per capita personal income over the same time period. If it is negative, this means that as income grows production of that item falls. If it is less than one, this means that as income grows the production, consumption, and waste of that item increases less than income. If it is greater than one, it tells us that production, consumption, and waste of that item is growing faster than income. You will notice that most of the income elasticities presented are greater than one. This fact leads directly to the dismal prediction above.

Of course a part of the problem, and that focused on by Professor Murray, is that we have a poor measure of income which includes a good deal of pollution directly. Another dimension of the problem, however, is that these summary statistics represent a summary of the individual and social values inherent in our economy. These items are produced—and produced in increasing proportions as income rises—at least partially because someone wants them to be produced. And, to the extent that our admittedly poor measure of income measures our ability to satisfy our wants, the more income, the more of these pollutants, and vice versa, as long as those wants remain unchanged.

These data tell us something about the rate at which the selected pollutants are being produced. Because many of these pollutants are not degradable, given the present state of applied technology, their production represents additions to the growing stock of such pollutants in the environment.

The stock of a particular pollutant in the environment at a particular time is equal to the sum of all previous production of that pollutant minus all of that pollutant which has previously been reabsorbed into the environment. Because the rate of reabsorption of certain pollutants such as plastics, stable and often poisonous hydrocarbons, and nonferrous metals is virtually zero, the rate at which they are produced is approximately the rate at which they are being

TABLE I

Elasticities, Per Capita Income,
Selected Sources of Pollution, United States, 1950-1969*

Source	Period	Estimated Elasticity
Electrical Energy	1950-1960	4.3208
Electrical Energy	1960-1969	1.6810
Electrical Energy	1950-1969	3.0984
Chemical Products	1950-1960	4.1575
Chemical Products	1960-1969	1.8011
Chemical Products	1950-1969	3.5205
Rubber and Plastic Products	1950-1960	1.8095
Rubber and Plastic Products	1960-1969	2.4087
Rubber and Plastic Products	1950-1969	
Nonferrous Metals	1950-1960	.0605
Nonferrous Metals	1960-1969	1.4795
Nonferrous Metals	1950-1969	.8995

*Source: Calculated from raw data from the Statistical Abstract of the United States, 1963 and 1970.

added to the environment. Thus, to achieve even a constant state of environmental degradation by these pollutants would require a zero level of production of these pollutants. We are, however, producing these pollutants at increasing rates as we grow "richer."

But this is only a part of the problem. The calculations in Table I are based upon per capita production of the selected pollutants, and per capita personal income. But the population is growing, so that the rate of production, and thus waste, of these pollutants is growing even faster than is indicated by the rate of growth of personal income per capita. For example, if the per capita income elasticity of a particular nondegradable pollutant is two, and if income is growing at 3 percent per year and population is growing at 2 percent per year, we would expect the production of the pollutant to grow at two times three or 6 percent due to the income effect, plus 2 percent due to the increase in population, a total of 8 percent.

Thus, as long as we continue to produce these nondegradable pollutants, even the prescription of a major economic depression won't fully solve the problem. It would only slow the rate of environmental degradation somewhat.

Then what can we do? The key to any viable solution to the problem lies in the phrase "given the present structure of individual and social values in this economy."

These values must be changed. We must both individually and collectively learn to recognize and treat the nondegradable throw-away approach to life as the menace to that life that it represents. Surely human life will remain the primary source of environmental pollution, but we can reduce, if not eliminate, the more harmful and more permanent pollutants which we produce

But what can we as individuals do to change these values? We can start by trying to change our own individual patterns of consumption and hopefully, through demonstration, those of others. Consumption patterns, of course, are habits and habits are difficult to break—especially on an individual basis. I thus offer the following proposal as a potential mechanism to both help us change our individual patterns of consumption and waste and to provide a financial base from which to support a wider political movement directed at changing the consumption patterns of society as a whole.

I will call the proposal the personal pollution tax. It involves the levying of taxes on particular items of personal consumption which are identified as especially harmful to the environment. At this stage it is nothing either new or unusual. Taxes have often been proposed as a potential solution to the pollution problem, the argument being that selective taxes will raise the price of particular activities and thus lead to a lower level of indulgence in that activity. These proposals have not been adopted because taxes are politically unpalatable and thus difficult to levy on an official basis.

This problem, in a reasonably democratic society, essentially means that a majority of the population must accept the idea of a tax before it can be levied on a general basis. Achieving such a level of consensus for a pollution tax will require a long and effective period of public education. Thus, my proposal involves the levying and collection of the tax on a personal basis, with the revenue from the tax being utilized for public education and political action directed at the pollution problem in the larger society.

This system of personal taxation could be implemented by small groups of individuals working together to decide the rates of taxation to be applied to various activities for their group and to decide how to utilize the proceeds from the tax. The process of deciding what items to tax and at what level will be immediately beneficial in educating those involved on the harmful effects of particular activities because the taxes should ideally be levied in proportion to the harmful effects of the activities being taxed. The process of deciding how to utilize the revenue from the group's personal taxes will be similarly educational, because these revenues will ideally be expended to support pollution reducing activities. Finally, the process of individually calculating and paying the tax will help to raise the level of consciousness of those participating concerning the harmful effects of particular activities.

Although the items to be taxed and the rates of taxation will vary from group to group, a few guidelines at least for initial discussion are probably in order. First, the items taxed should probably be pollutants which are utilized by most of the members of the group. Electricity, gasoline, and plastics are some examples. Second, the tax rates should be set sufficiently low to initially prevent discouraging people from participating. Finally, a mechanism for giving tax credit, or subsidies, to individuals for participating in environmentally beneficial activities—recycling programs, for example—would encourage participation by individuals with very low incomes.

While this proposal is not likely to solve the environmental problem immediately, it does focus attention on the changes in individual behavior which are needed in dealing with the problem. It also provides a mechanism for developing a growing base for political action and education oriented toward changing the larger social structure when that structure conflicts with the needs of environmental quality. It is thus offered as a possible approach to the problem that could be carried out on a small scale by small groups of people anywhere.

Panel Discussion

Dr. Vlasin (Assistant Chancellor, UWGB): The next order of business this morning will be some comments on the papers read by a representative of the corporate community, Mr. James Shipman, and a member of the student body in the Modernization Processes Concentration, Mr. Timothy R. Eggen. Mr. Shipman's vita is provided in the program. I'm sure you will be interested in this gentleman's illustrious career with the Kimberly—Clark Corporation. He has been responsible for almost every facet of that corporation's system of operations at one time or another, and he is presently a vice president and a member of the board of directors. We are most delighted to have a representative of the Kimberly—Clark Corporation officially with us because they are so involved with the evolution of this region, and we are happy to have a distinguished member of the business community with us on this panel.

Mr. Shipman (Vice President, Kimberly—Clark Corporation): As a commentator, let me first state that I agree with most of what has been stated today. This is a complex problem, very complex, and I would just like to add one or two observations. The production-consumption waste cycle and its ecological side effects is a problem, and I agree with Dr. Murray that the GNP is a poor measure of economic growth. It's a little like saying my sales are better, therefore I'm better as a corporation. It ignores some important facts. Not being an economist, I have to think of these in very simple terms, so you'll pardon me if I use a very simple example. Let's assume that I'm on an island, or any one of us is on an island, and the only source of our wealth is coconuts. I can gather maybe ten coconuts in a day. This is a simple economy—the gathering economy—and I also consume ten coconuts in the course of a day, and I also have ten coconuts of waste (in one sense or another) and this takes me an entire day to accomplish this task. Of course these coconuts are piling up, but it doesn't bother me right now because I'm too busy trying to collect them and eat them and that's all I can do. Now let's assume that through a technological innovation or something I discover I can gather eleven coconuts. Now my GNP, if you will, has increased by 10 percent—that's pretty good! However, if I consume them and waste them, my net wealth is, I submit, still nothing. I have no wealth. Now on the other hand I might decide I don't want to consume them; I want to defer my consumption of that extra coconut. And that brings me to something very important—time. In other words I might say, look, I have to gather eleven and I'm only going to consume ten, that's the surplus and I'll call this wealth. Now I have ten in consumption, but I have something else—I have one extra coconut. This gives me an option of what to do with this time. I could decide to do a lot of things with the additional time; I could just enjoy myself. I like this place and I haven't had much time to sit back and watch the sunset at night, so I will gather my eleven and spend the extra time enjoying myself. And this, of course, is what we do. Or I could say that I'm going to invest it in long-term capital goods. I might want to take the time that I have gained from the extra coconut and build myself a house. Because I have a lot of coconuts accumulating, I might begin to calculate, with the extra time the coconut gives me, what I'm going to do with the husks, and attack my ecological problem, if you will.

Classically, as the coconuts accumulate my wealth begins to accumulate. Usually we are not satisfied with this result. I probably wouldn't be, and few of you would find this a good idea. Thus, I invest some of my time trying to figure out how to obtain twelve coconuts. Conditions are improved, I can eat eleven, like I really wanted to do all along, and I still have one left over, so my storage of wealth is increasing. I almost hesitate to use this word, but as a businessman I use it many times, the excess is my profit. I use this business term and I might as well admit it, most businessmen are accused of thinking of nothing but profit, but that is the way they are oriented. On this little island on which I live, this so-called profit translates into time which permits me to do things to make life more meaningful for me. I think that most of the very difficult problems which were tossed about (in the papers presented) center about what to do with the extra coconut.

Mr. Smith offered an experimental device for exploring what to do with the extra coconut. Maybe I am oversimplifying the problem, but I do think the dilemma centers around the extra coconut and what do you do with it. It becomes as much of a problem to invest well—to invest your time well—as it does to place the additional coconut into extra production and increasing consumption, or put it into the removal of waste. Both alternatives have to be evaluated on the basis of, will I increase this total wealth—this total free time which I now have to enjoy the fruits of my labor, if you will? Admittedly this is a simplistic description of a very complicated social problem.

There is only one other point I'd like to make which the word waste brought to my mind. There are an awful lot of coconuts going through this system. Certainly as a representative of American industry and a personal consumer I think there is some chance of immediate improvement in my situation by examining it from the point of view, do I really need all those coconuts? Am I throwing away 25 percent of them when I could really get more free time to invest in improving the quality of my life, i.e., if I just ate eight or perhaps nine coconuts? In industry I know this is true because it goes on constantly—the trees that used to be sawed up into lumber wasted between 25 to 50 percent of the bulk that burned up—contributing to a long-term ecological cycle which comes back and makes more trees but still constitutes an immediate waste. Most of this wasted bulk is now made into paper.

To conclude my comments I would like to observe that the speakers have intelligently and professionally pointed out the problems associated with that coconut. I'll close by saying that in spite of the beautiful introduction that was given me, I am somewhat humble in the presence of all these gentlemen, these professionals. It reminds me of a story I have to tell you. They won't let me tell it at home so I have to tell it here. It's about these three professors who were walking along the campus up here and they began to talk about how groups of things get names, like a plot of land and a flock of geese. One of them noticed there was a house of ill repute across the street from the campus and he said, "I wonder what you would call the inmates of that place?" The first one replied, "I think you would call them a flourish of strumpets." The second one said, "No, I don't think that's quite right, I think I would call them a jam of tarts." And the third gentleman, who was an English professor said, "No, you are both wrong, the appropriate label would be anthology of pros."

Dr. Murray (faculty, UWGB, substituting as moderator for Dr. Vlasin): Thank you, Mr. Shipman, for your remarks and for the stories. Our next comments will come from Mr. Tim Eggen who is a senior at UWGB in the Modernization Processes Concentration, which describes his academic plan. He also has an option area or related interest in sociology and, of course, is particularly concerned about the environment.

Mr. Eggen: Rather than comment on what's been said, since it has been said much better than I think I could say it, I would like to direct a series of questions to the speakers who have already spoken. I would like to start with Larry Smith and his comments on a personal pollution tax. Even with the personal tax, the items are still purchased. How would this help to change our consumption habits? All these items are still being purchased and put back into the environment. Why should we buy some of these products, that possibly we don't need, and tax ourselves further?

Mr. Smith: Well, the idea of a tax or taxes in general is that they can be set at any rate from almost zero to prohibitive levels. In this case, it depends on how this particular group decides to tax themselves with respect to an activity and the harmfulness of that activity. Of course these rates can be adjusted. There are some activities we don't engage in right now because we think they are too harmful, and that is equivalent to saying we set a tax rate so high we just don't want to pay it. It is unlikely that we're going to persuade society, or even small groups of ourselves (if ten of us can't get together and try to agree) about what we want to do personally to improve the environment. It will be very difficult to have one of us say, "I'm going to quit driving a car totally and completely, I'm never going to drive a car again." Society has not gotten around to the point of supporting us in that effort by giving us an alternative means of transportation. We can say, "I'm going to ride my bicycle if the trip's less than five miles, and I'm never going to drive a car for a trip less than five miles." We can tell people, "I'm sorry I can't make it because it will take me longer to get there on my bicycle as I don't drive a car—the distance is too close!"

Mr. Eggen: I think I asked you to respond to what you said in your paper about the present amount of pollutants in the environment. Given the fact that we have an increase in nondegradable pollutants, plus a growing population, I'm wondering how effective a small group solution would be over time for the majority of the population?

Mr. Smith: It may not be effective enough. We may be past the point, as some people have suggested. The possibility of doing something like this leaves open to the participants the rate of speed at which they want to move. It's flexible and it's open to the individual. At this time the political dialogue hasn't progressed far enough to force our will on everyone, whatever our will is. I might wish that there were no automobiles, but I find it very difficult to make that come true. However, I may be able to get together with others in small groups and say, "Let's drive the automobiles last and try to find some substitute." The process of finding a substitute may actually, for us in a small group, generate a social substitute for the larger society, that's the idea behind the thing. If we don't have the time, then it's too late, because we don't have the power to make a change right now, even an immediate revolutionary change. Your question is well taken, but my answer is simply if we don't have time it's over, because there's no solution at hand that will immediately solve the problem!

Mr. Eggen: This is at least the starting point?

Mr. Smith: That is the way I feel about it, yes.

Mr. Eggen: I'd like to ask Dr. Murray something in connection with what he mentioned about durability. Could we consider the possibility of employing less people and creating more durable consumer goods and add to that the use of a guaranteed annual income? Would that be a solution?

Dr. Murray: The whole process of production is moving in the direction where we will have to face that prospect in any case. Economists considered this point some time before we even gave thought to the real environmental questions that we're facing today. I think the problem of technological displacement of employment is something that has been with us for a long time. Interestingly, technology creates and destroys employment opportunities, as we know, but the relation between output and employment is changing. In other words, it's clearly going to take fewer people to produce any given amount of output in the future. It depends on whether we want to try to continue to consume more and more goods. On the assumption that human wants are insatiable, we could continue to figure out ways of producing things that people would consume. I would say that we will and can employ fewer people to produce any given stock of goods we decide to produce. The question in doing it is both deciding production techniques and the level of consumption. But your suggestion that we need to accompany this by an alternative method of distribution is correct. The negative income tax or the minimum guaranteed income for all citizens is one of the proposals that would really start in the direction of accommodating this need for an income redistribution system. This is true not only in terms of what I said in my paper, where we're hung up on the notion of producing useful things all the time in the context of our own definition of usefulness, but we are also hung up with the notion that everybody has to be busy at something in order to justify any kind of income. We sometimes find if we look closely, people are being paid for activity which isn't really doing anything terribly productive. One person who is unemployed is looked at as not deserving of income, and another person who is employed at doing something that is quite useless is looked upon as deserving the income he receives. We are going to have to change our attitude towards these things.

Mr. Eggen: Another question I have relates to your suggestion for the development of a standard of value for our water and air. Would you care to elaborate on that?

Dr. Murray: Yes, the suggestion I made was that historically water and air were considered to be noneconomical free goods. In fact, they are now taking on the characteristics of economic goods. The traditional market process would place a value on them when people started indicating their willingness to pay for clean air and clean water. I suppose if we let the process go until the market could enter, we probably would get to the point where there would be domed cities. The new communities that are going to be built as model cities would indeed be domed cities, in which the air quality was controlled by a massive process of air-conditioning and so forth. Now you would pay to live in that city, not only for land but you would be paying for clean air and presumably clean water. This would all have to be artificially produced. That presumably will not happen as long as people can escape to a place where they can enjoy remunerative employment at the same time as they enjoy fresh air for free. So, I submit, if we are to do this without creating artificial environments under the ocean or on the land and charging for this in the traditional market process, we are going to have to undertake it collectively. In order to do that we will need the same kind of cross-benefit analysis that we employ in the case of an hydroelectric dam where we fix a value on flood control with the idea that we are going to prevent the destruction of cities and lives. What is the worth in a hydroelectric dam? What is it worth to have someone put a boat in the water and enjoy the recreation that goes along with a dam or reservoir? These things have been worked on and are being worked on by economists for the Bureau of Reclamation and the Army Corps of Engineers. The same kind of technique needs to be applied to the concept of clean water and clean air. If we decide to create an artificial environment where air and water would be marketable, then we're going to have to do it collectively as a society and deal with these things much in the way we have dealt with other aspects of conservation, the hydroelectric dams, the national forests and things of that sort.

Mr. Eggen: One more question, since this symposium is co-sponsored by Modernization Processes, I was wondering (if along with our technology and things we are exporting to other countries) whether we are also exporting the idea of planned obsolescence and the throw-away mentality, which could compound the problem tremendously.

Dr. Murray: I think there's no question about that. There was an excellent book written a few years ago by a man by the name of Mason entitled, *The Road to Huttersfield.* Huttersfield was the original industrial city in England. This particular book examines the experiences of The World Bank, The International Bank for Reconstruction and Development, and it very colorfully illustrates the fact that most of these countries first pursue the smokestacks of industrial development. To the "developing nations," economic progress is associated with the kinds of things we have associated it with for a long time. I think it's a very, interesting question to pose, I'm not sure if I'm the one to answer it.

To the question whether every institution or every society can only learn by experience, it is really a question of whether individuals can only learn by experience. Sometimes I reflect on our own university. I wonder whether we have to go through all the same things other universities have experienced before we get to the point of doing something different. Hopefully not, and hopefully the same thing can be true of other countries. If we can indicate how economic progress can be sustained, while at the same time focusing on environmental quality, I think we can share that experience with other countries before they have to go through the kind of experience we have had and then reverse trends. Perhaps we can help them anticipate environmental problems more systematically than has been true in this country. I think we are exporting problems, but I also think we can export our new concern.

Mr. Eggen: Thank you, those are the questions I have for you at the moment.

Dr. Murray: In the dialogue which ensued during the coffee break for this session, several persons asked me about the presumed argument between Larry Smith and myself concerning the question of durability. I would submit that we are open to questions from the audience whether a beer cooler made out of styrofoam is not as durable as a beer cooler made out of metal. In my concept of durability, it's true that maybe the metal cooler would disintegrate by rusting in the environment if left in the creek, but the very fact that the styrofoam cooler remains in the creek while the other disintegrates is my point. My point is that goods could be made out of better material, something which would last longer and thus demand a longer useful period of time rather than being cast away so quickly. I think also that in terms of generating income out of this process, durability will demand a higher level of input and higher income. In other words, we're simply going to have to pay more for durable things, there's no question about it. So it isn't as if I'm advocating destroying the income potential, income-generating potential of the goods that are produced. I submit that one beer cooler which lasts five years is better than five which last one year from an environmental perspective. That is what I really meant when I was talking about durability and beer coolers. Maybe we ought to just put our beer in the creek and forget about a cooler. Any questions that any of the audience would like to address to these gentlemen?

Anonymous (question from a community participant in the audience): Mr. Shipman, in regard to the use of the word wealth, possibly you meant income. The real wealth in your example is the island. If our life were pursued with that distinction in mind, the wage would be at least as great for improving the island as is the profit now received for the activity of just using the island and extracting coconuts. It is the use of the word wealth which I believe is the key to the whole problem. The value, in other words, the only value, is the island. Without it the whole thing disappears.

Mr. Shipman: Well, you're certainly right. In my simple approach I did not add the land assets or the other assets. I think Professor Murray did point out in his talk that you have to consider what you are doing to the assets you have when you are producing things. I agree that in order to increase your wealth you have to be careful about how you do it, and it could be just as destructive a process in the construction of the wealth as it could be a plus for human satisfaction. Certainly, your total objective is to increase your time to enjoy what you have, and if in so doing you destroy what you have to enjoy, then no one can say that that's good. But, if you don't have the time to enjoy it, then I don't know what good it is to you either.

Anonymous: But on the other hand if you overproduce hours of leisure there is no way to reimburse people, because one way or the other there is nothing left to enjoy or there is no money to enjoy it. Underemployment, rather than overemployment, could become an item maintained by management by improving or creating wealth. As it is now, a man or woman does not get money for enjoyment. In fact, they are further downgraded for it because that kind of labor is not rewarded in the way that we reward what is called skilled labor or unskilled labor. The preservation and survival of the environment itself should be rewarded more on the dollar scale.

Dr. Brewer: I would just like to make one observation. I think I would like to come back to Mr. Shipman's Robinson Crusoe example. First of all, we can consume endless hours on discussion of what really is wealth and income, and things of this sort. I think these are interesting lines of discussion, but somewhat difficult to carry forward in a symposium setting. I do think there is an array of very important problems which are much more down to earth. I would like to come back to the example and raise a specific one and pose a question about it to Mr. Shipman. Let's assume this increase in productivity which lets you gather one additional coconut is done with a mechanical means which increases the rate of the erosion on the island. Well, what you have got is a more efficient harvesting procedure, but you are imposing a cost on your own surroundings, or if there are other people, on my surroundings also. This is a real cost of producing coconuts, I think you would agree, and it seems to me quite appropriate under those circumstances to let the harvester—namely, you or the company doing the harvesting, whether it's Weyerhauser that goes into tropical agriculture—feel and experience the additional cost of production. This is a cost that is ultimately going to be passed on to consumers through higher product prices, but what it does mean is that the consumers will have a choice of consuming a coconut now valued properly—taking into account the environmental degradation that is entailed in bringing that coconut to the market. Assume the price will be up 15 percent. The consumer will make his choice whether he really wants to pay the full cost or wants to substitute an alternate food which is less damaging to the environment and therefore less costly.

This comes again to the earlier discussion we had about what means we will use, what are the policy instruments we will use to rearrange our activities to take account of the environmental impact. Will there be prohibitions in some instances? Clearly, yes. Mercury is something where we can't really tolerate consumers saying, "Well, it's still awfully important for me to use mercury, therefore I'm willing to pay a terribly high price." We simply are going to say for certain kinds of uses, mercury is out of the question and we are going to prohibit it. But for the other array of goods and services, many of them in the pulp and paper industry incidentally, which do involve particular loads on the environment and which subject the environment to particular stress, some means or approach to handling the problem is to find a method of folding that cost into the cost of production a company must undergo in order to produce its pulp, paper and wood products, oil or steel, whatever it is the company does. I think this would achieve several things. First of all, it would differentiate in pricing between those things that create environmental problems: for example, dyed papers that introduce difficult dyes into the water, or sizing or whatever the chemical may be. People would have a choice of buying those environmentally damaging products or buying, at a somewhat lower cost, a less damaging substitute. That really is why I think the tax approach, which would impose environmental costs on producers whose mode of production entails environmental degradation, is a very flexible and highly desirable one. I think it is more desirable than out and out prohibition, unless the environmental insult is so catastrophic that it just can't be tolerated. (To Mr. Shipman) Would you agree with this proposition?

Mr. Shipman: Well, yes, I think this is exactly what is happening. Let's take the stream pollution example. The increased standards against stream pollution have resulted in higher costs, and so ultimately everyone is going to pay more for paper products, including myself. This is what is happening, and I don't think that it is necessarily bad. I do feel that the decisions about how you improve the stream are going to be difficult, but that sounds like it's a cop-out. I think, for example, that illustration you mentioned about dyes in tissue is a tempest in a toilet bowl, as one person has said. There are, however, many important environmental problems like the one which exists at our Kimberly mill which is much more important and must be fixed, and will be fixed. But there is no question that the tax, if you will, on paper products will be higher because of it.

We accept that, and we presume that the consumers do. They will ultimately pay for it, just as when people demand different qualities in a product they are usually prepared to pay for it. So I guess I have to agree with what you said. How can I disagree?

Dr. Murray: The only disagreement is over the level of the tax, right?

Mr. Shipman: Well, you'll probably hear me in the next county if they seem to be taxing paper relatively higher in our area or relatively higher than other products on the market. Ultimately, we've only got the one coconut to work on. Obviously you've got to make adjustments and the cost will go up. I have observed that very few of us are willing, including myself, to give up the things we enjoy in order to gain an improved environment. I see I have caused some hands to go up. But at the same time I'm reminded that General Motors put an item on the market in Phoenix, where there are a hundred thousand cars, at the price of $9.95 plus installation. I don't know what the installation cost was, but they advertised the item widely as reducing the pollution from a pre-1968 car by 30-50 percent, or some such number. They sold only 900 of them, or maybe it was 500. On the other hand, if you survey the people in Chicago and ask whether they would be willing to pay $20 for such a device, they all say no. But if you would ask them to vote for a bill which would require every car to have it on and you would personally have to pay extra cost, they would all say yes. This is just a human characteristic.

Dr. Murray: I understand that we all have to force ourselves to pay income taxes.

Mr. Gorder: It is necessary to resolve the cost benefit situation and I think that people will be reluctant to give up things or sacrifice if they in turn do not gain an equal benefit. When I go into the gasoline station and pay 41 cents for a nonlead gasoline and I can buy leaded gasoline for 35 cents, I say to myself, "OK, I'm putting twenty gallons of gasoline in this car that costs me $1.20." Am I going to get $1.20 worth of benefit out of it? No, I won't. Society will, if all of society did this. We would all benefit because we would be buying better air, but I as an individual am not buying better air. Because Mr. Shipman is competing with American Can and all kinds of other competitors, he can't afford to be a good guy unless they're all good guys. He has to compete with them, not only with other paper companies but with other products. So it seems to me that what we have to do is solve the cost-benefit situation, and this is done through subsidies and taxes. I don't think it is done through laws of bureaucracy, because this simply increases the friction and therefore increases the inefficiency in production. A lot could be said about competition working toward better conservation. For instance, the iron and steel industry now uses about eight-tenths of a ton of coking coal to produce a ton of pig iron. Back in the 1920's it took over two tons of coking coal for the same operation. Now this happened not because the company considered themselves good guys or wanted to clean up the air or anything, it was done simply to maximize profit. It's less costly to use less coal. So I think what we need to do is preserve those aspects of competition which are conducive to efficient production and use, yet at the same time eliminate those aspects of competition which are destructive to efficient production and use of resources, and to do this through subsidies and taxes.

Dr. Murray: I don't think that requires any particular response. That is a succinct statement.

Anonymous: I was going to ask, probably due to my own ignorance or my own inability to investigate these things, but I really didn't know that dye made more pollution. I really didn't. And if they had written it in great big letters on the package I might have realized it and would have chosen white, because it doesn't really make that much difference. But when I see the color, I'm attracted to the color.

Mr. Shipman: If we believed or had any evidence that dyes in fact did cause major pollution problems, or caused any pollution problems, we'd put it on the package. We were probably the most surprised company in the world when we suddenly discovered that people were saying, "We don't want to buy dyed tissues because they pollute," or "Why do you make them—because they pollute?" Since then we have tested the damn things for irritation and everything else. Women still wanted them and we said, "We have tested them and they are safe." It was as if someone came here and said, "You know, salt is a very bad pollutant, and you had better stop using it." That was about our frame of mind, so we of course immediately said, "Who found that out, where did this information come from?" We never could find out. We went to the magazine that published the statement and asked for the source. Well, it turns out a reporter heard it from her roommate. As yet we can find no evidence that dyes pollute. Now I'm sure that they do in some small way. You can't add anything without adding something to pollution. Somebody's going to find that the dye in tissue affects the sex life of the red worm at the bottom of Lake Winnebago. And I'm sure this type of discovery will pop up. But I really believe the risk is very, very small. And so far we've put dye through septic systems, we have put it in the air, we have fed it to fish, and we still can't find any evidence that the dyes pollute. I think if you like colored tissue, you can buy it. If you like white, by all means buy that—it's a lot easier to make.

Mr. Kolshus (faculty, UWGB): Yes, I'd like to add to the tempest in the toilet bowl myself. I have one controlled experiment that I can refer to and, of all places, it took place in a high school in Sheboygan where a student in the science department, after having heard this and numerous types of responses from industry, collected two big bowls of tadpoles. In one of these bowls with the tadpoles he ground up white tissue paper and set it into the bowl, and in the other bowl he ground up colored tissue with rather striking results. Those who got the colored tissue died and the tadpoles with the white tissue did not die. I realize that this is probably a much higher concentration of dyes in the environment than we usually have, but if you have to print something on the toilet tissue why not print jokes or something like that, making the exercise a bit more enjoyable?

Dr. Murray: Do you want to respond?

Mr. Shipman: No, I was just wondering whether or not there are tadpole jokes. No, I sound flip about this, but I would very much like to know what that student did. If you can tell me his name I'd like to find out, because if this is a problem, and we don't think it is now, we want to know it before anyone else does.

Mr. Smith: Mr. Shipman, does your company make Pampers?

Mr. Shipman: No.

Mr. Smith: No, well Procter and Gamble does. On their package they encourage people to flush Pampers. That's a very expensive way to get rid of them. Why doesn't that company change such statements? These are the sort of things companies could do without any sort of law. There are lots of these types of things. Jokes don't take care of any problems.

Mr. Shipman: I guess I don't know. I don't think that's the way to dispose of disposable diapers myself. In most European countries they are collected and burned. I don't know why they recommend this practice. Maybe it's because some people do it. There is a lot of argument, as you know, but why should I be talking about Procter and Gamble's problems?

Dr. Murray: I might point out that in the book I referred to in my talk, *The Pursuit of Loneliness,* the author uses the concept of the toilet flush philosophy. He says that we treat many of our social problems, including the environmental problem, much as we do anything that goes into the toilet, and we won't really be concerned until the toilet doesn't flush. When the toilet stops flushing, then we will get excited about our environment.

Dr. Kolka (faculty, UWGB): This is really more of an observation and not a question directed to any specific person on the panel. When Professor Murray was talking about the word useful, it should be noted that it is a word which has a cultural value. In this culture, we value such things as automobiles, even though considering available resources it is not the most efficient mode of transportation for propelling people from one point to another—point A to point B. Our culture places a value on automobiles and, consequently, we produce such things. We have ideological attachments to certain types of technologies. Thus, we have to consider the psychic value which a culture places on such value-laden terms as "useful."

Anonymous: Right now we are jumping down Mr. Shipman's back trying to say that industry is the cause of most of our pollution and we are not questioning our own individual values. I think what Mr. Smith was trying to do was to question individual values and decide what we ourselves want to do in order to stop pollution. Instead of getting on Mr. Shipman's back, we should now question our own values in what we do to pollute our environment. For one thing, a question was raised by Dr. Murray about our human waste. An example of this point would be, when we die our bodies waste. I think they're made to be waste in our culture due to the mortician practices we follow. We would be a handful of dust if we were allowed to rot naturally, but we're not. We are embalmed, put in a casket, put in a concrete vault, and stuck in the ground. Much of the ground used for cemeteries could be used for other things. This is a definite value judgment that we follow, and it is questionable. Is this the way to do things, or should we be cremated?

Dr. Murray: Perhaps it would be better if we would make ourselves food for the birds. If you burn something you still insult the environment, but if you feed the birds there is no waste.

Anonymous: Or what about the possibility of having human beings eat human bodies that have died naturally?

Dr. Murray: I hope recycling doesn't reach that stage in my generation!

Mr. Gorder: I'd like to try to answer the question that was posed to Mr. Shipman on Procter and Gamble's throw-away items which flush down the toilet. Obviously, they are produced because it is profitable to produce them. If before the next stockholders' meeting the president of Procter and Gamble were to decide not to produce this profitable item and he reported to the stockholders at the next meeting that their profits dropped six cents per share because he discontinued this profitable item due to ecological considerations, he would no longer be president of Procter and Gamble. This is the reason it is produced, and it therefore seems to me that if you want to stop this type of production you should tax it either as a tax on production or on consumption, which would make it unprofitable to produce such items. Then, during the next stockholders' meeting the president could report the discontinuance of this product because it became unprofitable to produce. And, he would get a raise for doing it.

Mr. Barhydt (Assistant for Environmental Affairs, DuPont Co.): I have a comment. I'm from the DuPont Company and you will have a shot at me tomorrow. But I did want to support Mr. Shipman since we sell the dyes that go into toilet tissue. We also can find no evidence that dyes pollute. If there is evidence, we'd like to know about it too. I would also like to point out that very often we get set with an idea and we don't go beyond that idea. For example, the nonleaded gasoline which you are encouraged to buy. There is evidence, and it's pretty hard evidence, that the aromatics used to raise the octane in nonleaded gasoline are carcinogenic. We really haven't had too much public dialogue about this. So there are trade-offs you have to make in many of these areas. I just wanted to mention that even though in a lot of towns people talk about what they put down the toilet, they don't consider where it goes. Do they actually have adequate sewage treatment in their own town? Are they willing to back a bond issue to pay for sewage treatment and are they willing to go to the congressmen and demand that they get some federal money to support sewage treatment? I think these questions are very often not raised!

Dr. Murray: These are indeed serious questions and I think that if we, by having this symposium, exposed you to some energetic students in Sheboygan high schools, we will have accomplished quite a bit!

Mr. Smith: It seems to me that as far as this question of profitability is concerned and who makes what and why, we're the ones that make Pampers profitable. As far as disposing of them, if we don't want them to be profitable, if we don't want whoever makes an item to make it, we could mail our dirty Pampers back to the manufacturers in their plastic bags. I think that would probably make them unprofitable. We could do the same thing with our used colored toilet paper if we didn't want to flush it. There are ways to deal with these problems as individuals if we want to, and we can get together and do something. We don't really have to accomplish this in big groups either. We have to open our eyes to different approaches because it is the standard approaches which have led to where we are now. If we continue to use the same kind of approaches, we are likely to go in the same direction. I think we have to look for different ways of doing things rather than saying, "How can we go on in the same direction, just moving a little bit one way or the other?"

Student (Lawrence University): I was wondering if a gentleman from the university would comment on how the university as a group could be more effective than it is right now?

Dr. Murray: In any specific way? Do you mean more effective in environmental concerns?

Student: In environmental matters concerning, perhaps, changing values in the university and in the community.

Mr. Kirk (student, UWGB): I think a special concern would be this Saturday's nationwide demonstrations against the war in Viet Nam. I think that if you are openminded enough about it, you can carry that concern over and consider something against the war in Viet Nam which supports the whole system of consumption and income generation. We build ships, we build guns, and then we build men to go over and fight and consume. I think we should get out on Saturday and show the people in the country that we want this kind of thing to stop. We want to take the money that is put into defense purposes and rechannel it into other areas. The comment was made that empirical evidence is not easily come by. I think that if we had some funding for that kind of thing, we could have a cost-benefit analysis that would show us how expensive it is to pollute. So I think that a very good thing to do would be to support the anti-war demonstration as an extension of anti-pollution demonstration.

Dr. Murray: (To the panel) Would any of you care to address yourself to the question the gentleman raised about how the university could be more effective?

Mr. Shipman: Yes, I would. The first thing that comes to my mind are the lapel pins I see worn around here today. I would like to find out where they came from. I would especially like to get the one that has the little green half-moon on it with the inscription "Education is the Key" written around it. I think that's very true. Let us assume for a moment that dyed paper is worse than white paper. I won't assert that, I'm simply assuming it. But, you didn't know they weren't harmful and had you known you would have behaved differently. Well, that's an example of the value of education in this regard.

It seems to me, one thing the university could be doing that it's not doing is setting more concrete examples. When I was speaking earlier, I made a reference to the amount of light in this room. We really could do with less light in here and this thing would work. Many times in the classrooms we could do with less light. It has been tried. If the heat in the university were turned down a little bit over the winter it would be a small example of the types of things that could be done, but there are a lot of things. The university looks very much like any other university, and on the surface it doesn't really seem to be setting any really fantastic example of its commitment to ecological problems. We are here to talk about what we can do about ecological problems, but there is nothing that makes us look any different than a group of businessmen trying to figure out how to sell more colored toilet paper. We could set more examples that were more education-oriented, that were oriented toward identifying the problems and what can be done about them. I think the function of the university in this regard is primarily education, as well as the problem of finding out environmental relationships. This latter task is perhaps a more fundamental but a much slower process in which the returns will come in over a much longer period of time. There are two things: one is to spread the knowledge that is now available, and the other is to generate new knowledge.

Dr. Kolka: I would like to respond to that question in a couple of ways. That is why we are here in the symposium and that is exactly what we are hoping to accomplish. Too many of these issues are understood on a shallow basis. It's like going out and holding up a sign in front of a tree protesting against floods. So the flood comes and sweeps you away and you return saying, "Well, this didn't seem to work, I think I will try something else." The sign accomplished nothing. The need at present is to identify the real depth of these problems. I have had an opportunity to examine some of the papers presented here in advance, and I see some of the values and issues which need to be articulated. After we know the issues, we can move to the next phase and focus our energies on solutions. This is one type of response. It isn't the only response and it doesn't mean all people are doing it.

As a second type of response in which a university can get involved, I will use a different type of example. At present I am involved in a research project in Marinette County where a group of us are attempting to work with the county board to develop alternative management possibilities for problems of eutrophi-cation (lake aging or decay). I would hope that the university in the future would do more of this sort of thing and begin to throw its collective juices into articulating problems and integrating this material into the classroom. We need to bring new information, new perspectives into courses and begin to generate our own material. For the most part, UWGB is going to have to generate all of its own material because the texts and general information are inadequate in this area. The other portion of university activity is that we get actively involved in worrying about and solving local problems. In other words, identifying with our own environment. That isn't a total solution, and that doesn't answer all aspects of your question, but that is part of the reason we had this conference.

Dr. Khare (faculty, UWGB): I want to join two other speakers in relation to the role which the university could play in attacking the problem of environmental improvement. One certain way of doing that is that we attend both the aspects of the problem which are fundamental—social and technologi-cal. We talk about education, which basically means both communication and motivation whether on an individual basis or on a collective basis. Such a definition looks simple, but in practice it is far more complicated. Motivations may be easily acquired but are also lost equally quickly. The question is of continued motivation so that some social action is precipitated. Only a sustained motivation and effective communication bring about the so-called "grass root change" in a society. Normally, we do not have similar tracks of motivation and we don't communicate on the same level as we think we do. There are always certain differences in them that could go unnoticed and that's why Jim Kolka's remarks about depth studies are very important. That's where the contribution from the academic field comes in. The responsibility of The University of Wisconsin—Green Bay which considers itself to be a multidisciplinary, pan-disciplinary, and interdisciplinary institution devoted to problems of man and his environment is especially enormous in this area. We have charged ourselves with the responsibility of motivating ourselves constantly to be able to motivate the students and adults who come in contact with us. And one definite way of doing so is to make sure that it is done on both individual and collective bases.

In the context of motivation of the common masses, two broad aspects that must be constantly kept in mind are work and home. After all, we must realize that home and office, and home and the society-at-large are not separate worlds. These are worlds mutually interlocked, and if a problem like that of the environment has to be attacked, it must be attacked on both fronts equally strongly so that the individual as well as the collective get simultaneously motivated. Further, they must be motivated strongly enough to yield continued social action for the resolution of the problem. Once this is understood, such examples of "polluters" as automobiles, chemicals, synthetic fibers, etc., stand in a better perspective. Their engrained usage shows that the man creating and using them must ultimately change his own motivation towards these objects. Otherwise, the environmental issue will only remain a slogan. Finally, the problem of social change we face here is not new; one could compare it to the complexity of any other problem, including those of political and economic development and social inequality.

Dr. Murray: Thank you, Dr. Khare. We are nearing the close of this session so I am going to restrict our discussion and ask for one question from the audience and a comment from Dr. Brewer.

Mr. Sarns (student, UWGB): I didn't have a question per se, but just a point. I think the whole pollution problem is looked at differently by different people. Some here seem to think that it is production or industry, but I think Mr. Smith brought out the point also that it is not just industry, but our demand, want or need of this stuff. It also produces jobs people want. Ironically, jobs are produced in order for us to purchase goods. If you send all your polluting goods back, you are going to put other people out of work and reduce the problem and alter the whole interaction. We are really discussing a problem which is an aggregate cooperation or interaction between everybody.

Dr. Brewer: Actually, I had a similar kind of track in mind. I did want to pick up from the comment about motivation and the needs for motivation. I think that motivation is needed for a great many changes. This is a complex business that we are speaking of; it is not melodrama and there is no single villain, even though people may want to point the finger at industry, or government, or at the GNP, or at red towels. It is extremely complicated. We have many environmental systems within which we live. On this panel we have only been speaking, incidentally, about the natural biological and physical systems. We also have the social relationships which communities engender, the frictions, conflict, jarring of nerves, psyches, and what not. We are in the middle of many systems, and changes are needed in many of those systems.

On the motivational question, I would submit that these changes can best be made under conditions of economic prosperity. I haven't heard it today, and I was very surprised, but in many other colloquia of this type someone always pops up and says, "Well, we've got to end growth, we cannot grow, and it is the industrial system that is causing a great deal of the trouble. If we stop growth, our problems will be answered." What I am suggesting is that there are many transformations involved which will cause the displacement of people, their locating and assuming new kinds of professional and functional activities. These changes will probably necessitate psychological adjustments to longer periods of leisure time during the day. All of these changes are greatly facilitated under conditions of material prosperity. Under conditions of high unemployment and retarded growth or decline, I think the resistance to change of this kind is extraordinarily high. In a democratic political system such as the United States, I think it just increases the length of time that those changes will be made by orders of magnitude. So I really would suggest, for motivational reasons, that it is important to recognize material prosperity as a colleague of healthy environments. I think this is possible, and I think the changes in production, the changes in employment patterns, in locations of human settlement, etc., will require capital. That capital must come from an economic system which is basically a vigorous one, and one which is producing an accumulation of wealth from which these changes can be financed.

Dr. Murray: Thank you, Dr. Brewer. I was raised with the American Indian people and I know an old Indian chief who would argue with you vehemently, because he would contend that the American Indian economy could have lasted forever. But that's not the point here. Thank you for your remarks and thank you very much, audience, for your fine participation.

An Overview

In his concluding remarks in the panel discussion, Dr. Brewer accurately pointed to the primary dimension of the first panel's concern, namely, "natural biological and physical systems." Resource economists were among the first disciplines who evidenced a growing concern with environmental stress.

The resource economists share this honor with the ecologists who look at biological systems as interrelated, gradually evolving and mutually interdependent. Man the organism, rather than man the ruler, cast humans in the role of a species and raised serious questions about the quality and extent of human survival. (For a poetic exposition of this point, see Leopold 1968.)

The other major discipline to show alarm with environmental stress were the demographers, who began to speculate that Thomas Malthus might be considered a prophet, rather than a dismal chronicler of his times. Their mathematical projections for human populations and corrections for technological mutations accelerating population growth, revealed that human beings could outstrip the carrying capacity of their planet. (Best known among works with a demographic perspective would be Ehrlich 1968 and, Ehrlich and Ehrlich 1970.)

The combination of these perspectives is a natural bridge for resource economists, who direct a portion of their intellectual energies to examining physical dimensions of the planet earth and its ability to support rapidly expanding human technologies. This type of academic probing immediately raises political, economic and social questions; to whom do the resources belong? what are the political and social dimensions of their exploitation? what alternative resources are available for use? what costs will the extraction, production, consumption and waste have upon the physical and social locus of these activities? This type of economic search begins to unravel some of the biosocial complexities of the environmental problem. (For a most provocative analysis of this point, Boulding 1965, 1970a, 1970b.)

Although the primary basis for discussion in the first panel might be "natural, biological and physical systems," it should be noted that the two position papers concentrated on social interaction with the environment. Dr. Murray noted a most profound problem, namely, the sheer difficulty of interacting with (measuring) the environment. As humans, we are captives of our tools of measuring the economic universe. Yet, these very tools are the means used to identify reality or "problems of the real world." While the rewriting of this societal dilemma would make a most amusing satire, it illustrates the subtlety of dealing with environmental problems. We have to develop the capacity to competently identify, measure and account for the physical environment in our bid for a quality existence.

Since values are imbedded in every measuring device, a discussion of values would make an appropriate topic for consideration. It is to this point that Mr. Smith directs his paper. He is concerned that questions of a qualitative survival be made open to human choice and not left to the vagaries or caprice of an occasionally directed social evolution. Although questioned for its efficacy in the panel discussion, his solution is to encourage small group interaction with questions of choice.

Finally, the panel discussion brings forth another dimension of the economic analysis of environmental problems. It is apparent that economists have to draw upon related social science perspectives (political, social, cultural, psychological) in order to deal with the physical environment. For persons dealing with the day-to-day parameters of economic pressure, such as Mr. Shipman as a corporate representative, the questions are immediate survival and success in the business world. The ensuing discussion of that world revealed the degree of concern with short- and long-range economic questions. It is apparent that the removal of air and water from the category of free commodities will have a social cost. It is also apparent that a genuine understanding of the existing American economic world (as opposed to some of the more popular myths expressed in the discussion statements) will need the considerable energies of economists with an evangelical fervor for a new enlightenment. (Provocative works directed to this task would include the earlier cited efforts of Boulding, Galbraith 1958, 1967, Mishan 1967, 1970, Means 1969, Berle 1954, 1956 and Heilbroner 1970.)

J.W.K.

PART 2

Man Versus Nature

Environmental Approaches and Policies

Gerard A. Rohlich

I don't like to begin with an apology, but I must apologize to the other members of the panel here who did not have the opportunity to see a copy of my remarks before just now. However, I feel that because they weren't constrained by what I said, their remarks perhaps will be even more meaningful to you in terms of the total theme of the Conference on Environmental Quality and Social Responsibility.

I was asked to present some remarks particularly with regard to the impact of technology and its influence on the environment, some of the environmental problems that develop, and some of the questions in regard to policies and approaches that must be taken. I'm sure that both Professor Taylor and Professor Thompson will be giving you specific points with regard to these kinds of problems.

During the past 25 years, most of you know, there has been unprecedented activity and attention directed to the relationships between science, technology, and the humanities. It seems evident from these discussions amongst social and natural scientists and scholars in the humanities and also, of course, creative artists, that the impact of science and technology in shaping modern culture has become so significant that our modern society may justifiably be called a scientific culture, or perhaps more realistically a technological culture. Much of the early discussion amongst the scientists and scholars in the humanities centered around the need for more meaningful communication between these humanistic and scientific aspects of knowledge. More recently the impact of scientific and technological discovery, development and application in the environment and on the environment has become a primary consideration. As Rene Dubos (1965) pointed out some years ago, "the industrial revolution with mass production of energy and its rapid injection into all aspects of social life, is everywhere beginning to disrupt the great dynamic processes, which have so far maintained the earth in a state compatible with human life." The further point is made that, as a major institution or ingredient in our culture, the impact of science extends beyond the technological and engineering developments that have resulted from the application of the findings of scientists, and has, of course, a deep and strong influence on social habits. Many of the most important advances in science have been made with purpose and directly in recognition of a practical goal to aid man. In fact, technology has been defined by Bronowski (1956) as the "application of scientific knowledge to human problems and is a natural outcome of man's constant attempt to use his abilities in order to satisfy certain particular ends. Thus, in reality, technology has no meaning apart from humanity. It is, in fact, shaped by man's nature and by his historical and social circumstance." The interrelationship of science and technology and the feedback to basic research from technological developments, which themselves have been stimulated by science, have made it difficult "for the intellectuals as well as the wider public to find a basic difference between technology and science." (Holton 1965) As Sherwin noted a few years ago in an article in the *Saturday Review,* the combination of modern science and a highly sophisticated technology serve not merely as a basis for the nation's wealth and military power, but are also primary tools of social and economic revolution, which "have produced a crisis in the management of technology, particularly with respect to the public interest. Modern technology has become so complex that to manage it properly requires even more sophisticated technology and, as a result, it has become necessary to establish a man-machine partnership for successful organization and operation of business or government." This dependence on the machines and our daily conversations with the machine touch practically all of society. This is evident, of course, to all of you here, to the average citizen if you pay taxes or own an automobile or have a charge account, or register at the university, then you find it, of course, sometimes quite frustrating if for some reason or other you do reach disagreement with the computer.

We're all familiar, at least in a general way, with the history of mankind and the peculiar ability of man amongst the animals to exercise considerable control over his environment. Whereas most other animals must fit into the environment as best they can, man creates his environment, and through technology which is the sum total of all the different techniques he has developed, he may change his environment. If desirable, at least he can take the physical environment with him. . .in his automobile, in his home or in any other particular situation in which he may wish to control his physical environment. As I have mentioned previously, technology and social development are inseparable, and new discoveries, whether they be the use of natural objects such as sticks and stones for tools, or of natural processes such as fire for making pottery or glass or to work metals, have unfailingly resulted in social changes. Through his constant improvement of implements and mastery of the forces of nature, one cannot deny that man has enjoyed a succession of victories in his struggle for existence. The invention of the steam engine and the industrial revolution, although to say the least, had a disturbing effect on social traditions, freed many men from manual labor and brought new demands on science and technology, particularly in the development of power to make better, more efficient engines, grow more food and speed communications in an effort to further relieve man of routine manual labor. We are now more concerned with the development of new electronic devices which will be able to free man from routine mental work. This development has, in fact, become a necessity. The speed and complexity of operations in many communications control systems are so great that human vigilance and control are neither fast enough nor sufficiently dependable. The concept of feedback is by no means a new one, and the control systems in nature and the way in which animals grow and adapt themselves to changes or recovery from injuries or learn from experience are examples of the feedback system. The fundamental principle of cybernetics is that information about a system is the sole means of controlling that system. Or, as Forrester (1961) has stated, "an information feedback system exists whenever the environment [which is an input] leads to a decision [which is an output] that results in an action which affects the environment [back to the input] and thereby influences future decisions [again to the output]." The simplest physical example of communication and control is, of course, evident to all of you in the thermostat that controls the temperature of a boiler or a room. If the boiler is too hot, the metal rod expands, turns off the electricity to the fuel pump. As the boiler cools, the metal contracts and switches on the power supply. The information—this boiler is too hot or too cold—is automatically the control: feed less, feed more fuel to the heating unit. After all, Watts' flyball generator in 1798 was an early application of the cybernetic principle. The information about the process, engine turning too fast-too slow, is itself the means of controlling the process. This principle of information engineering is important in biological and social phenomena as well as in engineering and physical systems. Information engineering thus is a region of human activity which deals with the operation of components and systems to sense physical quantities, and from these inputs to generate operating commands for the machine and the organizations that serve the needs and desires of mankind. Although instrumentation in itself involves operations in excess of the billion-dollar-a-year level, we can say that it is still in its infancy as far as applications are concerned. Dr. Draper of the MIT Instrumentation Laboratory points out that because of its universal importance and its great remaining growth potential, instrumentation may reasonably be considered one of the most important frontier regions of today's technology. The shift from human operators to inanimate equipment will provide revolutionary new features in capacity, speed, reliability, accuracy, size, weight, operating cost, and general utility. The implications of automation are self-evident. "Greater productivity will result, but so will changes which seem to be a killer of skills that have been acquired to support men and their families. But automation is a cost control and cost-cutting process, and through automation, associated with a production and utilization of computers, the United States may well stay ahead in the competitive race despite high labor costs." Through automation, industry can achieve lower unit production cost by raising output per man hour. As a result it can afford to pay higher wages to its workers without impairing profit. Dr. Rader of the G.E. Company has pointed out that the criticisms of automation could have been said about the pen versus the typewriter or the mechanical calculator versus the electronic computer. There are, of course, many factors that are involved. Automation may change the skill required by the machine operator, it may change the educational level required, it may change the geographical location where the work is performed, it may require people to adapt themselves to a greater degree of leisure and for the man who can't learn the new skills or new job, or won't move to a new location, or can't adjust psychologically to rapid changes, automation may mean unemployment. The requirements placed on information systems by the complex electric power systems which depend on accurate adjustment to voltage and frequency, the use of high performance aircraft, the development of ballistic missiles and the design of space vehicles have forced performance much beyond the capabilities of human response in complexity, accuracy, speed, length of working period, reliability, and in environments too severe for comfort or even in some cases for survival of human beings. Self-contained guidance systems in space craft can receive, process and apply information to keep the object so controlled on course at great range. And we have come to realize that information systems are now recognized as necessities in business, industry and transportation.

Thus far the application of these principles embodied in cybernetics and information engineering has proved itself in the engineering and physical sciences and has had an important impact on biological theory in the recognition that the transmission of genetic properties from generation to generation is essentially a communication of information. As Brooks (1965) states, "one suspects that it may be possible to apply information concepts similarly to the study of cultural evolution and to the transmission of culture from generation to generation," and "in the case of the concept of feedback, the ideas appear to have an essentially quantitative and operational significance for social and cultural dynamics."

It's clear from this brief recital that technology does not end with the invention and application of mechanical tools and physical systems, but that we are in the infant stages of a new technology which we can call social or human engineering, which we must be aware of and apply properly to show how social life can be better managed. This, then, is the social responsibility aspect that becomes evident as technology and an understanding of technology and its implications develop. Involvement in this area is a reality and the application of technology in understanding and improving the environment is currently the subject of a number of research investigations at several universities. And, of course, it is a principal area of activity here at The University of Wisconsin— Green Bay. Fortunately, however, as evidenced by this symposium, we have come to recognize more fully the dimensions of environmental quality in the man-machine relationship. And it is clear as Dubos (1965) points out that "the disjunction between man's nature and the creations of science and technology inevitably manifests itself in social disturbances." These are the kinds of social disturbances and environmental problems that you are addressing yourselves to in this symposium. All the background briefing that I mentioned in regard to information systems and feedback may not have seemed particularly relevant to your specific questions. I think the important application is in the question of the impact that technology and science have in creating these social disturbances. As Dubos (1965) has said, "Land conservation, water resources, urban development, the physiological and mental qualities of the human race are but a few among the problems created by the impact of scientific technology. It is therefore a moral obligation for the scientific establishment to devote itself in earnest to the study of ecosystems." And this, of course, is the approach that is being taken. No longer are we willing to accept the deterioration of the environment as the price to be paid for progress. We recognize that the world's problems cannot be solved simply by making better machines or growing more food or increasing the speed of communication. For example, some recent statistical data would indicate that as the production of food has increased in the period of 1955 to 1965 by about 35%, the number of tractors to bring about that increased agricultural production increased some 63%, and pesticide production increased 120%. If we recognize that the increase in production of food takes even a larger percentage increase in technology, we recognize some of the environmental problems that can develop. So merely making better machines or growing more food or increasing the speed of communication is not in itself the only kinds of tasks that we look to. The environment is recognized as really "the aggregate of all the external conditions and influences affecting the development and life of an organism. In the case of man, this means not only the physical and biological environment but also the stresses and strains of the social environment."

Some thirteen years ago Dr. Kehoe, in a conference similar to this on Man Versus Environment (1958), made the pertinent statement that "the chief feature which distinguishes man from other animals is an ability to reason, and through his intelligence determine what he does to himself and his environment." In the future we will be finding that the selection of new technology will be determined to a large extent by the anticipated environmental effects. This is something that we have, I think, neglected in the past in our considerations of new technological developments.

As we come to the state of Wisconsin and some of the problems with which we are concerned, we recognize, of course, that in the water resources area, the particular area in which I have been working, many lakes and streams have been a subject of great pride to the citizens of the state. Exclusive of the Great Lakes, the more than 8,800 inland lakes and thousands of miles of streams cover in excess of 3% of the state's surface, and, of course, as it is well known to you people in this area, are assets of recreational and aesthetic value that are immeasurable and have played and will continue to play a dominant role in the economy of the state.

It is clear that the first priority use of our water is for municipal supplies, but many of our industries are dependent on water, not only for processing, but especially for waste disposal principally to streams. Rural nonfarm use as well as rural farm use for domestic purposes and livestock watering, and the expansion of supplemental irrigation makes significant demands in our water resources. Water-based recreation in hunting, fishing, swimming, boating, and scenic beauty has been a major factor in Wisconsin's attractiveness to the millions of tourists who look to the state as a leader in conservation. In addition to our bountiful supply of surface water, we are fortunate in having an abundant reserve of ground water, which supplies more than 90% of the municipal waterworks systems. Although less than 10% of our municipal systems obtain their water from surface supplies, these sources supply more than 50% of the population. If we add to our extensive water resources within the land boundaries of the state, the availability of Lake Superior (the largest fresh-water body in the world) on the north, Lake Michigan on the east and to the west the Mississippi River, it's evident that Wisconsin can be considered a water-rich state. Despite the favorable position of the state with regard to its quantity of water, there's an increasing and conflicting demand for its use which results in problems not only with regard to quantity but more particularly with regard to water quality. It's obvious, however, that water quality and water pollution control cannot be separated from the broader problems of the development and use of the water resources. In fact, we have come to realize that the inner changes which occur in the air, land and water resources must be evaluated when decisions regarding development and control of land and water resources are to be made. Residential and industrial development alters the land, often with major impact on the quality, not only of the water immediately adjacent but often for long distances downstream. Recognition of the need for the integration of water resource programs and land use is a primary thrust of the Wisconsin Water Resources Act of 1966. The provisions of this legislation present many challenges, not only to improve the environment in correcting the abuses of the past, but also with recognition of the need to prepare for the future. We must not separate present activity from contemplation of our future needs. Planning for the future in one sense is a much more critical requirement than the urgent measures now needed to correct the existing conditions, which are in a large part the result of inadequate planning in the past. This is by no means a new concept. For thousands of years mankind has been aware of the dangers accompanying disposal of human waste and other refuse and of the impact of technology on the environment. It's not the intent in these remarks to provide a chronological development of water pollution control since you are all aware that the problem is not a new one. It's of interest, however, to reflect on some of the earliest statements with regard to water pollution and in water quality and environmental deterioration and to note the parallel with the language used today. Let me recite this brief story which I told before and I'm sure some of you have heard before. On the 9th of July in 1842, which was noted as a summer of social protest in England, Edwin Chadwick, secretary to the Poor Commissioners in Great Britain, presented a report on the sanitary conditions of the laboring population of Great Britain. This was presented to the House of Lords. The report had been three years in preparation and although it drew information and statistics from many sources, it was in a large part an individual effort by Chadwick. Chadwick, as a civil servant lawyer, had been working in this area for some years, but it wasn't until this report of 1842 that action in the public health movement took place, leading to the Public Health Act of 1848. Time does not permit discussing the many details of Chadwick's report, but it is of interest to note that the greater part of the report was devoted to establishing "four major axioms": The first section, about half of the report, established the factual basis showing the correlation between insanitation, defective drainage, inadequate water supply, overcrowded housing and the relationship of these with disease, high mortality rates and low expectation of life. The second section was devoted to the economic cost of ill health. The third section dealt with the social cost of squalor, and the fourth point was concerned with administration in which Chadwick concerned himself with the inherent inefficiency of existing legal and administrative machinery. In this he argued, "The only hope of sanitary improvement lay in radical administrative departures which would call for new institutional arrangements." Flynn, Chadwick's biographer, pointed out that Chadwick was conscious that, "centralization would be resisted with all the vigor and fanaticism which landholders, commissioners of sewers and police in several hundred boroughs, vestries, and privately owned water companies could muster." It's obvious that today we are in many respects echoing Chadwick's axioms, first, in detailing the factual parts of the problem, then discussing the economic and social costs, and finally seeking legal and institutional arrangements to administer corrective measures.

In another historical parallel with the language used today, attention has been directed to the industrial waste problem. In 1865 the Royal Commission on River Pollution was appointed for the purpose of inquiring, in addition to other matters, "How far by new arrangements the refuse arising from industrial processes can be kept out of the streams or rendered harmless before it reaches them or utilized or got rid of otherwise than by discharge into running waters." It seemed that the problem had been solved quite readily, for the first report of the 1868 Royal Commission stated that "of the many polluting liquids which now poison the rivers, there is not one which cannot be either kept out of the streams altogether or so far purified before admission as to deprive it of its noxious character." Evidently the wish was father to the thought but the progeny never matured, and a third of a century later, in 1910, the statement was made, "The whole problem of trade wastes is one which must occupy a large share of our attention in the future. Such wastes usually offer such serious difficulties in connection with the ordinary processes of sewage disposal that it would in many cases be advisable to require their treatment by some special procedure before they are permitted to enter the public sewers or discharge into any stream." Twenty-five years later, in 1935, the United States National

Resources Committee had this to say about the industrial waste problem: "The essential approach to the problem of ridding stream waters of undesirable industrial wastes lies in the active cooperation of the industries involved. Always assuming, however, flexible in reasonably administered water pollution legislation. The problem cannot be solved by abstract studies on the part of the government nor by inflexible and arbitrary state or federal legislation. Waste materials are so diverse and so complex that each industry, and possibly each plant, represents a special problem." In the past 35 years since the publication of the National Resources Committee report, the number of articles written concerning the water pollution problems runs well into the thousands. Many of these present valuable information on the manner in which specific problems have been attacked and solved or partially solved. Many are of a general nature and nearly all contain a statement in the opening paragraph to the effect that the problem is a serious one, a fact that we are willing to accept without further comment. Throughout the past one hundred years the major effort has been directed toward solving the technical aspects of the water pollution problem. But until the analysis by Renshaw there had been far too little attention directed to the economic issues involved in pollution control. As Renshaw points out, "Although considerable resources have been used to pull together the costs of waste treatment, nothing has been done to determine the point or rate at which the demand to pollute breaks away from the alternative cost of waste disposal." Despite all that has been written and the unprecedented activity of recent years with regard to the problem of the conservation of the quality of our receiving streams and lakes and of the effects of pollutional materials on the quality of these waters, our progress has been painfully slow. To some extent we are running on a treadmill, barely fast enough in many instances to stay even with increasing pollutional loads and the introduction of newly uncovered environmental impacts from increased population, urbanization and industrial development.

Future policies and legislation must be aimed at preventive measures. As Mortimer stated, "prophylactic action should be preferable to therapeutic." It is true that in the field of water pollution control there exists a technology to treat waste waters to any level of purity, either for human consumption, maintenance of biological balance in receiving waters, or aesthetic enjoyment if the individuals concerned are able to expend the necessary resources to accomplish the task. Stated in economic terms, the state of the art is available to supply the quality of waste treatment that is demanded wherever the user is willing to pay the cost. Although we may believe that progress has been slow in improving water quality, as measured by the usual parameters of biological oxygen demand and solids reduction, as this somewhat more gross pollution is removed, we have come to recognize that even more complex problems confront us. One of these problems is eutrophication. The term eutrophication refers to the process of enrichment of water with nutrients. The literal meaning of eutrophication stems directly from the Greek eu, meaning well, and trephein, to nourish. Little distinction has been given to the difference between the terms eutrophication and pollution. These terms are not synonymous although it is true that the discharge of waste material often adds nutrients to receiving water bodies which increase the production of both free-floating plants such as algae and other forms of planktonic growth as well as the rooted aquatic plants. The process of eutrophication is one that goes on under natural conditions. What is disturbing is that the process is accelerated as a result of man's activities in altering the landscape by agricultural development, urbanization, and, in particular, by the discharge of sewage, industrial wastes and waste treatment plant effluents.

In confronting this problem and the problem of contamination of water supplies and degradation of water quality by pesticides, we see the need to develop a policy to control the discharges from nonpoint or diffuse sources as well as from the point sources of municipal and industrial waste flows. To control more effectively the quantity and quality of our water resources, it is becoming increasingly important that we take a comprehensive view of the total environment rather than approach problems on an individual basis. This, of course, is the main thrust as was pointed out by Dr. Klare in his opening remarks of this symposium.

In the past it was virtually impossible to consider large multi-use systems because of the lack of adequate accounting systems to evaluate these complex projects. The developments of computers and computer-use technology for information, storage and retrieval, simulation modeling, and optimization techniques have extended our capabilities to study these vast and complicated systems.

Development of conceptual models for systematic programs that identify units and factors that influence a system can include alternative methods and levels of control, including not only the budget constraints, the management control measures and enforcement schemes that may be employed to control the level of water quality within the desired goals, but such investigations will also make it possible to evaluate not only those direct costs and benefits which are normally identified, but also the social values which usually escape quantification. The development of these models provides a capability that may meet Chadwick's axioms of 1842 and can be followed by action programs. With the full development of factual information, economic and social costs and analysis that can be made by this technology, the protection of our water resources or land resources or air resources will have benefited from the professional advice, agency control, and the political and judicial decisions that are made in the light of the comprehensive approach rather than from the limited view that we have had in the past.

ed against the public's desire for a quality environment (and
to impose legal/political constraints upon the) activity—
to allow it to proceed unhampered—positive feedback.

l is obviously better equipped to enable decision-makers to
anagement strategy than the preceding two, it possesses
are readily apparent when long-range future time periods are
model still puts economic well-being against environmental
model fails to recognize that negative linkages exist between
health and deteriorating environmental quality, it fails to
cial economic disservices and external costs which tend to
se of time, or at locations remote from the origin of the
Second, the model still regards political and legal factors as
er than integral, highly mutable parts of a unified system,
environmental constraints. Finally, the model views the
the yes-no type. Either the activity can be continued or it
t least retarded). By failing to take into account the infinite
ent alternatives that exist respecting the use of a given
while it allows society to react to situations, fails to provide
r planning the future. (Figures 3 & 4)

THE "ECONOMICS VERSUS ENVIRONMENT" APPROACH

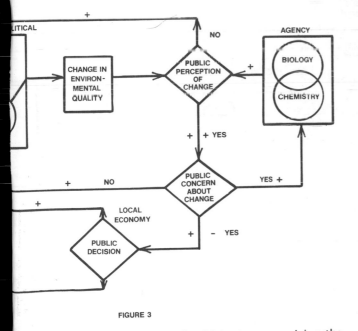

FIGURE 3

pose a new model (Figure 4) which, by recognizing the
s that can and do exist between the natural environment,
and legal/political forces, will allow us to make better
the way in which man will manage his environment. This
veral important respects from the previous ones. First, legal

Biophysical Environment
And Human Behavior:
Linkages and Feedback Systems

Thomas W. Thompson with Allen E. Bedrosian,
James E. Berry, and James W. Kolka*

As Dr. Rohlich has pointed out, human technology and human society are
interlinked in a complex manner and react with the physical environment,
forming a complex system that may be considered as a series of feedback loops
between decisions and the physical environment.

As we see it, the basic cause of the environmental problems facing society
today is a lack of appreciation and understanding of the intimate linkages

existing between the physical and the social environments. This lack of understanding leads to oversimplification of the models employed in reaching decisions which govern the management of society's resources, and subsequently leads to inadequate management strategies, programs and policies. (Figure 1)

THE "UNRESTRAINED MARKET" APPROACH

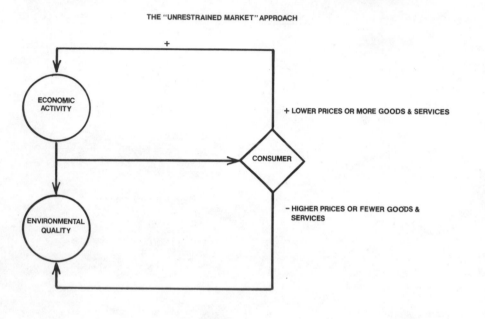

FIGURE 1

The simplest model employed with respect to environmental policy is shown in Figure 1 and is based solely upon decisions concerning product prices reached by agreement between a manufacturer and a consumer. Should the consumer be willing, according to this model, to include the cost of maintaining environmental quality in the price he pays for a product or service, well and good. If he desires ever-increasing quantities of goods and services at ever-decreasing prices, then environmental quality becomes a luxury his society cannot afford. A surprising number of individuals today insist on conceptualizing the relationships between the physical environment and human activities in terms of a negative feedback loop—increasing prices, or a positive feedback loop—lower prices, and place confidence in an unrestrained market and the concern of the consumer and manufacturer for their fellow citizens to maintain environmental quality.

*The work which enabled the authors to develop the information in this paper was funded by the Office of Water Resources Research, The University of Wisconsin—Green Bay and Marinette County through a matching grant (B—046—WIS) administered by the Wisconsin Water Resources Center. The assistance of these agencies is gratefully acknowledged.

largely as a result of increasing human populat has been created (Figure monitor the bio-physical findings, decisions are n economic activity. In this dominant, and on the government determines feedback, or must be term the "crisis" school of understandably, do some model, which places grea sometimes led to the ag intended to regulate. (Figu

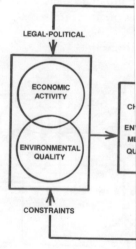

LEGAL-POLITICAL

ECONOMIC ACTIVITY

ENVIRONMENTAL QUALITY

CONSTRAINTS

Most thinking individua arbitrarily, whether by gove implemented without public is emerging in most parts of factors and environmental model, perception of cha individual's direct perceptio information relating to the investigative agencies, must are made. On the basis of t

society can be weig a decision is made negative feedback, o

While this mod determine sound n shortcomings which considered. First, th quality. Because the long-range economi internalize many cr appear after the ela environmental insul rigid constraints rat itself regulated by decision as being of must be halted (or variety of manager resource, the model the tools necessary

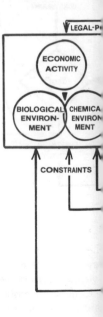

LEGAL-P

ECONOMIC ACTIVITY

BIOLOGICAL ENVIRON-MENT

CHEMICA ENVIRON MENT

CONSTRAINTS

We should p possible relationsh economic activity decisions regarding model differs in s

and political forces are integral parts of a total system. Like any other component of the system, they react to economic or environmental change. Second, the model insists that economic externalities and disservices can be measured and that environmental degradation can be defined in concrete terms rather than on the vague basis of aesthetics. Third, by integrating the efforts of economic, legal/political and bio-physical/chemical investigators, the model produces a variety of management alternatives rather than a single yes-no decision. We are aware that many of the interactions implied in our model are exceedingly complex, that the model still is in need of refinement, and that more factors may still need to be taken into account. However, we feel confident that, without a model which considers the relationships and feedback loops we have defined, it will be impossible to ask the questions necessary to the formulation of meaningful management strategies based on sound and complete predictive information.

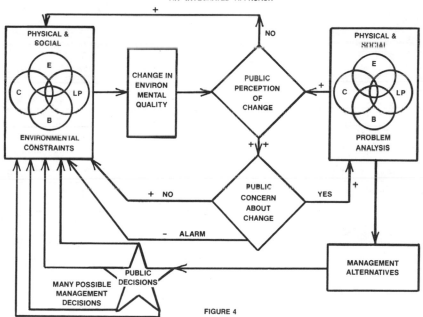

FIGURE 4

Some Social Costs
Of Population Policies

N. B. G. Taylor

Introduction

The purpose of this paper is to approach the theme of man versus nature in terms of social costs, and within the context of human population growth, or of overpopulation.

*This was originally presented with the title "Facing the Costs."

It is important to clarify two points: First, my subject social costs, concerns those matters not normally considered in monetary terms such things as satisfaction, privacy, aesthetic values, the discomfiture of change, good health. I may, however, shift occasionally into costs in the usual sense. Second, whereas I shall confine my remarks to population, this is not to say that all environmental and social problems will be resolved by changes in population growth rate or total numbers (Miles 1970, Coale 1970). It is to say that no proposed solution for these problems that ignores population will succeed. As an opinion, I say that of all the problems, excessive population stands first among peers.

There has been much discussion about what is wrong with the world (overpopulation [Ehrlich 1968], pollution [Dasman 1968], resource depletion [Milton 1968]) and many solutions have been proposed. Somewhat less discussion has been given to the costs of the solutions. Least attention has been directed toward the costs that will accrue after the solutions have become established. It is under these three broad categories that I wish to discuss the social costs of population policies.

The Costs of Continuing on our Present Course

This is a course characterized by absence of a national population policy of any sort except the pronatalist policy implied by the tax exemptions for children and heavy taxation of single persons. Family planning widely accepted today has the objective of helping couples have the number of children they want when they want them but has nothing to say about limiting family size for reasons of national policy. In fact, by increasing health of mother and child, existing family planning programs might increase the number of children. It has been very aptly said that millions of couples practicing family planning does not equal a population policy (Miles 1970). The social costs of implementing this nonpolicy are negligible just because it is *laissez faire*. The eventual costs—social and otherwise—of following this course are quite another matter, and are what many people fear. I refer to the contribution that continued population growth will make to the social deprivation of increasing numbers of persons in the urban ghettos (Hauser 1970), of the isolation and alienation of the suburban ghetto escapees of all ages (Mead 1970). Correlations have now been made between social deprivation and mental and physical illness. Studies have shown that the likelihood of postpartum psychosis increases with the distance from female relatives and friends (Mead 1970). When she made this last statement, Margaret Mead was doing so in the context of the fragmented social organization of suburbia. Every trend is in the direction of increased black-white segregation: blacks in the city centers, whites in the suburbs (Michener 1970). Population increase is not the sole cause of these trends (Miller 1970). But while population continues to grow and exact its demands for new schools, housing, utilities, jobs and recreational facilities, the massive amounts of social and economic capital, goodwill and energy needed to reverse the trend are not available (Wagar 1970).

So far I have done little more than give passing reference to environmentally related disease. Using dollars only to indicate the magnitude of the problem, the annual cost is estimated to be $35 billion in the United States

(Curtin 1970). It is probable, perhaps almost certain, that this is only the small visible portion of the iceberg of social costs which would include unreported disease, reported diseases inadequately treated, substandard performance because of minor intoxications, frayed nerves, irritability, family discords, and even violence, all the result of minor degrees of unhealth. Certainly asthma, impairment of lung function, chronic respiratory disease (including cancer), and eye irritation have been shown to be associated with community air pollution (Lave and Seskin 1970), and there is no reason to believe that those overt diseases are not preceded by varying degrees of dysfunction. Again I must emphasize, these social costs cannot be attributed to population alone. They are increased by increased population densities, which in turn are associated with crowding and social deprivation.

At this point, I deliberately omit any discussion of the social costs of crowded cities, decreased open space, overloaded recreational areas and the many other evidences of decreasing environmental quality which have been so well described by many (Ehrlich 1968, Rienow 1967, Marine 1969). I would allude, however, to some of the social costs in the form of inconveniences, if not discomforts, that are probable, possibly inevitable as increasing population places increasing strain on resources: greater reliance on public transport and bicycles or enforced living in proximity to work; changes in design and construction of buildings to conserve fuel; the need to plan ahead and remember to take reusable containers to the grocery store for foods no longer individually wrapped but sold from bulk; restrictions on the installation and use of flush toilets and the use of domestic water in general.

One would be foolhardy indeed to imply that the trends we observe around us, the widespread deterioration of general living conditions, will continue at the present rates, unchecked. The question is: "Will it be checked soon enough?" or "Will it be reversed in time to prevent deterioration of the environment in the U.S.A. to the level that we see in India today-or worse?" India's problem is poverty; ours could be widespread poisoning of air, water and soil. The social conditions can come about in North America. To reject the possibility out of hand is, I believe, to ignore the one characteristic which, more than any other, distinguishes man from the other animals—his ability to adapt socially or culturally (Dubos 1970). This adaptability has permitted man to survive and dominate other animals. But social adaptation takes social energy, and is a social cost vividly described by Rohlich (1970) as "a cruel killer of skills." Adaptation usually takes the form of an accommodation with the new condition. There is no reason to believe man will not continue to adapt socially to an increasingly deteriorated environment. The status of the 400,000 Calcuttans who are born, live and die in the streets, never having a roof over their heads, has surely been arrived at by this slow, insidious process. We are ourselves socially adapting to foul air, slimy beaches, congested roads, ambient noise and ghettos. Adaptation which has served man so well in the past may "do him in" today. Adaptation in this sense serves to block perception of the noxious condition. I suggest that a more appropriate response to present conditions may be a violent rejection of the impingement of these conditions on our living. Such rejection, however, will require very large amounts of human energy, the investment of large amounts of social capital.

Instituting a Change

The "change" in this case would be to establish a population policy. Do we need one? What would be the social costs?

The position taken here is that a population policy is long overdue. It is less easy to be dogmatic about the nature of such a policy—or perhaps better to say about the degree to which it should attempt to regulate population growth, or if it should be regulated at all.

Population projections are notoriously fallible, but with clearly defined assumptions some can be made with confidence (Frejka 1970, Miles 1971, Commission on Population Growth 1971). If the average number of children per couple immediately becomes two (the replacement rate), the United States population will continue to increase for about 70 years and stabilize at approximately 280 million. One can only guess at the date when, if ever, the two-child family might become the norm. If it is delayed until 1975, the population would stabilize at approximately 295 million. If the population is to be stabilized immediately, the one-child family must become the norm immediately and remain so for 15 to 20 years. One might ask why the immediate establishment of the two-child family would not stabilize the population immediately, or why with the one-child family as the norm there would not be a decrease in population. The reason is that the children of the post-war baby boom are now entering the reproductive years, the same reason that the annual number of births can continue to increase coincident with a decreasing birth rate.

If such stabilizations occur, how will they come about, and what will be the social costs? There will be changes in the genetic composition of the population (Bajema 1971). It will entail sharp changes in social attitudes if they come about voluntarily, or legal sanctions and other forms of coercion if there is not, in effect, universal voluntary acceptance of the need to curtail population growth. Changes of attitudes can be very costly, socially—I refer to changes in attitude toward marriage as an institution, the development of alternative life styles, delayed marriage and family formation, freely available contraceptive information and materials to all sexually active persons, the acceptance of nontherapeutic abortion as an indispensable backup for failures of contraception, and greatly increased practice of voluntary sterilization (Asimov 1971). Although United States attitudes are moving toward wider acceptance of these practices, one quails at the thought of the social upheaval that would result if an attempt were made to bring about a stabilized population within 5 years. The idea that population need never stabilize is, however, being rejected by more and more persons who analyze the problem. The further in the future the day of stabilization is placed, the less rapid is the needed change of foresighted attitudes. At the same time, the greater will be the final population figure (although reliability of projections decreases with time in the future), the more nearly will the situation resemble the "continue as at present" situation and the fewer will be the options—and the greater the final social costs of correction.

The Social Costs of a Stable Population

These will vary quantitatively (Frejka 1970), and to some extent qualitatively (Bajema 1971), depending on the length of time and the means taken to arrive at the stable population. They will be the result, to a large extent, of the

Biophysical Environment And Human Behavior: Linkages and Feedback Systems

Thomas W. Thompson with Allen E. Bedrosian,
James E. Berry, and James W. Kolka*

As Dr. Rohlich has pointed out, human technology and human society are interlinked in a complex manner and react with the physical environment, forming a complex system that may be considered as a series of feedback loops between decisions and the physical environment.

As we see it, the basic cause of the environmental problems facing society today is a lack of appreciation and understanding of the intimate linkages existing between the physical and the social environments. This lack of understanding leads to oversimplification of the models employed in reaching decisions which govern the management of society's resources, and subsequently leads to inadequate management strategies, programs and policies. (Figure 1)

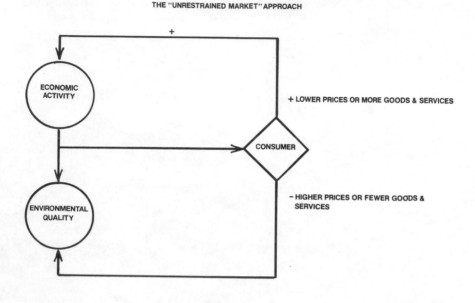

THE "UNRESTRAINED MARKET" APPROACH

FIGURE 1

The simplest model employed with respect to environmental policy is shown in Figure 1 and is based solely upon decisions concerning product prices reached by agreement between a manufacturer and a consumer. Should the consumer be willing, according to this model, to include the cost of maintaining environmental quality in the price he pays for a product or service, well and good. If he desires ever-increasing quantities of goods and services at ever-decreasing prices, then environmental quality becomes a luxury his society cannot afford. A surprising number of individuals today insist on conceptualizing the relationships between the physical environment and human activities in terms of a negative feedback loop—increasing prices, or a positive feedback loop—lower prices, and place confidence in an unrestrained market and the concern of the consumer and manufacturer for their fellow citizens to maintain environmental quality.

*The work which enabled the authors to develop the information in this paper was funded by the Office of Water Resources Research, The University of Wisconsin—Green Bay and Marinette County through a matching grant (B—046—WIS) administered by the Wisconsin Water Resources Center. The assistance of these agencies is gratefully acknowledged.

Largely as a result of the gross inadequacy of this approach in the face of increasing human population and mounting material demands, a second model has been created (Figure 2). According to this model, regulatory agencies monitor the bio-physical/chemical environment and, on the basis of their findings, decisions are made which impose political/legal constraints upon economic activity. In this model the agencies' concept of the public welfare is dominant, and on the basis of bio-physical/chemical measurements, the government determines that the economic activity can continue—positive feedback, or must be terminated—negative feedback. Many people belonging to the "crisis" school of environmental thinking adhere to this model as, understandably, do some regulatory agencies. It is worthy of note that this model, which places great power in the hands of regulatory agencies, has sometimes led to the agency being controlled by the very industry it was intended to regulate. (Figure 2)

THE "AGENCY CONTROL" APPROACH

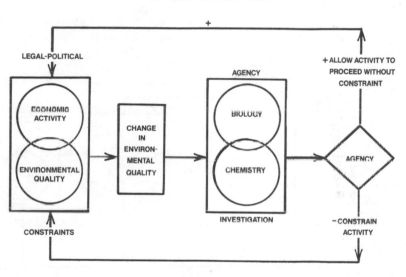

FIGURE 2

Most thinking individuals today realize that in a democracy, decisions made arbitrarily, whether by governmental agencies or private individuals, cannot be implemented without public support or in the face of public hostility. A model is emerging in most parts of our society which takes into account both economic factors and environmental quality, balancing one against the other. In this model, perception of change by the public, whether generated by the individual's direct perception of environmental quality or indirectly through information relating to the bio-physical/chemical environment generated by investigative agencies, must be translated into public concern before decisions are made. On the basis of this concern, the value of the economic activity to society can be weighed against the public's desire for a quality environment (and a decision is made to impose legal/political constraints upon the) activity—negative feedback, or to allow it to proceed unhampered—positive feedback.

While this model is obviously better equipped to enable decision-makers to determine sound management strategy than the preceding two, it possesses shortcomings which are readily apparent when long-range future time periods are considered. First, the model still puts economic well-being against environmental quality. Because the model fails to recognize that negative linkages exist between long-range economic health and deteriorating environmental quality, it fails to internalize many crucial economic disservices and external costs which tend to appear after the elapse of time, or at locations remote from the origin of the environmental insult. Second, the model still regards political and legal factors as rigid constraints rather than integral, highly mutable parts of a unified system, itself regulated by environmental constraints. Finally, the model views the decision as being of the yes-no type. Either the activity can be continued or it must be halted (or at least retarded). By failing to take into account the infinite variety of management alternatives that exist respecting the use of a given resource, the model, while it allows society to react to situations, fails to provide the tools necessary for planning the future. (Figures 3 & 4)

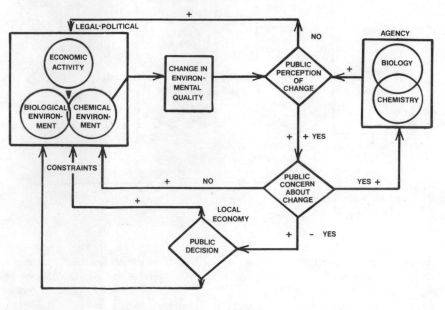

THE "ECONOMICS VERSUS ENVIRONMENT" APPROACH

FIGURE 3

We should propose a new model (Figure 4) which, by recognizing the possible relationships that can and do exist between the natural environment, economic activity and legal/political forces, will allow us to make better decisions regarding the way in which man will manage his environment. This model differs in several important respects from the previous ones. First, legal and political forces are integral parts of a total system. Like any other component of the system, they react to economic or environmental change. Second, the model insists that economic externalities and disservices can be measured and that environmental degradation can be defined in concrete terms rather than on the vague basis of aesthetics. Third, by integrating the efforts of economic, legal/political and bio-physical/chemical investigators, the model produces a variety of management alternatives rather than a single yes-no decision. We are aware that many of the interactions implied in our model are exceedingly complex, that the model still is in need of refinement, and that more factors may still need to be taken into account. However, we feel confident that, without a model which considers the relationships and feedback loops we have defined, it will be impossible to ask the questions necessary to the formulation of meaningful management strategies based on sound and complete predictive information.

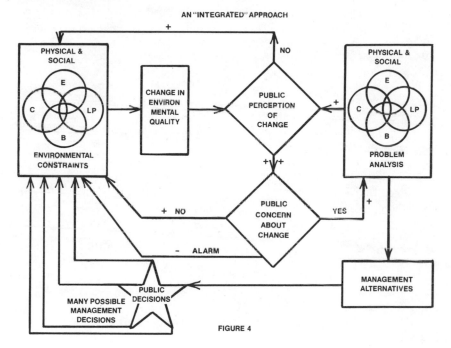

FIGURE 4

Some Social Costs
Of Population Policies

N. B. G. Taylor

Introduction

The purpose of this paper is to approach the theme of man versus nature in terms of social costs, and within the context of human population growth, or of overpopulation.

*This was originally presented with the title "Facing the Costs."

It is important to clarify two points: First, my subject, social costs, concerns those matters not normally considered in monetary terms such things as satisfaction, privacy, aesthetic values, the discomfiture of change, good health. I may, however, shift occasionally into costs in the usual sense. Second, whereas I shall confine my remarks to population, this is not to say that all environmental and social problems will be resolved by changes in population growth rate or total numbers (Miles 1970, Coale 1970). It is to say that no proposed solution for these problems that ignores population will succeed. As an opinion, I say that of all the problems, excessive population stands first among peers.

There has been much discussion about what is wrong with the world (overpopulation [Ehrlich 1968], pollution [Dasman 1968], resource depletion [Milton 1968]) and many solutions have been proposed. Somewhat less discussion has been given to the costs of the solutions. Least attention has been directed toward the costs that will accrue after the solutions have become established. It is under these three broad categories that I wish to discuss the social costs of population policies.

The Costs of Continuing on our Present Course

This is a course characterized by absence of a national population policy of any sort except the pronatalist policy implied by the tax exemptions for children and heavy taxation of single persons. Family planning widely accepted today has the objective of helping couples have the number of children they want when they want them but has nothing to say about limiting family size for reasons of national policy. In fact, by increasing health of mother and child, existing family planning programs might increase the number of children. It has been very aptly said that millions of couples practicing family planning does not equal a population policy (Miles 1970). The social costs of implementing this nonpolicy are negligible just because it is *laissez faire*. The eventual costs—social and otherwise—of following this course are quite another matter, and are what many people fear. I refer to the contribution that continued population growth will make to the social deprivation of increasing numbers of persons in the urban ghettos (Hauser 1970), of the isolation and alienation of the suburban ghetto escapees of all ages (Mead 1970). Correlations have now been made between social deprivation and mental and physical illness. Studies have shown that the likelihood of postpartum psychosis increases with the distance from female relatives and friends (Mead 1970). When she made this last statement, Margaret Mead was doing so in the context of the fragmented social organization of suburbia. Every trend is in the direction of increased black-white segregation: blacks in the city centers, whites in the suburbs (Michener 1970). Population increase is not the sole cause of these trends (Miller 1970). But while population continues to grow and exact its demands for new schools, housing, utilities, jobs and recreational facilities, the massive amounts of social and economic capital, goodwill and energy needed to reverse the trend are not available (Wagar 1970).

So far I have done little more than give passing reference to environmentally related disease. Using dollars only to indicate the magnitude of the problem, the annual cost is estimated to be $35 billion in the United States

(Curtin 1970). It is probable, perhaps almost certain, that this is only the small visible portion of the iceberg of social costs which would include unreported disease, reported diseases inadequately treated, substandard performance because of minor intoxications, frayed nerves, irritability, family discords, and even violence, all the result of minor degrees of unhealth. Certainly asthma, impairment of lung function, chronic respiratory disease (including cancer), and eye irritation have been shown to be associated with community air pollution (Lave and Seskin 1970), and there is no reason to believe that those overt diseases are not preceded by varying degrees of dysfunction. Again I must emphasize, these social costs cannot be attributed to population alone. They are increased by increased population densities, which in turn are associated with crowding and social deprivation.

At this point, I deliberately omit any discussion of the social costs of crowded cities, decreased open space, overloaded recreational areas and the many other evidences of decreasing environmental quality which have been so well described by many (Ehrlich 1968, Rienow 1967, Marine 1969). I would allude, however, to some of the social costs in the form of inconveniences, if not discomforts, that are probable, possibly inevitable as increasing population places increasing strain on resources: greater reliance on public transport and bicycles or enforced living in proximity to work; changes in design and construction of buildings to conserve fuel; the need to plan ahead and remember to take reusable containers to the grocery store for foods no longer individually wrapped but sold from bulk; restrictions on the installation and use of flush toilets and the use of domestic water in general.

One would be foolhardy indeed to imply that the trends we observe around us, the widespread deterioration of general living conditions, will continue at the present rates, unchecked. The question is: "Will it be checked soon enough?" or "Will it be reversed in time to prevent deterioration of the environment in the U.S.A. to the level that we see in India today-or worse?" India's problem is poverty; ours could be widespread poisoning of air, water and soil. The social conditions can come about in North America. To reject the possibility out of hand is, I believe, to ignore the one characteristic which, more than any other, distinguishes man from the other animals—his ability to adapt socially or culturally (Dubos 1970). This adaptability has permitted man to survive and dominate other animals. But social adaptation takes social energy, and is a social cost vividly described by Rohlich (1970) as "a cruel killer of skills." Adaptation usually takes the form of an accommodation with the new condition. There is no reason to believe man will not continue to adapt socially to an increasingly deteriorated environment. The status of the 400,000 Calcuttans who are born, live and die in the streets, never having a roof over their heads, has surely been arrived at by this slow, insidious process. We are ourselves socially adapting to foul air, slimy beaches, congested roads, ambient noise and ghettos. Adaptation which has served man so well in the past may "do him in" today. Adaptation in this sense serves to block perception of the noxious condition. I suggest that a more appropriate response to present conditions may be a violent rejection of the impingement of these conditions on our living. Such rejection, however, will require very large amounts of human energy, the investment of large amounts of social capital.

Instituting a Change

The "change" in this case would be to establish a population policy. Do we need one? What would be the social costs?

The position taken here is that a population policy is long overdue. It is less easy to be dogmatic about the nature of such a policy—or perhaps better to say about the degree to which it should attempt to regulate population growth, or if it should be regulated at all.

Population projections are notoriously fallible, but with clearly defined assumptions some can be made with confidence (Frejka 1970, Miles 1971, Commission on Population Growth 1971). If the average number of children per couple immediately becomes two (the replacement rate), the United States population will continue to increase for about 70 years and stabilize at approximately 280 million. One can only guess at the date when, if ever, the two-child family might become the norm. If it is delayed until 1975, the population would stabilize at approximately 295 million. If the population is to be stabilized immediately, the one-child family must become the norm immediately and remain so for 15 to 20 years. One might ask why the immediate establishment of the two-child family would not stabilize the population immediately, or why with the one-child family as the norm there would not be a decrease in population. The reason is that the children of the post-war baby boom are now entering the reproductive years, the same reason that the annual number of births can continue to increase coincident with a decreasing birth rate.

If such stabilizations occur, how will they come about, and what will be the social costs? There will be changes in the genetic composition of the population (Bajema 1971). It will entail sharp changes in social attitudes if they come about voluntarily, or legal sanctions and other forms of coercion if there is not, in effect, universal voluntary acceptance of the need to curtail population growth. Changes of attitudes can be very costly, socially—I refer to changes in attitude toward marriage as an institution, the development of alternative life styles, delayed marriage and family formation, freely available contraceptive information and materials to all sexually active persons, the acceptance of nontherapeutic abortion as an indispensable backup for failures of contraception, and greatly increased practice of voluntary sterilization (Asimov 1971). Although United States attitudes are moving toward wider acceptance of these practices, one quails at the thought of the social upheaval that would result if an attempt were made to bring about a stabilized population within 5 years. The idea that population need never stabilize is, however, being rejected by more and more persons who analyze the problem. The further in the future the day of stabilization is placed, the less rapid is the needed change of foresighted attitudes. At the same time, the greater will be the final population figure (although reliability of projections decreases with time in the future), the more nearly will the situation resemble the "continue as at present" situation and the fewer will be the options—and the greater the final social costs of correction.

The Social Costs of a Stable Population

These will vary quantitatively (Frejka 1970), and to some extent qualitatively (Bajema 1971), depending on the length of time and the means taken to arrive at the stable population. They will be the result, to a large extent, of the dislocations associated with an altered age distribution in the population. Whereas the "population pyramid" of a growing population (such as at present) is a fair representation of the pyramids of Egypt, that, for a stable population is a bit like a fire hydrant--top heavy with old people, small-based with few One of the costs associated with such stable populations is the likelihood of slow, highly competitive rise through the hierarchy—fewer new chiefs are needed because the number of Indians is not increasing. This could force development of the social phenomena described as "knowing one's place," well known in Britain but strongly resisted in the socially mobile United States. The large proportion of older people over 65 will present its own problems quite apart from the (tax) burden of supporting them. Ways will have to be found to utilize their potential and to avoid the loneliness increasing the lot of the old. These trends have already been shown and described as "the unanticipated results of the unconscious family planning that has been practiced for the past century." (Falk 1971) Characteristically, the 19th Century couple married at about the same age or later than today and continued to have children throughout the reproductive years. Survival beyond the reproductive years was not prolonged, and there would be a reasonable expectation that at least one of the children would be at an appropriate age and economic status to look after the parents in their old age. The characteristic 20th Century couple marry young, have fewer children close together and early. Because of this they have a considerably longer post-reproductive life expectancy, which is further lengthened by modern medical care. One demonstrated result of this is that parents and children grow old together and that when parents need support through ill health, the children, because of their own ill health, or of a spouse or their own post-retirement financially straitened circumstances, may be unable to take care of the parents.

A social cost arising out of sudden changes in the birth rate with serious implication for young adults is what may be called an effective change in the sex ratios. Men normally marry women some years younger. Because of this, a sudden decrease in birth rate would result in due course in a shortage of "right age" women for men of marriageable age, tending to force men to marry women more nearly their own age.

By way of summary, this paper supports the position that whatever course is followed the social costs will be great. If a foresighted population policy is followed, there will be options for defraying the costs. If a *laissez faire* course is pursued, options will decrease or costs increase. In plain English, we're damned if we do, if we don't, and while we're doing it. I close with a philosophical question: Man has long sought to subdue nature and now seems close to being able to do so. Will he succeed only to find another nature to confront—his own? Will he find, in Walt Kelly's words that "He has seen the enemy and he is us"? or will he, by controlling his numbers and his activities, yet learn to live with nature and himself?

Panel Discussion

Dr. Byrne (faculty, UWGB, moderator of the panel): In discussions with our next speaker it turns out that he is a graduate of the University of Kansas and was there about the time that I was teaching at Kansas State University. The term applied by the KU people to Kansas State was Silo Tech. In reference, of course, to the land-grant status of that fine school. Now it happens that both Kansas State and the University of Kansas are located along the Kansas River known as the Kaw River, so in retaliation, the K. State students used to refer to the University of Kansas at Lawrence as "the flaw on the Kaw."

Mr. Louis Carmouche has been with Dow Chemical in Midland for many years in a number of administrative and supervisory capacities. He is going to react to the very fine papers that have been presented earlier in this afternoon's session. So, Mr. Carmouche.

Mr. Carmouche: Ladies and gentlemen, fellow panel members, and students of the environment. Frank has forgiven me for going to the University of Kansas and I have forgiven him for teaching at Kansas State University. I had no real problem with Kansas State because I found my wife there and so I kept the railroad tracks hot between those two places for about three or four years while I was going to school.

As a representative of industry, commenting on the environment sometimes causes some hesitancy about knowing how to approach that kind of problem, because we usually are painted somewhere in the "black hat area" as to what we are doing to the environment, in spite of all the things that anyone can do to prevent us from doing that. I thought today that I would take a different approach rather than comment on the other papers. I want to tell you that I am a chemical engineer by training, I am a manager by the sufferance of my fellow employees, I am a conservationist and a mountaineer by choice, and I thought perhaps you'd like to know what that kind of a representative of industry thinks about the environment (his attitudes toward it and what he is doing about it). I can tell you in honesty and sincerity that the views I am going to express to you are the kind of views you would get from most of the executives of my company. At present we have 40,000 people working for Dow so I'm sure there are a few who really don't hold these views and really don't act in the manner I'd like to see them act, but I can sincerely tell you that those who hold the destinies of this company in their managerial hands feel about it in this way.

I'm encouraged by your approach to the problems of the environment and the ills of our ecological system as we now see them. About a year and two or three weeks ago I spent a day like this one on the highly seasoned Ann Arbor campus of the University of Michigan. They had their Earth Day a little bit ahead of the regular Earth Day last year in order to perhaps act as a model for other universities and schools. It was our great pleasure to have been able to meet with the youngsters who actually organized that first Ann Arbor Earth Day. We had interchange with them on some ideas several months before they planned their Earth Day activities. As you recall, our President was there on the program, as were Senator Muskie and others who represented various viewpoints. Quite an interesting day! On April 22, 1970, I was able to talk to the Cleveland Society of Engineers about the environment and what I thought they ought to do about it. At that time I mentioned that the four objectives, it seemed to me, of Earth Days were to create an awareness about the environmental problems, to create concern on the part of people for that problem, to learn something about causes and effects, and to then take action to restore the proper balance in the ecology. I told them I didn't know how long those things would take nor what route anyone would go to get there, but first the awareness factor had to be made evident in the United States and the rest of the world. You've certainly done that. In fact, people are so aware of the environment at the moment that it almost becomes redundant to talk about awareness as the problem. They are concerned at the moment because it doesn't do any good to make your fellow inhabitants of the earth aware of something without causing some concern. If they don't have any concern, they don't have any cause for learning anything more; if they don't learn some causes and effects, their concern doesn't do any good because concern alone doesn't cause action. You can't have proper action unless you learn the causes and effects, and so that seems to me to be the point at which you are.

As I read your program, it looked to me that you were plugging into the system at the cause-and-effect level, having assumed that awareness and concern were present. I think that's the place to tune in, and I think that the kinds of programs that have been talked about here and kinds of data presented indicate that the cause-and-effect relationship is the next step. My feeling about the point is that it is going to be a major accomplishment to learn those causes and effects. It seems to me that what we know now causes us to be able to state the problem quite simply. The human society as I see it has gained sufficient knowledge about the physical sciences to be able to upset the ecological balance and plans. It's that simple. We actually may be upsetting the balance in some areas where people are concentrated. And I say *may* because I don't really know that until we know the causes and effects. We may be causing irreversible or at least difficultly reversible changes on a planetwide scale.

The thing that makes it really a crisis in some areas is that, as someone has said, people of the earth persist in having all the population "ruled" by one percent of the land area, and you're likely to have problems of extreme crisis in some of those areas. I think it's worthwhile taking a short look at how we got where we are. The human race in general has not been and is not now a frugal species. We have had vast resources and we have used them. We are still using them. We are still not in control of that using process.

Our culture has placed a high value on singleminded specialization. Up to now people who have specialized and have acquired certain skills in certain areas, whether it be making automobiles or whether it be making plastics or whether it be in any of the other multiplicity of industrial activities. Those people who have specialized have been successful and our culture has granted them all of the earmarks of success. The only problem is that when you have several singleminded individuals even-running down a road, where these roads tend to cross each other you're very likely to have collisions and sometimes a real crisis of one sort or another. With our culture and value system up to now, I think, we have caused these collisions in ecology and we have done so through some detriment in the environment. Along those lines I think we have pursued narrow, technical goals with absolute brilliance and we have been successful, but the goals have not been broad enough and have not widened themselves out to major objectives.

We have had an amazing, consistent and massive lack of priority sight. It matters little to some of the people who are finding it difficult in this land of ours to be educated properly, it makes little difference to the fellow in the ghetto who does not have a job, it makes little difference to the people who do not have proper housing to have somebody concerned with the environment.

Their environment is all too obvious and it is under extreme stress and extreme crisis, but we continue to set priorities. Now, until you have set some priorities, you don't even know what direction to go, and more importantly you don't know what kind or how many resources to allocate to each of your major concerns. What do you want? Clean air or better education? Clean water or better housing? A better environment or jobs? Frankly, I think you need all of those. You need all of them. But again you have trade-offs and you must make up your mind. There are not enough resources right now to do all of them at once. But until we sort them out and begin to focus in on the major problems of each of those areas we will not be able to allocate our resources properly.

We have gotten where we are because of two other factors. One of those is procrastination. We have many tools at our disposal to help control ecological damage and we have not used them. We are not using them now; we don't enforce the laws we have; we don't enforce the social pressures we have available to us. The other side of that coin is lack of conviction. We really are not ready to say we want that environment that we talk about. We have failed to have that kind of conviction and that kind of dedication. That is not to say that one should run off blindly and do inconceivably stupid things. There is no reason for that. I do not believe that we are at an incipient disaster point in this environment in which we live. I think it is in danger but I think we have time to do something intelligent about it. Part of the reason we haven't and part of the reason that the priorities are not set and conviction is lacking is that you just have a fantastic problem, and it really is fantastic.

Tommy Thompson has shown you a model of some of the kinds of things that go into a decision-making feedback circuit to control what people do. And he said that you are able, probably, to measure the effects of pollution and perhaps to put in predictive data into that model that was definitive enough for decision making. Tommy, I quarrel with you a little bit. It is only to this extent—the predictive data of those definitive characteristics that will allow you to make decisions is one whale of a job. I defy you to do it for this county. And when you've got that done I'd like to see you do it for the state of Wisconsin, and then the United States. But this is not that small a problem. This is a global problem and we are in the midst of it. Incidentally don't mistake me, I think it's absolutely imperative to be doing the kind of model work that Tommy and his cohorts are doing. Without that you're going to be in trouble. You're going to have to have some kind of model towards which you're working so don't mistake me that that is not good work. But when you have so many equations to take into account that their numbers and dimensions are fantastic and the only constant in any of those equations is change, the matter is difficult.

I quarrel with you, Dr. Taylor. I do not want people to cease to adapt, I do not want people to settle for status, I don't think they have to, so to that degree I quarrel with you a little bit, although I do agree with Professor Taylor that if we assume that we are bound to this one planet in a completely closed system and can go nowhere else and have no outlets, we must have some population control. I'll talk a little bit about that in a minute. Everything that we have said this morning (Mike Brewer and Jim Murray, Larry Smith), is couched in the context of social systems. Mike said you need new social processes, he said you even need "new" kinds of people, at least new kinds of thought in the people we've got. Jim Murray talked about new measuring sticks, including how we can measure what we're doing and new input into the social account. Those are the things that concern us if you are familiar with social change, and I know well you are, because you're in the midst of causing some of it. But social change takes a long time. Then what should we do right now? What can we do right now? I think the most important thing we can do is start sorting out those priorities. Consensus is a difficult thing but it can be done. It can be done with the old town hall philosophy, and I suggest we get at it. Everyone of you is some center of activity, or could be, in your own communities to start that kind of dialogue going for two reasons: first, to find out what people really think, and secondly to give them information which they badly need to sort out priorities.

We talked only a little bit about the political situation and the fact that politics could be a messed up thing on occasion. We don't have anyone represented here (and that's too bad), but there are several facets to politics, one of them is the statesman-like end of it and the other is the ordinary "garden type" of politics that we all think of in the cartoons. I will guarantee you that I have never met a statesman who did not respond to an informed public. I will also likewise guarantee you that I have never found an ordinary garden-type politician who wasn't scared of a well-informed public and that he will do what they wish. The statesman will do it by leading, the politician will do it by following, but a well-informed public that knows what it wants can get it.

I also think we need to understand the deployment of power—by power I mean energy—"energy *en masse.*" I submit to Professor Taylor that it doesn't make any difference today whether or not you stop the population in its tracks tomorrow morning. You could cut the number of people in the United States in half tomorrow morning and if our use of energy *en masse* (all the masses of things we use) increased per person at the rate that it now is increasing, we could desolate the United States of America in the next 50 years with no problem at all and no more people. The problem is one of how to use that energy and how to learn to use a portion of that energy to control the deleterious effects of the rest of it; and that can be done. Most of that technology is available. It still is desirable, I agree with you, to control the population. But that alone won't do it. We have so much ecological fire power right now that we could ruin this earth if we want to; we can ruin it whether we want to or not if we stay inactive about it. I think that we can understand the real cost of goods and services and give people a chance to understand the cost-benefit analysis. Engineers have the unique ability to at least put down costs objectively, they can find out what those data are and they can present them in a way that people can understand them. That was one of my messages to the Cleveland Society of Engineers—that I thought they had a responsibility to carry correct information to people, not the kind you find in literature or newspapers, most of which is wrong. But I am referring to the true cost of what we're doing and how it can be presented in a way that people can understand it. It may take Tommy's model to help do it.

We need some tough and uniform pollution laws but we don't need taxes. And I'll tell you why not. Taxes are a crutch. Taxes are a political expedient and the governments usually get so used to taxes that there is the distinct possibility that if they tax you once because you were polluting, there would also be a time when they would encourage you to pollute in order for them to keep raising the taxes. I think taxing is a poor substitute for deciding on criteria and then enforcing those criteria. Actually, the problem has to be approached with intelligence and it has to be done with some understanding of what the criteria are to be. Local people have to understand what those needs are and they have to enforce them. But they have to do so with a general, overall set of criteria in mind which provide a minimum basis for the environment. If you don't do that at a national level and make things somewhat uniform, you will simply find industry moving around all over the place to take advantage of those places where restrictions are not so great. It has happened already, it happens now, it's a foolish long-term policy for the nation, the state, the county, and the industry, but it happens. We need good, tough pollution laws that are uniformly enforced. When the enforcement is left to the local area, and usually it appears not very uniform, that's no good either. I think these are the things we could work on now. Never losing sight of the fact that we are in the midst of a very complex situation that will take a long time to change. Social systems do not change quickly unless by revolution. And that would be the most stupid "pollutant" that I could think of anybody introducing into the system. But the system will change if intelligently guided. A great deal of industry these days has been sacrificed and brought to the position of understanding that they must help in this education, dissemination of data and accepting some responsibility for what they're doing. I think you will find most of the corporations in that camp, although you will not find all of them. But, nevertheless, the responsible ones are there. I'd be happy to answer any questions you may have later on about industry, if I can answer them. If I can't I'll tell you so, but if I know the answers you'll get them.

Dr. Byrne: Thank you, Louis, for sharing your thoughts with us, and thank you also for sharing the source of our wives—in other words, Manhattan, Kansas. We both have been very fortunate in finding girls from Manhattan, Kansas, who are very ideally suited to us. And thank you also for showing the poetic philosophy. You are a chemical engineer, I am an environmental geologist. Our technological evolution has hurt us because our sociological evolution has not kept the pace with it. We need to emphasize much more the evolution of our social structures and until we do so we are in deep trouble. That's one of the reasons I like these conferences so much. One of the advantages of UWGB and its program is the contribution that is made to it by our students, so we have asked Bob Barnstable, a student of Modernization Processes, to comment for our benefit on his reactions. Bob?

Dr. Barnstable (student, UWGB): Thank you, Professor Byrne. I have some very general comments I'd like to put before this symposium. Man as a biological organism is capable of an infinite amount of variety of adaptations. Human populations with all their diversity are capable of existing in that physical environment and adjusting to just about anything man has conceived. And they are also capable of producing a viable offspring which itself can produce an offspring which can survive. But we have a conflict in technological society because when we as a biological organism turn ourselves over to a technological order we might be ultimately cutting down our chances of survival. Conversely, our entire survival may depend on the strength of our technology. But what has been the record in the past of this technological area? Well, if you consider briefly the east coast as an example, what would have been the result if these past power failures there had lasted three months instead of just three days? It doesn't take a vivid imagination to project the kind of chaos that would have ensued from this type of a situation. And what the evidence indicates thus far is that in areas of problem-solving in the technological area we tend to be like the little Dutch boy. When a problem develops we rush to the spot and put in our finger and try to solve the situation. Well how long can we continue to put our fingers in the dike before we run out of fingers and this whole thing comes tumbling down? Some people feel that if you sit on a street corner in New York and breathe the toxic air from automobiles, the emissions from smokestacks, etc., lungs can adapt to this type of situation. But this might be an utter fallacy. One immediate result could be that the individual will have a shorter life span. Adaptation—physical adaptation—takes thousands and thousands of years and our technological-environmental considerations now are couched in decades or less, and it seems obvious that man as a biological organism may not adapt to this particular plan, not at least with the same speed. So we have to be very careful as to what courses of action we intend to pursue in the future.

The second area I wanted to touch on is that problem fallacy that exists in our society—the idea that the public consumer, you and I, all of us together, controls products and production. We find here that the cart is now leading the horse. Products are conceived, created and developed by manufacturing firms, put on the market, and then a need is created for that product by their advertising. But what we are being fed is coming in the large part from people who are sitting down and trying to devise consumption patterns that are to a large extent far beyond the normal biological and social needs. A complex chain of dependence is started to undo the bad effects of one product by another. Thus I feel a guideline in the area of production is that we, the consumers, do not necessarily control this area. If a product can match a concrete human purpose, then we should give consideration to having it produced and having it put on the market. And if it cannot pass this criteria, then we should take a long look at the product and see whether it merits being produced at all. Perhaps we should also be concentrating our efforts on more durable goods, ones that are long-lasting and have some meaning rather than all of the ephemeral products that seem to creep into our society and clog our environment.

These lead to the third area of consideration which will probably rack the most votes, and that would be in the area of what I would call "environmental tokenism." Such a tokenism would be crushing a can, breaking a bottle, or using a degradable detergent for our clothing and dishes, and although the jury is still out, we haven't yet determined just how valuable this sporadic action is going to be to the environment. The tokenism which I would like to point a finger at and feel would be most serious is that which occurs within the industrial personnel, the management personnel and their supporting agencies, in direct relation to what they do in the area of public welfare. Thus, a corporation which would donate a building in the park for the boys would be widely applauded by the public, but at the same time out the back door of that particular industry, pouring into the stream, might be this toxic element which has made that stream unfit for swimming or to boat in, and aesthetically ugly. So on one hand they may be applauded for their actions, but what is taking place behind them is really of concern. Another would be going out and soliciting funds, collecting for cancer, cancer research, cancer institutions. This is great, but at the same time industry behind you is pouring these things into the air which ultimately help contribute to the cancer, which, in turn, helps to put people in the very institutions that they're collecting money for. There seems to be a contradiction here. I think the effort should be to make management and personnel of industries realize all the consequences that result from their actions. Let them look within their own home, let them clean up their own backyard before they start whitewashing the porch. If we as a public can try to push them to realize this contradiction, ultimately we'll all be much better off. I feel industry has been remiss in their responsibility and it's time they should take care of it at home instead of waiting for legislation which forces them to do so.

Dr. Byrne: We would solicit some comments from you and our panelists have indicated their willingness to respond to such comments as you may have. I talked briefly with Mr. Stratton and, Mr. Stratton, would you direct your question as you have it to Dr. Thompson.

Mr. Stratton (student, UWGB): Dr. Thompson, when you were talking and described a diagram, which I though was excellent, I felt that you had left out one pertinent variable. I was here this morning, and I'm here now, and it seems like the most important thing, our purpose of the symposium, is to educate the public. But nowhere in your diagram did I see education. While you have a labeled public opinion, that's good, and you call that a start. Yet I'd like to know if this is really the place to start and why did you not include education in your diagram?

Dr. Thompson: I'd like to address myself to that problem. Education does appear on the last diagram. It doesn't appear in an overt fashion, but it is part of a positive feedback loop in the diagram (see Figure 4). You will notice over on the righthand side of the chart a box labeled physical and social problem analysis, and an arrow from that block to public reception of change. I suspect before any education comes about, the public is going to have to request some investigation, which would also be a public indication of concern—the righthand side of the arrow leading down from the large diamond. If the public is concerned, then it requests problem analysis. There you see you have an arrow leading through that block and the arrow leads back to public perception of change. This is a positive feedback loop, a self-reinforcing feedback loop, and the linkage that is indicated between problem analysis and public perception of change could very well be labeled education. Does that answer the question?

Dr. Byrne: You've got a question from the minority group. A lady over to my right would pose a question for the majority group.

Mrs. S. Terry (from audience): I just want to say that I agree with Bob that industry should start cleaning up its own backyard, but in towns like Green Bay, if we wouldn't have the men in industry behind things like United Fund drives, Red Cross, Scouts, and Boy's Clubs, those goals would not be successful and our community would lack a lot. You have to remember that even though many of the big companies give their men the time to work for such organizations, it is the man himself that believes in the project and does the work. He is not only taking company time and the company name, but is also probably spending evenings and weekends working on that sort of thing. It's just like the speaker here being a mountaineer while he's a chemical engineer. You can't say that it is only the company that's trying to make us think that, because they are helping the community in several other ways.

Dr. Byrne: Thank you. Are there further questions from the audience?

Mr. Lingelbach (student, UWGB): I'd like to call upon the people from Dow Chemical and Kimberly-Clark to assist UWGB in helping to understand and to know their products and their own employees, and that they would grant money to the university for appropriate studies. In other words, I'm calling for a joint effort by both industry and the university for development of our society. As far as creating meaningful jobs and meaningful products are concerned, I think here is something that both can do together. We don't have to call upon legislation for development of our society. Can I have a reaction to that by people from Dow Chemical and Kimberly-Clark?

Mr. Carmouche: You can certainly have one from me. I agree with him 100%. We do this and we are involved in many projects with the universities; I am not sure we have any with you, but we're helping sponsor this activity, friend. And we would like to have some more of this kind of interchange. We would like to have some of you come over to Midland and visit us and see what we do over there, and we would also like to have your definition of meaningful products

Mr. Lingelbach: I'm a little more familiar with Kimberly-Clark than Dow Chemical. What is more ecological minded, say, a Kleenex tissue or the recycling of linen that is washed? What's better for society in terms of environmental pollution—whether the water and detergents go into the stream after washing linens, or the possible recycling of the paper fiber? Further, creating meaningful jobs should be the emphasis in the industry, we can put people into society for education and for social work, rather than the kind of manual labor that causes us, in essence, to look for leisure time but not really have a leisure.

Dr. Armstrong (faculty, UWGB): I have a question for Mr. Carmouche which I think follows up to a certain extent on Mr. Barnstable's remarks and also Mr. Lingelbach's. I see great hope when you describe the bulk of the 40,000 employees of Dow Chemical as being ecologically minded and concerned individuals. I have no doubt this is true. But it seems to me that there is at least a possible paradox in your remarks when you suggest that the best alternative that society can follow is a stringent set of all-embracing laws and regulations to force industry to do what it ought to do. Your statement was that, if there were no universal legislation concerning pollution abatement policies, in fact, industry would move from place to place to find those areas which had been lax in propagating such policies. I'm curious, I suppose it's one you get asked over and over again. Why is it that industry cannot on its own initiative show a social conscience? Undoubtedly, industry knows the costs of pollution at least as well as anybody else. Why is it that it would take an outside force such as governmental intervention to get industry to do the kind of thing that it might do on its own?

Mr. Carmouche: I think it's a good question. I think it's legitimate. I think it deserves an answer. And to the best of my ability, here's one I have prepared for that question before and will undoubtedly be preparing from now on. In the first place, I think we should understand what a corporation is. And I don't believe very many people really understand that. So I give you what I think it is, whether anyone else thinks that or not. I think that a corporation is a problem-solving organization that generally sees as its mission the conversion of materials and energy into other forms of materials and energy that society desires. Granted all the nuances you know, it does not really work that way, but, yes, in theory it does. Its success in performing this task is measured by whether society rewards its efforts by providing more materials and energy to be converted. The corporation seeks to optimize its reward but it must operate within the constraints set by society. Now a corporation per se doesn't have any moral conscience and it doesn't have any moral responsibility. The people in it of course do. But a corporation per se is a tool of the society and the culture of which it exists, and it will operate within the constraints which that society sets for it. It is a problem-solving, reward-seeking organization, set up that way. That is its mission in life. Whatever the rules of the game it will seek to optimize its reward. And if you have badly formulated rules and have holes in them, the corporation will seek optimization there, too, whether anybody wants it to do that or not. That is the machine, and that's the way it's built. That's why it exists and it's yours, friend. And if you don't want to constrain it and if you don't want to put it where it belongs and tell it what the rules of the game are likely to be, it will seek its own rules, and as Bob had indicated, very often it will try to create its own market. It will try to create its own need for being. It's that kind of entity. So understand the corporation as to what it is and as to what it can do. Properly used, it's the strongest force in this world for gaining you the things you need to have, for a proper environment, and an enriched life. But you've got to understand the tools. There are a lot of bad workmen who do bad work and then blame the tools they've got for doing it. The human race is sometimes guilty of that syndrome.

Mr. Gorder: I think from my comments, some people will think I'm way off in right field, when, in fact, I am an economic liberal. But I am also a pragmatist. I believe in policies that get something done. And the gentleman from Dow Chemical said that we have a lot of laws. Our problem is to enforce them. Yet at the same time he says that taxes should not be invoked. Well, we had prohibition and it didn't work. We had price controls at the end of the second World War and that didn't work very well. And I think any laws that people don't want to follow on an individual basis, they're not going to work. In any case, it requires a bureaucracy, a police force, which in turn requires taxes. And I think that we have precedence of economic incentives in the way of taxes and other subsidies working, for instance, in the state of Wisconsin—the forest crop laws. I think we're largely responsible for reversing our forest situation in this state. Those laws were put forward in 1920. Our forests are in better shape today than they were before.

And I'd like to make one more comment that relates to that of the student who mentioned about the corporations being over there and we ought to do something about those organizations. Well, I get the impression that the corporations are formed by households who have contributed land, labor, and capital as means of production and for which these households are getting rent, profit, and wages, which they, in turn, spend on the products of this production. So I wouldn't separate the two in this way. And I think along the same vein.

Mr. Carmouche: No question about the fact that laws are the least desirable way to do anything. In a society like we have there are just too many interfaces that simply are different in as many states as we've got in the United States (and around the world) and you have to have some kind of general policy. That policy, I submit, ought to be carried as a coordinated compliance as near as you can get. But you're going to have to have some kind of constraint to measure performance against. Certainly you have to finance it. I just simply said that to tax on a pollutant going into a river or SO_2 going out the stack seems silly to me. There are better ways of financing than that, and taxes per se I didn't include in my previous discussion. Taxes on a pollutant I do think are silly.

Dr. Taylor: I'd like to respond to the remarks that Mr. Carmouche directed toward me. And all I can find in my heart to disagree with is your interpretation of what I said. I didn't mean to imply that failing to adapt meant spaces or would involve spaces, in fact I used the word "violent rejection" of the impingement of these conditions on our living to replace adaptation to those conditions. And I stressed, I thought sufficiently, that the population was not the sole problem but any solution that ignored population control or growth was fated to fail.

Dr. Byrne: I have about two pages of comments that I was going to direct to these various people, questions to ask of them, but because the time was so pressing, I would save them for another opportunity. Actually, I do not have anything to say. To Dr. Taylor, Mr. Carmouche, Dr. Rohlich, Dr. Thompson, and Mr. Barnstable, I wish you would join me in expressing our appreciation to them for sharing with us the thoughts and experiences they have had.

An Overview

The first thing that may strike a reader of this panel is that it has encompassed a wide variety of materials—empirical, sociocultural, theoretical, and conjectural. It may be only expected on a topic that is paradoxically both obvious and obscure, and has received only piecemeal and casual attention by several desperate specialists. Integrated perspectives on the problem of "Man versus Nature" may be harder to come by. While aware of such problems, our first panelist, an engineer of wide experience, wove in bold but firm strokes a pattern of fundamental relationships between society and technology that characterize contemporary U.S.A. His inclusive notion of technology is noticeable: "...we are in the infant stages of a new technology which we can call social or human engineering, which we must be aware of and apply properly to show how social life can be better managed."

The following two "position papers" remained more specific in orientation while relating to several themes set forth by the first speaker (e.g., of "social costs," "information feedback system," and performance control and prediction in natural systems). One (Thompson with his associates) undertakes to construct a model illustrating multilateral exploratory interrelationships between man, nature, and culture, for it is they that stand at the back of "environmental problems and policies," and they need to be more fully appreciated than heretofore. The other contributor (Taylor, a trained physician interested in population problems) views the same triangle from the end of population studies. His central point is that while reviewing man versus nature relationships, population is an important variable since its size always entails "social costs" (including noneconomic ones) which affect the quality of life of a social group. He argues for a population policy which should dovetail with environmental policy. His remarks about population size, technology, and public health costs should be especially noted in this regard.

The comments made by Mr. Carmouche, and the discussion that ensued thereafter, bring attention to the sheer diversity of topics that could be found related to the theme of the panel. Presenting industry's viewpoint, Mr. Carmouche argued that a corporation, while seeking to "optimize" its reward "per se does not have any moral conscience and it does not have any moral responsibility," and hence it should be regulated from the outside (e.g., by government imposed constraints) to bring it in line with the theme represented by man in (and of) nature. Thus, if an industry contributes to antagonistic relationships between man and nature, the zone of voluntary adjustment is limited, according to Mr. Carmouche. As is evident from the discussion, such a contention is controversial, leaving the possibility of many more questions that could not be raised for the lack of time.

In contrast stand the remarks of a student who finds curious contradictions that are being nurtured by the industries: Industry environmentally contributes towards the causation of those very diseases (e.g., cancer) that it attempts to remove by its philanthropic action later on. The remark may be trite but it remains significant for correcting the negative skew that industry produces in relationships between man and nature.

And then, obviously, there was much that could not be covered by the panelists who always have to work under the limitation of time. However, one may like to bring to attention several more general lines of inquiry that are fast developing on the theme of this panel. In themselves, man and nature relationships are neither recent in origin nor simple in structure, function, and cognition. Whatever research is done seems to be helpful in providing us with a "start" in the right direction. Much more remains to be understood in relation to that which is not so apparent but vital for human survival in the company of nature. For some fundamental relations between nature and man, one may refer the reader to such readings (for full citation, see bibliography) as: Burton (1968), Comfort (1967), Crile (1969), Hare (1970), Iltis, Loucks and Andrews (1970), Kahler (1968), Lee (1968), McKinley (1969), Watson and Watson (1969), Wheeler (1968), Wissler (1926). For a study of more complex interface between man, technology, and nature, one may see: Odum (1970), Rickover (1965), Russel (1970), and Wagar (1970).

R.S.K.

PART 3

The Urban Social Environment: Problems of Affluence, Membership, and Security

Lee Rainwater

Welcoming Remarks

Dr. Edward Weidner (Chancellor, The University of Wisconsin—Green Bay): I have been asked to make some comments. This is a very dangerous thing to ask a Chancellor to do because he is unlikely to cut his comments appropriately short, but it does seem to me that our entire thrust in Green Bay at The University of Wisconsin—Green Bay is in the direction of social responsibility. I would like to introduce a few thoughts along that line which underline our own academic approach and our academic plan. In my own field of political science, I was once known as a young logical positivist who was interested in the quantitative measurement of human behavior. I am not sure my colleagues would still consider me to be a young political scientist, but I am still interested in that kind of approach. And yet as I look back, I think there are a couple of things which strike me as unfortunate in higher education, and maybe in higher education as a whole. In one sense, there are two implications which might be considered equivalent to the separation of church and state for education, similar to the implication which the logical positivist movement had for education. I am impressed that both movements had the same impact, namely, to separate affective learning from cognitive learning. For the last twenty years, maybe even stretching to thirty years, we have traveled this route with blinders on either eye bent for cognitive learning and with utter distaste for anything that is affective in nature, relative to learning. From my personal point of view, I don't believe that these activities constitute turning the cold shoulder within the behavioral sciences on quantitative methods or turning the cold shoulder to logical positivists, John Dewey or anybody else. Unfortunately, we have forgotten that the accumulation of knowledge in this world is based upon value assumptions. I once had an instructor who always used the example that a person could spend his life in a room describing it and never quite finish the task, and that would be quite a foolish thing to do. Likewise, in any substantial library one could go down just a few rows of stacks, spending his lifetime in those particular rows and never really finish the task; that also would be a rather foolish thing to do! It is obvious that the facts we select as significant or important in this world are guided by things we consider to be important.

To avoid the entrapment of spending a lifetime in foolish approaches to education, we have developed guidelines at The University of Wisconsin—Green Bay. It is high time that we develop guidelines at the elementary, secondary, adult education and higher education levels. I think that this is the beauty, the stimulus and the challenge of environmental education because it does provide a framework for us to examine meaning in our society and our social behavior. Specifically, this approach provides us with a framework for examining the meaning of our avocational interests, regardless of the time of year, time of life or level of life (if we want to speak of levels), and it also provides us with a meaning for our particular chosen vocations or job orientations. This approach also permits us to combine the two elements of education which have been traditionally separate: citizenship education or the complete man education over in one corner and the job orientation over in another corner. Naturally, we have better terms for this phenomena. Job orientation, for those of us who are snobs in higher education, is relegated to the vocational schools. In counterpoint, we prefer to talk about our disciplines and our professions in the upper reaches of higher education, but that is really job orientation under a different kind of color. Presumably our disciplines, professions, job orientation or graduate school orientation have little to do with citizenship education. Citizenship education is a kind of preliminary activity. I am impressed that we are ignoring the fact that we are more frequently citizens than we are adherents to a specific job orientation. To forget this fact ignores the whole unity of life! Yet, to develop a rationale for social responsibility, it is necessary to be aware of the whole unity of life.

Environmental education is not the only answer to higher education, elementary education, secondary education or any other kind of education, but it is a subpart of a problem orientation in education which is a very important step toward social responsibility at all levels. There are many problems, and environmental quality is not the only set of problems which beset this world. There are problems of human conflict and conflict resolution. There are problems of human rights and brotherhood. There are problems of population and urban growth. One can look at many facets of problems, and, as one does so, I think that one develops an educational system with a kind of undergirding philosophy that combines affective and cognitive learning. This sort of philosophic approach puts values, ethics, and morals not just as freshman and sophomore prerequisites for getting a real education, but as a guideline for all education, and as a guideline for selecting those things which are significant in this world. This allows each student an opportunity to develop guidelines for his role as a human being, as a citizen and as a person having occupational and avocational interests. We are very pleased that you are here to sample the kind of thing that we are trying to become concerned about as an institution and as individuals. We welcome your contribution and your insights and we also welcome those community members who have joined us for this session. We hope that your fellowship will continue to be associated with us in many different ways.

Our program this evening is divided into four parts—one of which you have already had. The second part will consist of introduction of the speaker. The third part will consist of the address by Dr. Rainwater, and the fourth part, assuming that we all have zip and vitality suitable to this part of God's earth, we will have a brief discussion and reflection period and then close the evening. For the second part of this four-part program, I would like to call upon the ambitious chairman of this wonderful concentration. I think it's a wonderful concentration because if I were no longer Chancellor, I would become a member of this concentration. Seriously, it has been a particular pleasure to see the Modernization Processes Concentration gain shape, meaning and definition, and to develop a true sense of mission within itself under the leadership of Dr. Ravindra Khare.

Introduction and Address

Introduction

Dr. Khare (Chairman, Modernization Processes Concentration, UWGB): I'll only briefly introduce Lee Rainwater, who is a Professor of Sociology in the Department of Sociology in Social Relations at the John F. Kennedy School of Government at Harvard University. He is also currently participating at Harvard and at M.I.T. on a program of Family and Urban Studies. Many of you, I am sure, have come across some of his writings and you know he is a prolific writer. He has been associated with *Trans-action* magazine, and his latest book is *Behind Ghetto Walls: Families in a Federal Slum* (1970). Before coming to Harvard, Dr. Rainwater was associated with Wahington University, St. Louis. We are very pleased to have Professor Rainwater with us this evening.

Address: The Urban Social Environment

For all of its seriousness, for all that things are likely to get worse and not better over the next few years, and for all that we understand the problem only very partially, there are good reasons to be optimistic about the solution of our environmental problems; more optimistic than I think we can be about the solution of certain other persisting problems of American society, particularly those of poverty and race. After all, the principal causes of pollution problems are technological; and are therefore, in most cases, amenable to technological solutions. Most environmental problems are common to everyone, and there is a common interest in resolving them—for all that the cost of that resolution may fall differentially on different groups within the society. And, the particular technological arrangements that produce problems are probably, we can't be sure yet, not centrally tied up with the sense of social identity of significant groups in the society the way some of our problems are (like our hang-up on being the policemen of the world or the various arrangements that continue to support racism and poverty).

Therefore, if the social, economic, and technological resources for problem solution are brought to bear over the next few years on the problems of the environment, we shall probably see solutions to most of them. I will be talking tonight about the ways of life of various social groups in urban America and suggesting some of the implications those ways of life and aspirations have for how problems of the social and physical environment will need to be approached to have the best chance of constructive resolution. Too often those interested in particular social problems tend to think about those problems in a narrow way that does not take into account the fact that all problems exist within the social matrix of the ongoing life of individuals and groups in the society and not in isolation. If those who want to solve problems understand too little about how people in this society live and what they want out of life, then they run the risk of suggesting solutions that are either irrelevant or anathema to their countrymen. This is a particular danger because the problem identifiers and solvers tend to come disproportionately from a particular segment in the society—the intellectual middle class and elite—a segment that in terms of lifestyle, values, aspirations and interests is quite different from other groups in the society. The initial flush of enthusiasm for the environmental issue has produced more than its share of nonsense, but so far the nonsense has not had catastrophic effects. In any case, the real danger of misunderstandings and projections on the rest of the society isn't so much that of negative effects as it is of no effect at all, of an evanescent thrust toward problem resolution.

One way we often mislead ourselves in thinking about social problems is to fasten too much on the present and the immediate past in developing the paradigms by which we seek to understand and control the problems. As antidote for that, let me start off by sketching what seems to me to be the most likely course of development of the broad segments of the American society over the period of the next 15 years. Some of the trends are now well established—we know fairly exactly what the adult population will be in 1985 since all of those people are born now. We have some experience in predicting economic growth, income distribution and things like that over fairly long periods of time. Unless there were to be very, very major exogenous changes in the future (like nuclear war, a depression that would curl your toes or such), the margin of error for predictions in the economic area is probably not too wide. For lifestyle changes we are on much if-ier ground, but I believe that from what we know now about how Americans of the various social classes live and of what they are interested in, it is possible to make some educated guesses as to how people will want to live in the changed circumstances of the 1980's. First, let's start with some of the simpler demographic facts.

The nation is now, of course, heavily urban in its pattern of settlement. By the mid-1980's, it will be slightly more urban—the proportion of the population in metropolitan areas having increased from 70 percent to 73 or 74 percent. But there is another side to this increased urbanization. Because of the transportation revolution brought on by the automobile and the superhighway within the urban areas, the population is less and less densely settled—the population per square mile in urbanized areas will have decreased from 6,580 in 1920 to around 3,800 in 1985. This is what suburbanization is all about. It is a trend that can be expected to continue into the future. This means that more and more land will be subjected to the stresses of suburbanized development.

The population will, of course, grow but current indications are that the growth will not be nearly as great as has been previously thought. The rate of population growth seems to be slowing down and some of the most experienced demographers in the area of family size and family planning believe that somewhat greater perfection of contraceptive technology will lead to zero population growth without any special need for exhortation. The population of the mid-1980's is likely to include some 240 to 250 million Americans: 35 to 45 million more than today.

This growth is not particularly dramatic although it will certainly require a great deal in the way of new facilities. The most dramatic aspect of population change is the change in the age distribution. If the 60's and the early 70's have been the generation of youth—of the teenager and early 20's adult—the late 70's and 80's will be the era of the young marrieds. The number of men and women between the ages of 24 and 34 will increase by almost 50 percent; the younger group will increase less than 15 percent. There will be a small decrease in the number of adults between 35 and 45, and a 20 percent increase at the over-65 level. The big demographic impact on the society, then, will be in the years of youthful maturity.

Most indications are that the economy will grow fairly steadily through the 1970's and 80's. This will result in an increase in the size of the GNP from 975 billion to 1.7 trillion dollars. It is expected that the service sector of the economy will grow, of course, much more rapidly than the goods sector, but the growth in that area is not inconsiderable.

In the daily life of members of the society, the concomitant impact of this growth is a very large increase in personal income. The median income for families is expected to grow from around $10,000 to about $16,000 (in dollars of 1970 purchasing power).

However, there are no indications to suggest that this income will be distributed more equitably in the future than it is at present. As has been true for the post-World War II period, it seems likely that although each income class will participate in the rising personal income, those at the bottom will not be increasing their share of the pie. That would mean that in the future, as today, the richest 20 percent of families would still be receiving over 40 percent of all of the personal income, and the poorest 20 percent would still be receiving less than 5 percent of the money income. We will speak in more detail about the implications of such a dismal prediction later.

We are so used to the steady increase in affluence (despite occasional periods of two or three years of relative stagnation) and we adapt so rapidly to each successive level of affluence, that it's often difficult to realize how very large the shifts in personal income are. For example, the median income of families and unrelated individuals is projected to increase by $6,100 from 1968 to 1985 (1968 dollars). One way of looking at this increase is to say that over a 17-year period, median income will increase as much as it has over the previous fifty years. The result of these increases will be that by the mid-1980's, half of the population will enjoy the level of living that characterized only the top 3 percent of the population in 1947 or the top 15 percent of the population in 1970. The very large bundle of goods and services that goes with this very large absolute increase in median income can be expected to have important interactions with the emerging lifestyles of the 1980's, both affecting and being affected by those styles.

The increase in knowledgeability will be less dramatic, but nevertheless important. While the upward shifts in educational attainment projected for the 1980's are not particularly dramatic, the small increases there, in addition to numerous other forces expanding the knowledgeability of the population (and shifting its tastes in a more "sophisticated" and "cosmopolitan" direction), will combine to make important changes in the world view of adults in the 1980's. The continuing urbanization of the population and the impact of modern communications has the effect of exposing the average citizen to a much wider range of information and a much wider range of perspectives for interpreting that information than has ever been true in the past. The citizen in the 1980's is therefore likely to be less insulated from national and, indeed, worldwide trends in taste, style and innovations than has ever been true.

Capitalizing on these forces, there will likely be the rise in cultural pluralism. Lifestyles will increasingly be built out of a rapidly expanding multiplicity of choices—choices made possible by the interaction of affluence and cosmopolitanism. One of the most striking things about American society since World War II (or longer than that) has been the extent to which the lives of most Americans involve what they put together out of the choices available to them rather than to what they are constrained to do by their socioeconomic situation. Much of the conflict and turmoil in the society probably has as much to do with anxiety and uncertainty engendered by continuing massive increases in the range of choices available to people as with more frequently commented-upon factors. Indeed, the "oppression" that many who "protest" feel (aside from war-related issues and the problems of blacks and other minorities) is probably more the oppression of having many choices and not knowing how to choose among them than of being "forced" to do things one does not wish to do.

Out of the current ferment about "lifestyles" is very likely to come the institutionalization of a set of pluralistic standards which legitimate a far wider range of ways of living in American society than has previously been the case. From the various liberation movements (black, brown, red, women, gay men, gay women, youth) will probably come a more widespread ethnic of pluralism in lifestyles. (And this will be more than "toleration" in that it will involve recognition of the legitimacy of different kinds of identities and lifestyles.)

The ability to pursue a lifestyle more tailored to individual choice (and less constrained by standards as to what a respectable conforming person should be like) is tremendously enhanced by the increases in material affluence and cultural sophistication.

For the most part, these shifts in opportunity for choice will not involve dramatic changes in life for the great bulk of Americans because their exercise of choice will tend to be in the direction of elaborating and perfecting the existing class-related lifestyles. However, because of the resources available to them it is likely that their particular version of those lifestyles will become increasingly distinctive, increasingly tailored to the needs and identities which they bring to their life situation and which evolve out of its year-to-year development. It is likely that more and more individuals and families will find it possible to elaborate particular areas in which they can indulge one or another special taste or interest in a major kind of way.

Lifestyle trends of continuing importance. In the post-World War II period, the lifestyles of each of the major social classes have evolved in terms of a logic dictated by the values and needs of families in each class as these interact with the increasing resources and possibilities available. The dominant trends of each class can be expected to continue to be important as families from these classes use the resources that come to them to further accomplish their goals and aspirations.

For the working class, the dominant theme has been the solidification of the nuclear family base. Traditionally, the working class has been much enmeshed in kinship, ethnic and peer group ties, and the nuclear family has tended to be relatively "porous" to influences from the outside. Already in the early 1960's, the affluence of the post-World War II period had produced a "modern" working-class family in which husband and wife interacted in a closer and less rigid way, and in which they directed themselves, together, toward the goal of perfecting a secure, comfortable and pleasant home as the central focus of their lives. Their relationships, particularly the father's, with the children also reflected this sharp focus on the home as opposed to previous external ties. This development was central to the consumer goals of the modern working-class family which were strongly oriented toward investment in the home to perfect it as a secure, comfortable, cozy place. In many ways, this modern working-class family seemed to be adopting the styles of the lower middle class. But that class was also in the process of change.

The lower middle class has traditionally centered its lifestyle on a necessity to achieve and maintain respectability. While respectability certainly continues to be a touchstone for the lower white collar way of life, it is increasingly taken for granted and decreasingly an issue of preoccupation for lower middle class men and women. The growing economic affluence and the wider horizons that come from higher education and constant attention to the messages of the mass media have highlighted the striving after wider horizons as perhaps the central theme in the development of a "modern" lower middle class lifestyle. Affluence allows the working-class family to turn in on itself since it no longer has to be so deeply enmeshed in a mutual aid network of community and peers. Affluence allows a lower middle class family to reach outward to experience and make use of a wider slice of the world outside the family. This is true both for lower middle class individuals who move toward expression of personal interests and for the lower middle class family as a whole, which is able to increasingly define as central to family interaction the experiences they have as individuals or together in the outside world. These wider horizons, however, are pursued from a very solid family-oriented base, and with the assumption that the experiences of the wider world will not change the members in any essential way or change their relationships to each other. Therefore, the traditional base of family "togetherness" as a core goal of the lower middle class lifestyle is not challenged. Thus, lower middle class people come to have a wide range of experiences and possessions that have previously been considered characteristic of the upper middle class taste and way of life. Here too, however, the reinterpretation of new lifestyle elements and the changes in the class above result in a continued distinctiveness about the lifestyle.

In the upper middle class, the push out to the larger world is intensified. The central characteristics of the upper middle class orientation towards living have always been self-sufficiency and the pursuit of self-gratification. It is a more egocentric class, in that the claims of either respectability or membership in diffusely obligating groups such as kindred are subordinated to personal goals and desires. Increasing resources and knowledgeability intensify the striving after exploration and fuller self-realization. This is particularly apparent among upper middle class youth where parental indulgence, current life situation and family resources combine to maximize the possibilities for fullest realization. At the level of older upper middle class persons, the experimental approach to perfecting lifestyles is more subdued but also pursued with greater resources. Upper middle class people are in a position to afford and are likely to have the knowledge to select major new additions to their way of life—whether this be a vacation home and the frequent use of it to develop an alternative social world, or the development of a fairly systematic plan of vacation travel that, for example, allows one to see the USA, then Europe, then Asia, with in-between excursions to the Caribbean and Latin America. Because of the extremely large absolute increases in income that will accrue to this group, one can expect a considerable strengthening in the 1980's of this propensity toward elaborate lifestyle innovations. Thus, while the median increase in family income projected for 1968 to 1985 is $6,100, the median increase for the upper middle class will more likely be on the order of $15,000 to $18,000. Such a large absolute increase obviously provides a very rich resource for upper middle class experimentation with new lifestyles without the necessity to sacrifice the material base that supports the more traditional lifestyle.

New trends affecting lifestyles. In addition to the unfinished agenda of the social classes discussed above, one can expect lifestyle changes in response to the changing circumstances that future developments will bring. In some cases (as in fertility) these changes represent a reversal of previous trends, in other cases simply an intensification of changes that have been taking place over a longer period of time.

Changes in family living. Adults will spend less time in the "full nest" stage of the family life cycle. This will come about through a later age at marriage and birth of the first child, an unchanging age at the birth of the last child, and an unchanging or perhaps slightly declining age at which the child ceases to live at home.

First, the later age at marriage: As a lasting legacy of youth and women's liberation thinking, we are likely to find that young people marry somewhat later than they have in the past. There is little evidence of a major revolution in the extent of permarital sexual relations—the Kinsey study of college youth completed in the mid-1960's showed essentially little change over the first Kinsey study in the proportion of women who had had premarital relations. However, there do seem to be important changes in the pattern of sexual relations for that portion of the female population that has premarital sexual relations at all. Sexual relationships are likely to be more frequent and more institutionalized, more open and more accepted within the peer group than was true in the 1930's. Since there is reason to believe that the trend toward earlier marriage in the middle class (the lower and working classes had always married young) was in large part responsive to an effort on the part of young people to establish their maturity and adult status, the development of alternate modes of being "grown up" should mean less of a rush to marriage. The beginning of legitimation of premarital sexual relations in the context of youth peer group relations rather than as furtive and hidden activities should go a long way toward reducing pressure for marriage to establish legitimate adulthood. (For that matter, the eighteen-year-old vote and the consequent courting by politicians may bring somewhat the same result.)

It seems likely that at the level of the "class mass" (at least the highly urban and more cosmopolitan portion of it), relationships that involve young couples "living together" will become fairly widespread. Under these circumstances, marriage will come when the couple decides to "settle down" either to have children or to begin seriously to build incrementally a career and its related family base. For large numbers of other young men and women, less institutionalized patterns of heterosexual relationships may serve to allow a sense of adulthood without marriage. We have already seen the development in a few cities, particularly on the West Coast, of a wide range of "singles" institutions. One can expect this pattern to continue to spread across the country and to become more elaborate as the level of affluence of young adults permits.

Social and heterosexual relationships of the kind sketched above (involving as a common if not universal pattern, reasonably regular participation in sexual relations) depend, of course, on a high possibility of preventing unwanted births. The continued development of more and more effective contraceptive devices (and by the 1980's a once-a-month technique such as the prostaglandins should be well established) means that the technical base for this pattern of social relationships will be available. Legalization of abortion on demand (which should be the case by the 1980's in the states with the great majority of the population) allows for the clearing up of "mistakes" which often currently precipitate marriages (apparently approximately one-quarter of all brides are pregnant at marriage). While there is ample evidence that the availability of contraception does not have much impact on women's willingness to give up their virginity, the willingness to establish a regular premarital sexual relationship is much more responsive to the possibility of effective and interpersonally simple contraception.

Of course the same contraceptive techniques and the availability of abortion which make possible lower rates of premarital fertility also allow couples to space births and to have exactly the number of children they want. Analysis of surveys already conducted suggests that if couples had only the children that they chose to have—that is, if pregnancy was completely voluntary—the average completed fertility of married couples would be on the order of 2.6 children (whereas, in fact, average completed fertility has been running more on the order of 3.3 children).

We have almost no information as to why there seems to be a shift towards smaller family ideals during the past decade. There is no way of predicting with much assurance what fertility desires will be in the late 1970's and 80's However, the clear indication in fertility survey data that (even in a period of fairly high fertility) a great deal of the expressed preference for medium and large families may well have been a rationalization of "accidents" and unplanned pregnancies makes it seem most reasonable to predict a continued trend toward lower fertility.

The product of these various changes in mating behavior would be that women would, on the average, complete their fertility in the late twenties as they do now, having (again on the average) started their families somewhat later than they do now. The children would be grown and old enough to leave home while the parents are, on the average, somewhat younger than they are now. For example, the typical case might be one in which the mother marries at 22 or 23 and has two children. The last one is born when she is 27 or 28 and the children leave home for college or a job, and then "singles" living when the mother is not yet 50. Whereas the typical time period between the marriage and the last of the children leaving home is now between 25 and 30 years, given these patterns of marriage and fertility, the more typical range in the 1980's might be 20 to 25 years. The lifestyle elaborations both prior to marriage—the various "singles" styles—and those after the children leave home would loom larger in their influence than is presently the case.

Interacting with these changes in the timing and structure of family composition will be social-psychological developments—particularly ones connected with the changing role of women. The new feminism seems to contain two strains of thought and aspiration for women, one of which may very well have a pervasive effect and the other a more limited effect. The first involved a greater self-consciousness on the part of women about their subordinate status within the family and in the larger world, and a drive for more autonomy, self-respect and self-expression.

The second involves a challenge to the still-established notion that a woman's place is (really) in the home. The implications of the new feminism are easy to misconstrue because of a peculiarity of the interests of the leaders versus the subjects of the movement. By definition, women who seek leadership or elite positions within the Women's Liberation Movement are persons whose major identity goals are bound up with activities in the public world, and often also with career aspirations. Such interests, aspirations and the relevant skills are entailed in elite roles. Therefore, the leaders of Women's Liberation will probably consistently underplay the importance for the women in whose name they speak of equality goals and aspirations that do not relate in one way or another to the larger, more public world. More specifically, the leaders will tend not to regard the homemaker role as a legitimate major commitment on the part of women. The mass of the followers, however, will be much concerned with their ability to fulfill the homemaker role in a way that is personally gratifying, in a way that allows for the development of autonomy, self-respect, and a sense of valid identity within the narrower and more private worlds that they themselves construct. Even though they will often find the public level of discussion of feminine equality frustrating because it doesn't take these aspirations as fully legitimate, they probably will prove remarkably tenacious (as people do generally in such a situation) in pursuing their own interests and in reinterpreting a great deal of the public ideology of the movement to support the actual roles that they play in their private worlds.

As quickly becomes apparent in any discussion between men and women on this subject, the liberation of women also involves a very significant change in attitudes on the part of men, and also in the nature of the relationships between men and women. The kind of thinking that is apparent in the new feminism (except in its more radical version) clearly points in the direction of greater equality between husbands and wives in their functioning, a strengthening of the trends apparent over the last several decades in the middle class family toward more sharing of power and duties and a less sharply defined division of labor. It has, in the past, been a point of considerable ambivalence among middle class women as to whether they are the servants of their families, the hidden bosses of their families, or persons of equal status whose duties happen to be those of keeping things running smoothly within the home. It is the latter definition which is likely to be strengthened by feminism. As incomes rise, the need for the woman's management of the home and the complexity of that activity of manager, purchasing agent and doer of tasks also rises. If more and more goods and services are brought into and used within the home with increasing affluence, the woman's work there becomes more valuable rather than less. Yet, women have the problem that the values of the society do not define the wife's work as general manager of the home as productive and worthwhile in the same sense that paid-for labor is regarded as productive and worthwhile. Thus, women can define themselves as oppressed and "underpaid" for their valuable work for other members of the family. Thus, the first impulse of many women is to try to get out of the home and to earn self-respect and respect from others by work in the labor market. Such work not only earns a clear-cut status, but the demands in jobs are much more specific and less diffuse than are homemakers' tasks. Women sometimes find it easier to feel that they are doing a good job at those more specifically defined tasks than at home where a woman's work is never done—nor unambiguously judged. Yet, with the rise in affluence and productivity in the commodity sector, the kinds of services that a woman might buy to take care of her home become increasingly expensive so that women will be loath to buy on the outside market much of the labor that will be necessary to maintain the home.

There may well be a class difference in response to the combination of affluence and a continuing emphasis on feminine equality. Very likely at the working and lower middle class level the two will combine to give women a greater sense of worth and to encourage them toward more autonomous functioning within the homemaker role. At the upper middle class level, however, there may be an increasing emphasis on career for purely self-expressive goals. (At all class levels there will be some increase in the proportion of women in the work force because of the decline in fertility and the fewer years in which a woman has children in the home.) Upper middle class women have always included activities outside the home (either in voluntary activities or at work) as a central part of their role definition. They will certainly expect, as part of rising affluence, to be able to engage in these self-enhancing and self-validating activities more fully. This will put a strong premium on homemaking products and work organization which facilitate labor and time saving. While on the one hand the home will be a more elaborate and complex place, on the other hand the woman will want to spend less time there. This will create a great demand for innovations which make homes easier to keep clean and neat, meals quicker to prepare, etc.

The increasing impact of the wider world will stimulate needs for both more stimulation and more privacy. Modern communications, combined with the greater sophistication of the audience, have the effect of bringing the world in on the average citizen in more and more forceful terms as the years go on. He reacts to what he sees in various ways—sometimes with fright and intimidation and other times with interest, approval and fascination. Both of these responses can be expected to be at least as characteristic of the 1980's citizen as of today's, assuming that all the world's problems are not solved between now and then. The need to pull back, to disengage from exposure to the world's events (not just the large scale events seen on the evening news but also those observed and important in one's day-to-day life at work, on the street, in the local community and elsewhere) strengthens people's commitment to home as their castle, as well as encouraging them toward seeking for relaxation and vacation other locales which are tranquil, isolated, private, etc. The feeling that the world is too much with us leads to an interest in getting away from it all, getting "back to nature." The fascination with the wider world leads to an interest both in bringing into the home more and more that reflects, expresses, symbolizes that wider world, and also a stronger interest in travel, in exploring the wider world. Both sets of needs combine to create trends toward freeing the family in its lifestyle from a particular territorial base. There grows, instead, an emphasis on the mastery of space, distance and amenities so that one can pursue gratifying activities, individually, as a couple, as a family, in a variety of places. People strive by using their resources of tailor-made environments in ways that fit their particular interests, their moods, their desires for new or repeated preferred experiences. We would predict from these trends a rapidly increasing demand for all kinds of products and services related to travel, both those which are used personally by consumers, and those which provide the product base on which services such as hotels, airlines, etc., are based.

There won't be enough time to spend all the money. People become busier the more affluent they are. Paradoxically, people whose affluence is increasing tend to make choices which result in their having less free or uncommitted time rather than more. There is considerable evidence to suggest that with increasing affluence workers do not choose greater leisure rather than more income; work hours tend either not to decrease at all or to decrease very slightly. None of the predictions made in the early 1950's concerning shorter working hours seem to have held up. Indeed, in the few cases where unions have bargained for a short work week the slack seems to have been taken up for a fair number of the workers by more moonlighting. This makes good economic sense. After all, a man doesn't have to have anything extraordinarily interesting to do with his leisure time if his only choice is earning 50 cents an hour. On the other hand, at $10 an hour the leisure time activity needs to be pretty gratifying to cause him to forego the money.

With increasing affluence, people are able to buy more and more goods and services but then they run into the hard fact that the using of the products and services requires time. And the time available for consumption does not change. One can't really buy time; all one can do is try to buy more efficient use of time. This fact has profound implications for lifestyle and consumer behavior—many of these implications are discussed within the framework of economic theory by Steffan Linder in *The Harried Leisure Class* (1970).

In general, when there are so many products to use and things to do and gratifications to be derived from both, people will tend to become impatient with routine, purely instrumental activities which seem to consume a great deal of time and effort relative to the gratification they produce. Similarly, people will tend to shift their consumption in the direction of products that seem to provide more gratification per time unit and away from products which seem time-consuming in relation to the amount of gratification they provide.

A principal effect is to make daily life more "commodity and service intensive." That is, people will tend to use more and more products and services in ways that maximize the satisfaction in a given period of time. Linder argues that with rising income, pure leisure time (that is time in which you do nothing much) tends to decline because the degree of gratification that is available from goods and services that were previously too expensive is now greater than the gratification that is available from leisure and from one's own efforts to turn leisure into gratifying activity. Similarly, activities that are less productive of gratification tend to be given up or the time devoted to them sharply curtailed in favor of activities that are more productive and more expensive. The less time goods take per unit of satisfaction provided, the more in demand they will be. The cheapness of the product in terms of time becomes more and more important as the importance of their cheapness in terms of money declines. Individuals tend to give up relatively less productive activities such as reading or taking long walks in familiar territory, or leisurely engagement in lovemaking, in favor of activities that require less time investment. The same activities may be pursued in more exotic settings as a way of heightening satisfaction through the use of economic resources. Thus, the man who would hardly waste his time to view nature in the city park a few blocks away from home may be ecstatic about the beauties of the Scottish countryside. People are notorious in not being tourists in their own cities because they are "too busy," but they will spend a great deal of money to visit a distant city and will end up knowing more about its interesting sights than they do about the ones in their own home town.

These trends, coupled with the trends toward freeing women even more from household duties, will tend to heighten awareness of the home as a "system" involving shelter, furnishings, production processes and their maintenance. The home will become a more and more "capital intensive" place as the cost of both externally supplied labor and the household labor increases. The interconnection between the various parts of the home system may prove to be particularly frustrating as the drive toward time efficiency increases. (This trend will not proceed as rapidly if the cost of housing rises as sharply as increasing construction costs over the past few years suggest it might. In that case people will be spending higher and higher proportions of income for housing and would have less available to make the household more capital intensive.) Assuming that shelter cost does not increase as a proportion of income, then rising affluence and a static supply of time will mean that the operating of the household will have to become more and more capital intensive if it is not to prove burdensome to the family. There will be an ever higher premium of labor-saving devices that actually do save time (as, for example, a dishwasher does and a disposal does not).

The consumption of services will grow and broaden. A large segment of the multiplicity of choices that become available to people as their affluence rises has to do with the wider range of services which they can afford. People are able to buy expensive services which they previously had to forego (like regular medical care) or perform for themselves. As their own time becomes more and more valuable, they are more willing to pay others to do things for them if those others can perform the task more efficiently (often at the cost of possession of special equipment) or in a more satisfying way. This trend toward having others do work previously performed by household members is most dramatically evident in the rapid growth of franchise food operations.

A second area in which a large expansion of services is likely has to do with the public sector. If the current national consensus toward disengagement from worldwide empire (a consensus that seems widely shared from the middle of the Republican spectrum leftward) becomes a more or less permanent feature of the nation's stance towards the larger world, then one can expect an even greater rate of growth in public sector services than has been apparent over the last decade. The basis for support of demand for a broader and more fully developed range of public sector services is provided both by increasing affluence and by the broad exposure of most of the population to "informed opinion" through the mass media. Also, a higher proportion of the population attends college and is exposed there to welfare-oriented teaching which emphasizes public sector services of all kinds.

One area in which there will likely be rapid expansion of services has to do with cleaning up and neating up the environment. This ranges all the way from public activities to reduce pollution and to facilitate recycling, over to expansion of public recreation facilities both in local communities and in national and state parks and camping facilities.

The current propaganda in favor of day care services may presage a growing consensus in favor of publicly supported nursery schools and day care services which will have the effect of lowering the age at which children enter the public child care/education system to perhaps as low as three years. These programs are now often phrased as anti poverty programs but I think they represent a projection onto this issue of a widespread desire on the part of women to get the kids out of the house at earlier ages than five or six. These children's services could be developed fully in the public sector as with the public educational system or in a public/private mix involving vouchers used to pay tuition at privately operated nursery schools, day care centers and the like.

So much for likely lifestyle developments affecting the fortunate majority of Americans who are above the level of economic marginality. But what of the groups that have occupied so much of the public attention during the decade just finished—the poor and the oppressed minorities?

The future of the underclass. Perhaps I was being overly pessimistic earlier when I emphasized the fact that there is no evidence to suggest that the distribution of income in 1985 will be different from its distribution today. Perhaps that's not important. Certainly the group at the bottom of society, the underclass, will experience tremendous growth in their level of affluence just as will those who are better off—that is what an unchanging income distribution means. If we consider the underclass includes those families who consistently live on incomes of less than half of the median family, that encompasses 20 percent of the population. That same 20 percent in 1985 will have experienced a 60 percent increase in income, and the top of the underclass will be defined then by an $8,000-a-year family income—the underclass will be as well off in 1985 as the average American was in the mid-1960's. What is there to complain about in that?

Just as there are reasons for predicting no change in the income distribution, there are good reasons for predicting only small changes in the relative incomes of white and black families by 1985. The 1960's saw significant increase in black family incomes relative to whites—from around 53 percent of white income to around 63 percent of white income. However, there has been no improvement in that figure in the last couple of years—emphasizing again the crucial role of high unemployment rates in black economic oppression. Indeed, an economist, Harold W. Guthrie, has projected the comparative experience of white and nonwhite families from 1947 through 1968 into the future by calculating the number of years required for equality of family income between the two races under various employment conditions. His results suggest that at current unemployment rates, equality of income between black and white families would take well over 100 years to achieve. At the so-called full unemployment rate of four percent—the Administration's current target—it would still require 30 years to achieve equality of income. Only with a sustained unemployment rate lower than three and one-half percent, would black and white incomes be equal by 1985. (And it's important to note that these very low unemployment rates which could be expected to produce equality of income would have to be sustained over the required number of years. There seems little reason to believe that it will be possible to sustain such low rates.) Given the kinds of swings in unemployment experienced in the 1960's, we could perhaps expect black family incomes to increase to between 70 and 75 percent of white family income. At 75 percent of white family income, blacks would be enjoying the standard of living purchased by $12,000 a year, significantly better than the median family income for whites today. Their incomes would have almost doubled. Yet, relative to whites, the absolute difference in income would be slightly larger than it is today.

There are obviously two ways to look at what happens to disadvantaged groups under these economic circumstances. If one focuses on the absolute changes, one can say that they are far better off than today. If one focuses on changes relative to the majority segments of the society, one can say that they are not at all or only slightly better off. Knowing which judgment best captures the human reality of living as a member of the underclass or as a black who does not receive his equal share of what society has to offer, requires a more thoughtful consideration of what income and material standards mean in our kind of society than is usually accorded that issue.

One useful way to begin to examine this issue is to look at the results of the first decade of our war on poverty. In some ways, that war started in 1961—the focus was not on poverty but on the "grey areas" of the cities and on such problems as juvenile delinquency and public housing. But, the issues encompassed in the grey areas—juvenile delinquency, concerted welfare service programs of the early 60's—were essentially the same as the issues which came to be included under the general rubric of poverty.

The reduction of poverty in the 1960's. When the War on Poverty was launched, one of the most immediate needs was for a yardstick by which to measure the prevalence of poverty. In the end, the chosen standard was one based on a low-cost food budget which represented a presumed minimum subsistence level of nutrition. This budget was multiplied by three to get the annual income which was to represent the poverty line. (The logic there was based on studies of the buying habits of low-income people which had established that they spend approximately one-third of their income on food.) By 1971 the poverty line for a nonfarm family of four members was at about $4,000 a year, a budget that would allow approximately $25.60 per week for feeding a family, or $3.67 a day or 91 cents per day per person. A poverty line varying by family size, farm or nonfarm residence, and male or female head, was initially adopted in 1964, and has been updated each year to take account of price increases. Otherwise it represents an unchanging standard for assessing the prevalence of poverty.

Assessed against this standard, the prevalence of poverty has declined dramatically over the past decade—from 22.4 percent of families in 1959 to 12.8 percent in 1968. These figures represent proportions of the population; in absolute numbers, the poor declined from almost 40 million to around 25 million persons. There were 20 million fewer poor people than there would have been had the proportion of poor not declined.

Another way of assessing the change is to look at what happened to the "poverty gap," that is, the amount of money that the poor would have to have in aggregate in order not to be poor. That poverty gap amounted (in 1968 dollars) to 18.3 billion dollars in 1959 and to only 9.8 billion dollars in 1968, a decline of about 40 percent despite the 20 million increase in population.

This reduction in the prevalence of poverty, simply viewed, should be regarded as evidence of a dramatic success for public policies related to poverty. One can well imagine that over the next decade and a half a similar proportionate decrease in the incidence of poverty will occur, reducing the prevalence of poverty to a mere 5 percent of the population.

One would expect, given this kind of success, a mood of elation to characterize professionals and politicians particularly interested in social welfare. One would expect that any time inroads of such significant magnitude were made during a decade against a kind of social problem which has previously proved remarkably persistent, there would be a strong sense of success on the part of those responsible. Quite the contrary is, of course, the case. The statement that the nation is well on its way to eradicating poverty is greeted with disbelief, there is no sense that the disadvantaged are significantly better off today than a decade ago, etc., etc.

What is interesting is that although the figures have changed, the social reality the figures were supposed to capture doesn't really seem to change at all. The people who would have been considered poor on an "eyeball-to-eyeball basis" in 1959 are still considered poor today. The people who felt themselves poor and deprived, oppressed and wasted by their society in 1959 seem still to feel themselves poor, oppressed, deprived and wasted today, despite the fact that their incomes have increased by one-third in dollars of constant purchasing power.

An examination of the attractiveness of a War on Poverty in the 1963-64 period suggests that the political leaders and the general public did not undertake that war out of altruism. There was the expectation that significant inroads into the problem of poverty would result in parallel decreases in the prevalence of various kinds of social pathologies that had traditionally been related to poverty—the kinds of social pathologies that disturb the nonpoor and the political executive because they make for a threatening and unattractive social milieu. The hoped for reductions in crime, welfare dependency, racial conflict, deterioration of urban institutions like the schools—all these hopes have been in vain. Despite the reduction by almost 50 percent of the proportion of poor Americans, we have seen increases in the intensity of all of the other problems. Thus, there is no sense in the nation of triumph over poverty or of mastery of the nation's problems related to deprivation.

There are several ways of looking at the absence of change in connection with problems that have always been considered poverty-related despite the dramatic decline in the prevalence of poverty. One popular way of explaining this phenomenon has been to emphasize the cultural aspects of poverty and to say that "of course" the social pathological phenomena do not disappear simply because fewer and fewer people live below the minimum subsistence level. If one believes there is an independent lower class culture or "culture of poverty," which is a cultural tradition not responsive to the socioeconomic situation in which people find themselves, this apparent paradox is not a paradox at all. I think, however, one can argue that this kind of cultural determinism is, in fact, not an adequate explanation of the paradox. The other explanation for the paradox lies in examining what was meant by poverty in the first place by trying to disentangle some of the variables that tended to be collapsed into the one concept of poverty at the time the War on Poverty was announced—variables that have also been confounded historically in scholarly discussions of socioeconomic deprivation.

One can say that the basic error of diagnosis in establishing the independent variable called poverty was to conceive of the poverty situation as that of suffering from the absolute deprivation of not having enough resources to establish a "minimum subsistence level of living."

If, instead, one concerns himself with socioeconomic deprivation as a problem of inequality as one facet of the class structure of the society, then there is little cause for surprise at the lack of change in "poverty-related" social problems during the decade of the 60's. One discovers that while the proportion living below the poverty line established by the Social Security Administration has declined 43 percent since 1959, the proportion of families whose incomes are less than half of the median family income has changed not at all, not only over the last decade but since 1947 when family income statistics first began to be systematically collected.

The people we would have called poor on the basis of an examination of their way of life in 1950 we would very likely call poor in 1970 because their way of life is much the same despite the fact that it includes slightly more in the way of material goods. Their affluence has increased somewhat, but in absolute amounts the affluence of the bulk of the population has increased even more and they will find themselves further away from the going standard of American life now than they did in 1960. The issue of poverty, then, and the apparent progress toward eliminating it has concealed all along the issue of inequality and the fact of no progress toward eliminating it. Oscar Ornati captures the issues exactly when he observes that the huge social escalation in standards of living over the past 40 years has carried with it no significant decrease in income inequality:

"The rich and poor have continued to 'keep their distances' while the entire structure has shifted to a higher plane. In 1940 the top 5 percent of U.S. families received about 25 percent of all income and in 1961 this group still received about 20 percent. The real per capita income of the average nonfarm family in 1960 was almost as high as the real per capita income of the wealthier 5 percent in 1940. What has happened is that the problem of poverty, because of a very real social escalation, has slipped away from under the neat and reasonable theoretical formulation which equated the problem of poverty with the problem of income distribution. One might almost say that the economic base has moved out from under the theoretical superstructure, leaving the analysis in theoretical limbo." (1966)

However, while the economic issues of income distribution have entered in a kind of theoretical limbo, the social issues related to lower class behavior appear in much the same light today as they did in the 1930's. Contemporary sociological analyses of various lower class related social problems do not read that differently from those carried out in the 1920's and 30's if one makes allowance for shifts in rhetorical style. One would hardly know that a huge social escalation in income had taken place.

This underclass defined in relative terms as living below half of the median family income has experienced an enormous increase in its living level since 1947 (when median family income data were first systematically collected). Then its yearly income stood around $2,500 whereas today it stands around $5,000. The income of the underclass has literally doubled in a 24-year period. By 1985 that income will stand at $8,000 a year, an increase of $3,000—even larger than the absolute increase since 1947. However, the gap between the underclass income and that of the man in the mainstream also grows—from $2,500 in 1947 to $5,000 in 1971 to $8,000 in 1985.

Compared to these kinds of considerations, the current absolute poverty line projected forward to 1985 is obviously ludicrous. It would still stand at around $4,000 a year in current dollars since it is adjusted only to compensate for inflation. By its standards there would be about three and one-half million poor families. By the standards of the relative poverty line at 50 percent of the median family income, there would be closer to 13 million poor families.

There is one bit of evidence concerning how the public evaluates living standards which suggests that the relative standard is by far the most meaningful. If, in relation to the median family income, ordinary people maintain fairly constant judgments as to what a decent minimum income is, then we can assume the relative standard of poverty (or affluence) is the one that actually influences behavior. Fortunately, since 1937 the Gallup organization has been asking a question (with slight variations) which gets at the issue of a decent minimum income. Their question is, "What is the smallest amount of money a family of four (husband, wife, and two children) needs each week to get along in this community?" In late 1970, that amount stood at around $6,500 a year—about two-thirds of the median family income. All during the 1960's the average answer given by the Gallup samples has been around two-thirds of the median family income. In the 1940's and 50's it was somewhat higher but the range between two-thirds and three-quarters of the median family income has been remarkably constant over a 25-year period. This figure is, of course, higher than the poverty level but its stability suggests that there would be a similar stability at the lower standard of living also.

If we project this standard forward we could find that Americans are likely to believe that an income of around $10,000 is necessary for a family of four just to get along in 1985. Again the absolute gap between just getting along and the median family would have increased markedly. There would be 19 million families living below this standard.

In order to understand something of why, in human terms—in terms of the social psychology of individuals and families living their daily lives—these relative standards are so crucial, we need to consider for a moment what might be called the social psychology of materialism.

We want to explore, from the perspective of family lifestyles and individual life careers, an issue which unfortunately has not received, from behavioral scientists, the attention that, given the realities of industrial society, it should have. This is the social psychology of materialism, or "consumerism," if you will. I believe that an understanding of the role of materialism is crucial to an understanding of the problem we call poverty and minority disadvantage. I think it's obvious that an understanding of materialism is even more crucial to the development of successful policies to cope with environmental problems.

A materialistic society can be defined as one in which members achieve and act out membership in their society and its institutions through the use of objects and paid-for services. It is a society in which objects and services are essential to the achieving and acting out of membership, and in which these objects and services are not in sufficiently plentiful supply that one can have them simply for the asking or the reaching out. While all societies have their material underpinnings, distinctive to industrialized society is the incredible proliferation of material objects and services for sale through which individuals in the society live out their identities and perform their roles. The social psychology of materialism, then, rather than simply damning the "overly materialistic" nature of modern societies, must chart in detail the connections between the individual's sense of place and purpose in social space and life, and his access to and command over the resources represented by the goods and services provided through private and public markets.

Equality and membership. The Council of Economic Advisers, at the beginning of the War on Poverty, defined the prevalence of poverty as involving "the number of families who do not have the resources to provide minimum satisfaction of their own particular needs." But the Council went on to observe that, "By the standards of contemporary American society most of the population of the world is poor; and most Americans were poor a century ago. But for our society today, a consensus on an approximate standard that is based on the presumably absolute logic of "low cost" or "economy plan" budgets. If we are to define the poor, as the Council does until it tries to develop a measuring instrument, as "those who are not now maintaining a decent standard of living—those whose basic needs exceed their means to satisfy them," then one must recognize that the standard involved is inevitably relative.

The issue of inequality and the goal of equality have tended to be eclipsed in modern political discussions and in social science scholarship and research that is responsive to major political issues. The approaches to equality which occupied so much of the attention of political philosophers in the nineteenth century seem to have reached a dead end. For all the emphasis on equalitarian values in our traditions, the issue of inequality per se has tended to be fragmented and refocused into a number of other concerns, one of which has been poverty defined according to some absolute standard of subsistence. To base a social science analysis on the effects of inequality has a kind of old-fashioned ring to it. Equality as an ideal has come to seem an arbitrary or abstract, unreal ideal since it is so obvious that people have different tastes, want different things, experience life in different ways, and so on. The sameness which is conjured up by the idea of equality seems both impossible and unattractive. The impasse that equalitarian thinking has reached was a result of concentration on models of the process by which society might be equalized which tended to make the idea seem either impossible of achievement or irrelevant to issues of social justice.

One model of equality dominated a great deal of early socialist thinking. It might be called the "top down" model. The emphasis was more on taking resources away from the rich and powerful than on distributing those resources to people who were less rich and less powerful. Such a model tends to reach a pragmatic dead end when it is discovered that distributing all of the personal income of the very rich would have a fairly small impact on the economic status of everyone else. So the writers on equality have generally had to admit that confiscatory approaches would not accomplish much for the material well-being of those at the bottom (even though it might have great consequences for political and status equality). This approach has also seemed to reach a pragmatic political dead end with the discovery that of course the rich and powerful will fight tooth and nail any approach which takes away what they already have.

Another model, one which has received increasing emphasis as the confiscatory approaches were discarded, is one which emphasizes not so much the production of equal results as it does the equality of opportunity to achieve rewards in a society which it is accepted will continue to be highly stratified into haves and have nots. This kind of concern dominated a great deal of discussion of racial inequality and led to the symbolic importance of Negro "firsts," that is, Negroes who are the first to win some important position or reward. The logic here tends to emphasize the extent to which the disadvantaged minority is excluded both from participating in the unequal reward system and from making outstanding contributions to society—as in the rhetorical question that used to be popular before the latest civil rights revolution: "Think of how many Negro Nobel Prize winners have been lost because we denied Negroes equality of opportunity!"

This model of equality has met with considerable frustration from the discovery of how tenaciously interconnected inequalities are so that it becomes almost impossible to produce equality of opportunity except in a situation in which there is, in fact, also equality of result [as Nathan Glazer (1966) has nicely observed in his comments on Negro family studies since Frazier's (1939) landmark study]. Thus equality of opportunity has come to be seen as a kind of will-o'-the-wisp. But, the long effort to provide a social science base for policies based on the goal of equal opportunity has had a great impact in teaching us what, for a society that might even approximate the achievement of equalitarian ideals, the real implications of those ideals are.

Much of the earlier discussion of equality assumed that who men are and what they want are given (by human nature, genetics, etc.) and that the discussion of equality and equalitarian social forms must proceed without taking as problematic the question of how the person is formed in society and by its institutions. The increasingly strong evidence that who men are and what they want are social products, even to such apparently innate characteristics as intelligence, recasts the whole issue of equality, of equal opportunity, and, most importantly for our discussion, of what represents a "subsistence" level of resources. Much discussion of equality foundered on the question of what one does about the presence in society of individuals whose productivity would not merit an equal reward, and what one does about problems of incentive if people are rewarded in excess of their contribution to society. Once one admits the perspective that men's productivity is itself a product of society and not just of their own innate ability and motives, this latter issue appears as the problem of how a society can be structured so that it does not produce persons of low productivity; that is, how a society can be structured so that problems of unmerited reward would be trivial rather than significant.

This leads one in the direction of a model of equalization which might be called a "bottom up" model as opposed to a "top down" or equality of opportunity model. In the "from the bottom up" model of equalization, the central question is: "What material resources are necessary to be a fully contributing member of the society?" It is a question of the level of resources necessary in order for individuals to enter the mainstream of society and be self-sustaining within it. Interestingly enough, many definitions of poverty take this into account but then back away later from the equalitarian implications of such a definition. John Kenneth Galbraith defined poverty very much along these lines when he said that "people are poverty-stricken when their income, even if adequate for survival, falls markedly behind that of the community. Then they cannot have what the larger community regards as the minimum necessary for decency; and they cannot wholly escape, therefore, the judgment of the larger community that they are indecent. They are degraded, for, in a literal sense, they live outside the grades or categories which the community regards as respectable." (1958:251)

Harold Laski faced this issue in an even more direct way, and his choice of words for discussing equality makes it easy to begin to see some of the connections between traditional behavioral science concerns with socialization, personality development, motivation and the like, and the apparently abstract issue of equality. Laski characterized equality in its social implications along the following lines:

Equality means that no man shall be so placed in society that he can overreach his neighbor to the extent which constitutes a denial of the latter's citizenship.

Equality means such an ordering of social forces as will balance the share in the toil of living with a share in its gain also. It means that my share in that gain must be adequate for the purposes of citizenship.

In institutional terms (equality means that) the urgent claims of all must be met before we can meet the particular claims of some. The differences in the social and economic position of men can only be admitted after a minimum basis of civilization is attained by the community as a whole. That minimum basis must admit of my realizing the implications of personality.

Equality involves rendering to each man his own by giving him what enables him to be a man. It is only by making identity (that is equality up to the point of sufficiency) the basis of our institutions, and differences the answer to the necessities of social function that we can make our society call into the play the individuality of men. (1938:153-165)

In these quotations is embedded a theory of socialization and of the just society that is congruent with the dominant thrust of behavioral science development over the past several decades. The image of the good society contained here is that of a society in which each man is who he knows he should be. That is, each man is a fully formed member of his society. Much of cultural and psychological anthropology has been devoted to describing and analyzing in detail how primitive, traditional societies operate to prepare for their members the "minimum basis of civilization" that realizes for them the implications of personality. Much of sociology has involved cataloging the various ways in which exploitative societies deny full membership to their members—exploitation which commonly takes the form of tribal and ethnic subjugation or of exploitative capitalist (or other) economic arrangements.

The central social science issue becomes that of how a society positions its members by its stratification of the experiences and resources available to them. Erving Goffman's (1959) concept of virtual social identity is relevant here. He suggests that both in general and with reference to particular social situations, persons in a society develop expectations as to what attributes, characteristics and possessions an "ordinary" person is likely to have, and that we convert these expectations into demands on others, demands that are usually smoothly met because the other person is, indeed, the ordinary person whom we expected. The characterization "in effect" of others appropriate in a given society, or a given situation, constitutes a virtual social identity appropriate for that society or situation.

The person who is able to fit into that identity is then characterized by himself and by others as a "whole and usual person." When, in fact, he possessed attributes that make him different in a less desirable way from persons in the category in which he is supposed to fit then, Goffman (1959) shows, he is subject to processes of stigmatization that deeply affect his life career and his personality. People who feel comfortable in their role as members of a society are those who perceive themselves to possess those attributes and resources which go into the construction of a virtual social identity for persons in their society. Following from Laski's (1938) observations is the judgment that the good society is one which programs the experiences of its members as they grow to adulthood and as they make commitments as mature adults in such a way that they experience themselves as, and are treated by others as, being "whole and usual" persons—so that there is a concordance between a virtual social identity appropriate for their society, and an actual social identity that they possess. (Elsewhere I have discussed the relationship between social identity and ego identity, and the importance of congruence among these for the development of a sense of valid identity.)

The discussion in the previous section emphasizes the importance not only of identity at any one time but of identity through time. One's sense of identity involves a conception of a likely life course (or of alternative life courses with subjective probabilities attached to each possible development). And just as the actual social identities of individuals are matched against virtual social identities which represent society's conception of who its members are, the actual life careers of individuals are paralleled by the virtual life careers which members of the society carry around in their heads to summarize their understandings of how members of their society progress through life.

Much of the discussion of socialization, particularly as it varies by social class, can be seen as turning on the question of the prospective life career the child sees for himself and the extent to which there is a disjunction between it and a virtual life career he has learned is appropriate for full members of the society. A virtual life career, when it seems a possibility for the individual, becomes a powerful stimulus for anticipatory socialization in ways that facilitate adaptation and productivity in the society. A marked disjunction between that society's virtual life careers and individuals' conceptions of their likely life careers tends to set up identity processes which reduce the degree to which the individual commits himself to activities which are likely to earn him a reward in the larger society.

The much discussed measures of subjective perception of control over one's fate may be a kind of a roundabout way of tapping the extent to which there is or is not a disjunction between the life career the individual projects for himself and ones he knows to be appropriate and desirable for members of his society. It may be that because social scientists are career-oriented and mobile they have tended to develop concepts with an activist bias like "control over one's fate" rather than concepts which go more directly to the issue of the way individuals calculate the probability of good things happening to them if they behave naturally, if they are themselves. That is of the extent to which they perceive themselves as so positioned that things will go right for them if they behave in what seems like a reasonable and congenial fashion. Part of the fascination of books such as *Black Like Me* (1960) is that they provide dramatic illustrations of what happens when the "person" doesn't change but the contingency of "good things happening" when he continues to be himself changes dramatically. (Much the same kind of consideration probably also applies to the concept of "inability to defer gratification" which has been used in a great deal of discussion of lower class behavior. Here again the central factor involved seems to be that of the subjective probability assigned to different kinds of futures.)

A focus on life career as opposed to identity and life situation at any one time tends also to shift our concern with economic resources from income at any one time to the income stream through the individual's life. Thus, there is an important parallel between subjective sense of life career and economic concepts of permanent income which direct our attention to the ability of the individual to sustain a given level of consumption through time. (This kind of longitudinal emphasis is approximated statistically by measures of lifetime income.)

In the best possible data world, one would discuss poverty and income inequality not so much in terms of cross-sectional comparisons of income as in terms of lifetime income, or more exactly, lifetime command over goods and services. As it is now, a good deal of discussion of poverty confounds the question of the allocation of income for a given individual to different portions of his life cycle (e.g., the problem of the old poor) with the question of the total amount of resources that are likely to be available to him throughout his lifetime.

From the point of view of the individual's sense of membership in the society, it is probably the latter that is the most important. That is, it is not so much the amount of money he has available right at the moment that is important to him, as the stream of resources that he has good reason to believe will be available to him into the future.

If one defines the good society as one in which individuals have those experiences in life necessary for them to regard themselves as members of their society, that is, as persons who are who they know they should be, then it is possible to assess the goal of equality against this more general standard for judging the good or just society. The first response of at least the cross-culturally sophisticated social scientist is likely to be that, in fact, equality is not a necessary avenue for the development among the members of a society of a sense of valid membership in their society. Thus, the anthropologist is likely to point to societies in which stratification and elaborate systems of varied roles based on positions in kinship, age grade or other kinds of hierarchies are central to the society, and yet there seems little evidence that the members of those societies do not regard themselves as having a valid place within them. In fact, of course, the anthropologist would also note that the vast majority of cultures are highly equalitarian in resource distribution for all the elaboration and specificity of their role systems, and that even when there are enormous differences in sacred or political status, the material differences tend to be fairly small. We would note that the crucial characteristics for the highly stratified societies in which individuals nevertheless have a sense of place, of valid membership, is that each of the individual positions in those social systems or each of the classes of positions is clearly defined and articulated with the overall system so that there is nothing anomalous about the existence of varied and invidiously ranked positions in the system. Thus, one could say that one way of abolishing poverty is to make the poor content with their lot by convincing them that their status has meaning and purpose within the overall design of the society. However, the moment one considers such caste-like arrangements as a solution of the problem of the destructive consequences of inequality, one is immediately struck by how totally dysfunctional such arrangements would be for industrial society. In industrial society, people are positioned in the society principally by their relationship to the economy. No other role system challenges the importance of that central positioning institution. Industrial societies seem to require a considerable degree of openness in their operation; they require mobility of labor, they challenge competition from other sources by their own dynamic, etc. Therefore, industrial societies are stuck with being relatively open societies. The individual's command over material resources becomes the central measure of the extent to which he is a fully participating member of the society at any one time, and prospectively.

And it is apparent from a wide range of sociological studies that people know this about their society. People tend to define themselves and others very much in terms of their judgments about individuals' command over the resources produced, whatever the going definition of a satisfactory standard of living is. The study of lower class behavior and lower class subculture becomes a study of how groups experience themselves in history as removed from the going definition of a member's lifetime trajectory (that is, the going definition of virtual social identity and virtual life careers). We discover that when a group finds itself so removed from command over resources that it cannot participate in society in these terms it adapts to its position by developing a lower class culture. The daily experiences of the group, as well as its accumulated wisdom, tells its members that they are not part of the society, that they are not able to function in an ordinary way, and that, therefore, they must develop extraordinary techniques for adapting, for making a life from day to day, and from year to year.

If membership is the key issue in the human's effort to find a meaningful life, and if in affluent industrial societies membership can be achieved only through the command over the goods and services that are required for mainstream participation, then it follows that we will continue to have poor people and oppressed minorities so long as a significant proportion of Americans have incomes far removed from that of the average man. It follows that the underclass will be alive and well in 1985. And all of the pathologies of the city which are generated by the oppression and deprivation which produce the underclass will also still be with us.

As we have seen, without marked improvements in their economic situation, the black underclass will continue to grow in numbers. Because the black migration from the rural south to the major metropolitan areas does not seem to be abating very fast, it is likely that the size of the urban ghettos will continue to grow, in some cities spilling over into the suburbs. In any case, the ghettos will remain the locales of concentrated trouble and violence that they are today.

I don't think we can be particularly sanguine about the efforts during the 1960's to direct new resources and leadership into poverty and black areas. Because of a combination of sociological and political reasons, it seems to me that the most likely end result of the ferment and militancy of the 1960's will be the institutionalization of a new bureaucratic class staffed by members of poor and minority groups, and functioning—for all of the possible continuance of militant rhetoric—primarily to keep the minorities in their place and to limit their encroachment on affluent white America. While the cost of social control of and welfare for the underclass will continue to increase, all evidence is that the relative costs of these programs will probably not increase very much. Thus, while the affluent will complain mightily, they will continue to pay the price they have been paying for many years now for some modicum of urban peace.

Because the underclass will still be there, and because of the much higher level of affluence, property crime rates will probably continue to increase, and crimes of violence will probably not decrease very much. There may or may not be recurrent periods of urban rioting but then the riots are really less important to the day-to-day lives of people living in the ghetto than the more random and individual violence to which they are subjected. One can expect larger and larger areas of the city to deteriorate and become abandoned, and one can expect more no-man's lands to develop in cities—areas where no one wants to go for any legitimate purpose, and which are abandoned to whatever use marginal persons may want to put them. Again, although the financial cost to individuals with whose commercial or residential investments in the areas of deterioration may be great, the net cost of the deterioration of the cities will continue to be fairly small, relative to the general level of affluence and relative to the opportunities that the expanding suburban and exurban rings provide.

Finally, while one can expect to see a very large growth in the "human service" industries—with perhaps a large part of that growth directed toward doing something about the problems of the underclass—it seems likely that these service-oriented programs will continue to prove to be failures. They will provide opportunities for middle class professionals and, hopefully, for a few mobile persons from the underclass to earn a good and steady income, but will not do much, in fact, to improve life for the "clients" of these services.

Only if there is a very major shift in the way Americans think about and cope with the problems of poverty, race, urban distress, and the like, is 1985 likely to appear much better to us in these respects than 1971.

Solutions for a better urban environment. Let me try to draw some implications from the foregoing for the main tasks that confront us in improving the quality of the urban environment over the next two decades.

First I'd like to say something about physical environmental problems. This is not an area of my expertise but I think some fairly obvious conclusions follow from what has been said about likely lifestyle and economic developments into the 1980's.

We may hope that the population will begin to stabilize. If we approach replacement level birthrate soon the population will still grow until around the year 2020, but the rate of growth will be very small compared to what we have experienced in the last two decades. In any case, I don't think population size is really a problem for this country; even at the 1950 rates, population growth probably would not be a really pressing problem until the end of this century. Population distribution does represent a problem in terms of the physical environment, however. In many ways the management of metropolitan areas would be much easier if there were smaller metropolises and fewer of the megalopolitan size. We don't understand nearly enough about why urban areas grow, and what combinations of individual choices and public policy produces the megalopolis. We need to understand that better so that we can adopt policies which would encourage the growth of smaller urban areas away from the big East Coast, West Coast and Great Lakes conglomerations. Thus, one of the principal tasks for the next two decades is to learn how to manage the dispersion of people over the land so as to meet their needs best and yet not destroy the land.

It's likely that part of the solution to what might be called the land problem will be the development of intervention devices that make economic growth much more attractive in small cities and less attractive in big ones. Part of the solution will mean also that in the large metropolitan areas people will have to learn to live on less land and to preserve more of the land for the public use in and around urban centers.

But the big environmental problem is not the problem of population growth but the problem of affluence. It is not clear to me that environmentalists have yet come to terms with how much of a problem affluence and materialism are. The hostility with which many environmental advocates regard the high level of consumption which most Americans hold dear has and can continue to distract from a meaningful grappling with the issue. The "eco-freaks" who want to substitute bicycles for automobiles, eat natural food, package things in returnable bottles, and so on, may serve some small useful function by heightening our consciousness of mundane aspects of the ecosystem, but the very terms of the definition of the issue are so far removed from the ordinary realities and wishes of most Americans that they provide little in the way of a guide for action. Environmentalists should start out with the assumption that

Americans will not easily give up their high standard of living nor their wish for an ever-higher standard. If the environmental issue is subjected to the kind of moralizing and expressive dramatizing that many of the social problems of the 1960's were, it seems likely that the issue will be converted into merely another amusement for the alienated intellectual elite.

The problem, instead, is to learn to manage affluence, not to abolish it. The broad positive response to the environmental issue suggests that the chances for that management are pretty good. As it is now American consumers are anxious to adapt themselves to consumption patterns that are less destructive to the environment. But those constructive impulses are based on the assumption that they will not have to give up those things they value most about their standard of living. Successful resource and environmental management will require that those expectations not be violated. It seems to me that there are a number of rules of management that, if systematically applied across the range of environmental and pollution problems, could command fairly widespread support.

First, now that an awareness of the environmental implications of production and consumption are more and more clearly understood, there must be a rational allocation of costs based on this understanding. The cost to the environment, so to speak, must be included in the costs of all economic transactions. And so as far as possible, these costs should be allocated to the specific products involved. Sometimes these will be the costs of disposal to nature's recycling mechanisms; other times these will be the costs of developing and operating effective recycling systems.

Ultimately, economic growth will need to be redefined. To speak of a cessation of economic growth is to be unrealistic in terms of what Americans (let alone others in the world) demand. But economic growth can be redefined as the speed of recycling rather than the using up of plentiful resources. This is, in effect, the outcome of any redefinition of cost to include the environmental cost of production and use.

Finally, there will have to be the recognition of the value of scarce natural resources. There are some resources that cannot be recycled at all, and somehow we have to learn to place a value on those resources commensurate with their irreplaceability. Land and water that are available for recreational and leisure time use, for example, must be managed as irreplaceable resources and not used up in unnecessary ways.

In these ways, the environmental issue raises, in a particularly clear-cut form, a general problem we have. This might be called the policy rationality problem. The problem is in essence how to mesh the healthy conflicts which a democratic/pluralistic society generates among varied interest groups with the goal of a rational pursuit of benefits for society as a whole and for its various groups. The conflict of political forces often produces situations which are even worse than the proverbial zero-sum game. It's not just that interest groups compete and what one wins the other loses. As society becomes increasingly complex and interdependent, the most common outcome of competing interest groups may well be that everyone is worse off, the winners and the losers. Somehow there must be institutionalized in society a way of making politically relevant the actual consequences of action. Somehow we must increase the chances for public action to be effective in dealing with problems, and decrease the tendency of politicians to substitute symbolic actions as a way of cooling out the opposition for more difficult and demanding policy initiatives.

The current welfare crisis provides a host of examples of the substitution of symbolic for effective action. Clearly, a great deal of money is spent on welfare to little good purpose. People are kept from starving, but they aren't really enabled to move on to better lives or to become self-sufficient. We are apparently now seeing the beginning of a new round of attacks, much like those of the late 1950's, on welfare recipients and on the welfare system by mayors, governors, and federal politicians. If the system is not effectively reformed at the national level, we can expect several years of sniping at the programs, fake cuts, and hunts for welfare chiselers. The current maneuvers by Governor Rockefeller in New York provide particularly rich examples of symbolic actions. One of them probably will cause very little damage, and reduce welfare costs hardly at all—for example, Rockefeller's subterfuge to try to deny benefits to new migrants to the state.

However, some of the symbolic actions that have been suggested are incredibly stupid since they would not only not reduce welfare costs but, in fact, would very likely increase them. The New York governor's proposals include no longer paying for abortions under the Medicaid program, thus saving the state somewhat under $300 per abortion. The stupidity of this action lies in the fact that since it will produce unwanted births because not all women will be able to afford abortions out of their own welfare payments, the state will end up paying in child support, educational costs, and other subsidies many times over the amount the abortion would cost. The pressure on politicians to do something in a situation in which, in fact, there is very little he can do leads to these kinds of symbolic actions. (It is interesting that commentators are always commenting on the inability of lower class people to defer gratification, yet do not observe that politicians share this characteristic. Seldom are they able to forego the gratification of diverting the political heat from themselves no matter what the future political and other costs.)

Finally, the problems of the social environment of the metropolitan areas can be resolved only if the central thrust of public policy is to eliminate the kind of inequality that produces an underclass. The nation must set goals that are realistic in terms of this problem, and give up the silly notion that what we really mean by poverty can be eradicated by insuring that no Americans have incomes of less than $4,000 a year a decade from now when the average American will have more than three times that much. Let me suggest two simple goals that could be used as yardsticks for measuring the seriousness of public policy directed toward the problem of inequality as the central "cause" of urban social ills.

There should be a guaranteed annual income for families with children equal to one-half of the median family income. That guaranteed annual income would be $5,000 now and would rise to about $7,500 by 1985. This guaranteed income figure should be the floor of a family assistance or negative income tax plan. Those families who also have earnings should have their family assistance payments lowered by less than their earnings in order to preserve the incentive to work. Because population growth must be a concern, and because government policy must be consistent, the guaranteed amount should not vary in terms of number of children. A family with one child should get as much as a family with five children—at least once family planning services are truly available to all American women.

But this goal is not sufficient for the achievement of a stable equalitarian society. To provide a guaranteed annual income at one-half of the median family income is only to do away with the worst oppressiveness of underclass life. The nation should also set as a goal the creation of a labor market in which all Americans have the opportunity to earn a family income equivalent to 80 percent of the median family income. Obviously this can't be done by transfer payment. You can't give families who don't earn it an income of $8,000 today or over $12,000 in 1985. Instead, workers must have an opportunity to be sufficiently productive that they earn that minimum income.

This means that the nation must discover ways to redirect the economy so that jobs are provided for everyone. And the goals of jobs for all who must work in order to provide these kinds of incomes should be treated as of equal importance as other economic goals such as limiting inflation, insuring economic growth, and the like.

It is easy to say that this should be accomplished by manipulation of public sector employment—the policy of government as "employer of last resort." But if one really wants to institutionalize greater equality in society, it is necessary that somehow private sector employment be equally affected. One way of doing that is to insure that government-generated and influenced demand policies be made in terms of a first priority for full employment at all skill levels. Indeed, the unemployment rate that should guide government policy is not the unemployment rate for all workers, but, rather, the unemployment rate for the least skilled third of all workers.

So the real issue is that of how to redirect demand so that those with less skill can still work and have productive and self-respecting lives. In all likelihood, within a generation's time the problem of guaranteeing work for unskilled and other low-skilled workers will have disappeared, but in the meantime we have to do something other than provide job training programs which are dead-ends.

Crucial in this is a halt to the growth of the defense budget because, without that, demand will never be shifted away from the high-technology/high-skill industries. But there is a danger that even if the growth of the defense budget is halted (or more optimistically the budget itself is sharply cut) those resources will be used in ways that do not benefit the lower and working class. If we make investments in big science or investments in highly skilled professional manpower of any kind, then we will have foregone the opportunity of doing anything significant to reduce inequality.

(We are not talking about the spending of a few billion dollars on big science. It's unfortunate that people who support the cause of equality spend as much time as they do damning things like the space race. The total cost of the space race has been a drop in the bucket compared to the resources that would be necessary to do away with the low-income class. Similarly, while the SST may be a tremendous environmental danger, the money spent on it is piddling compared to the needs of the underclass. It is, rather, the investments that might be made in activities that eventually would amount to tens of billions of dollars a year that must be assessed against the goals of reducing inequality.)

I think that one of the main areas where decisions can be fateful for the underclass has to do with the growth of services. Clearly, as the economy becomes more service-oriented, the staffing of the service institutions will have a crucial effect on job opportunities. If we continue to pursue our treatment of education and of professional qualifications as sacred, we will not do much toward eliminating inequality. If, on the other hand, we use the expansion of service industries—particularly publicly-supported service industries—to insure that there are many, many well-paying low-skilled entry-level jobs, then we can make a major impact on the problem. Two examples come to mind.

There is now a great enthusiasm for day care. Indeed, some people offer day care as a solution to the problems of poor children. That I think is nonsense since the yearly cost of providing day care for a child would do him and his family much more good if turned over to them in the form of a guaranteed annual income payment. But the issue is larger than that. As I have suggested, American families may become receptive to the idea of publicly-supported nursery schools for everyone. Those schools will involve tremendous investments—there are apparently people in Washington today who don't blink at the idea of a future 20 billion dollar a year price tag on day care. If those day care centers are staffed the way that day care centers tend to be today, with three college-level teachers and five professional consultants consuming the great majority of the payroll, then nothing will have been done to resolve the problem of inequality. If, on the other hand, day care centers and nursery schools are designed in such a way that the bulk of the payroll goes to low- and medium-skilled employees (some of whom can look forward by a combination of on and off the job training to moving up into more professional roles), then the impact of the child care payroll can be tremendous.

This has been called the strategy of cross-commitment by Roger Starr and James Carlson in their discussion of the problems of poverty and pollution (1968). In most general terms their argument is that the poor should be put to work solving the problems of pollution—and by extension of applying their energies productively to other problems of society. They find that the decision to undertake the "modest" 30 billion dollar expense of complete separation of sanitary and storm sewers would result in direct wage payments of around 2.5 billion dollars to unskilled laborers. In 1968 dollars, that would be enough to provide jobs of one year's duration for three-fourths of all males in the nation who are unemployed for five weeks or more (at "full employment" levels).

While housing constructed by conventional means does not provide nearly the same proportion of jobs at the low end of the scale, there is good reason to believe that if the nation manages to develop the manufactured housing industry as the major source of housing production for middle and low income families, then these housing "factories" could have a similar impact at the lower wage levels.

Another example of the strategy of cross-commitment, or the failure to pursue that strategy, has been in the news recently. The new enlightened police chief of Miami has recommended that the Miami police department take seriously the fact that the police are the major social service workers in any city and that a large proportion of the police force be assigned to neighborhood duty in these less threatening roles. This makes good sense in terms of the kind of public demands that are made on police in low-income areas, and clearly we are going to see a fairly large expansion of police forces in the country in the next few years. Miami could be a model for that. Yet at the same time that this enlightened approach is taken toward the function of the police, the Miami plans indicate that in the future only policemen with two years of college will be hired. Instead of reducing crime, these requirements increase crime since they impose an artificial and unnecessary barrier between the young lower-class man and a potential job which he could do and in which he could find self-respect and a sense of service.

In short, somehow we have to learn how to use a low technology to meet many of our needs instead of constantly seeking to solve all problems with the highest and most expensive technology possible—high physical technology in the form of complex machinery and high human technology in the form of constantly increasing the educational credentials required to do society's work.

We must learn to do away with what sociologists S. M. Miller has called "credentialisms" and Ivar Berg has called more forthrightly "the great training robbery." (1967) That is we must stop subsidizing education as our substitute for a state religion as a way of meeting all problems and must, instead, seek to create job definitions and requirements in such a way that the minimum education and training necessary is required, rather than the maximum the market will allow.

If one makes comparisons between the kind of policy stance necessary to deal with problems of the environment, problems of equality and, I think, the problems of the nation's foreign involvements, it seems to me there is a common thread that runs through them. Somehow in the future we have to become a modest society. We have to pay more attention to the human reality which is the object of public policy, and less attention to symbols and ideology. We have wasted hundreds of billions of dollars and participated in the murder of one and one-half million human beings in order to make the world safe for capitalism—only after that orgy are we finally coming to understand that perhaps that's not the most constructive stance for a people to take. We have focused our attention so exclusively on building the most productive industrial machine in the world that we have ignored the cost of destruction of the environment until it now seriously threatens our survival. And because we have pursued these grand goals and others, we have systematically concealed from ourselves the tremendous human cost of maintaining an inequalitarian society.

Panel Discussion

Dr. Weidner: Thank you very much, Professor Rainwater. We have a few minutes left during which we can pose a question or two or an observation or two, although we have almost run out of time. Does someone have an observation or a question?

Anonymous (question from a community participant in the audience): Professor Rainwater, I am particularly curious about your thoughts concerning the institution of marriage. Do the existence of communes mean that marriage is breaking down in this country? Is the church no longer important, or put differently, what is the future of the church and the future of marriage? Finally, does the institution of marriage mean the same to black families as it does to middle class white families?

Dr. Rainwater: Well, I haven't really thought about the future of the church. I can't think of anything sensible to say at this time. As for the future of marriage, part of what I was trying to say was placed in the context of a great deal of discussion these days of new styles of marriage and communes, etc., I don't think that these new styles represent a beginning of a major change in the institution of marriage or serial polygamy, serial monogamy or whatever you want to call it that we have now. That is, I assume that we will continue to have a high divorce rate. Perhaps it will go up somewhat higher than it is now. Among other things, the more money you have, the easier it is to buy a divorce, and that's why the divorce rate goes up. But, I assume that the preferred form for raising children will continue to be the kind of nuclear family that we have now and the changes we get will be developments on either side of this type of family. That is, a great deal more men and women living together without marriage before they have kids and a great deal more comfort and openness about that type of behavior. Perhaps after the kids have gone away we may see some increase in the divorce rate, although I doubt that as I think those divorces will take place earlier in marriage. What you will have will be a high divorce rate and a high re-marriage rate. So it's not the state of marriage that most people getting divorced are complaining about, it's the particular partner that they have in that state. It seems as soon as they get divorced, by and large they rush off and get married again. One of the reasons that we have such a high proportion of female headed households in black families is not that they have anything against marriage, but that the cost of getting married is high. It is the sense of trying again an experience that you are pretty sure is going to be a failure. It's kind of hard to find a man who can provide a good and steady income, and this produces a long period of time between marriages among blacks. I guess overall I don't see much reason to believe that there will be major changes in the marriage institution.

Anonymous: Are you taking into account the winding down of the Vietnam War and foreign involvement in general? Will a decrease in foreign activity mean an increase in domestic aid and domestic programs?

Dr. Rainwater: I don't take it systematically into account because I think partly the first effect of pulling back will be a period of some years of re-thinking the nation's role in the rest of the world. No one knows quite what to do with it. Most people these days seem to consider foreign aid a failure; certainly foreign military adventures are a failure. After that, I would assume that some other kind of international activity will be of interest to Americans and they may be more confident about what to do, but what that is I really don't know. Perhaps you can hear something about that from the other speakers.

Mr. Kolshus (faculty, UWGB): I used to be a sociologist before I saw the light and became an economist. As I listened to your paper, I had the strange feeling that I had heard this theme before. Then I remembered that many of your comments parallel ideas expressed by John Kenneth Galbraith (1958). It seems to me, you are suggesting that we are going to experience unequal, and unlimited affluence without suffering environmental costs. I would suggest that the achievement of this new level of affluence or unlimited growth may abruptly end by suffocating the society in its own garbage!

Dr. Rainwater: Well, I don't know, we may just suffocate in garbage. I'm not sure if what I had to say is optimistic or pessimistic because it depends on what's done about that, but what I was trying to suggest was that it would be very hard to resist this kind of growth and to knock it down more than 5 percent. It would seem to me, then, that the strategy would be not so much to try to stem the rising affluence, but, rather, to make investments that enable you to live in spite of it or with it. Of course that will, to some extent, have the effect of reducing the affluence, because it will make everything more expensive. Somewhere somebody has to pay the recycling cost, but it seems to me that is where the push has to go, unless it proves to be really impossible to recycle in a way that makes any major difference. Because if you don't go that way, you have a head-on confrontation between what is the major and most earnest desire of most of the people in the country and the needs of the environment. Theoretically it ought to be possible, I suppose, except for the one possibility of power. Whether power is available to do recycling and solve the other social problems is an open question.

Dr. Clifton (Assistant Dean, College of Community Sciences, UWGB): Professor Rainwater, what you say is very disturbing. With the pressure of a rapidly increasing population and rapidly diminishing resources, it is difficult to share your expectation that affluence will continue unchecked. It would seem that the natural resource box is signaling a decline in the standard of living. Don't you think that people will have to become accustomed to a lower standard of living and take satisfaction in a different lifestyle?

Dr. Rainwater: I don't think so. If you look back over time with peoples' satisfaction with life, certainly people whose median incomes were $1,500 when the median income was $1,500 were reasonably satisfied with life. From all we know from history, they had problems, but they had a sense of being alive and well in their world. But, at the same time, the people who had an income of $500 a year, for example, had a sense of being out of it, not being a part of it. Now we have people who have incomes of $4,000 and $5,000 who have exactly that same sense about themselves in the world. And, the people who have $10,000 have a sense of being reasonably alive in their world. Since it would be hard to point to anything that's not social; that is, anything that is biological about man which would signify that a move from $5,000 to $10,000 would significantly affect man's biology in the future, all that you are left with is the comparative social factor that makes a person satisfied or dissatisfied with his lot in life. As long as one has an open society, a society in which there can be mobility and freedom, then I don't think there is any way in which people will be happy with $5,000 a year if everybody else has $10,000. Naturally, this is an overly concrete way of expressing the point. It's really more the individual's sense of where he is going to be able to participate throughout his whole life, so he can tolerate $5,000 now if he knows that he is going to have the median income in three, four, five, or even ten years. It's sort of his average, the average life that he can expect for himself relative to other people. The only way to make people content with the average is to give them something else. But then as soon as you shift away from dollars to satisfaction, you are simply re-defining income if you give people something else to make them happy. So, no, I really don't think there is any way at all out of that situation.

Mr. Howlett (student, UWGB): As an aspiring ecologist and one who is environmentally concerned, I am upset that you are treating this question so lightly. I am wearing a button now which has the phrase, "Education is the Key." Don't you think that education can help people to understand the nature of environmental problems?

Dr. Rainwater: What I am saying to you is that to hope that education is the key is a grave misunderstanding of the people. Because, in fact, there is no way of educating the people to live on less than they have now or less than they think (in one way or another) they will need in the future. If that is truly necessary, I mean if it really turns out there is no way out of this natural resource box, then I think what will happen is that we will proceed along this course for however long it takes, until that becomes a very, very big squeeze. Then, there will have to be some kind of major dislocation in the way the society operates to take that into account. There is just no way of persuading people they should give up a thousand dollars worth a year of what they consider good living in order to deal with the problem of the environment. It will have to come through experience and not through education.

Dr. Kolka (faculty member, UWGB): I am curious about your remarks that the urban ghetto will produce a "no man's land" for police action. Due to your association with *Trans-action* magazine, I imagine you are familiar with the guerrilla police force which developed in the "no man's land" on the frontier of the eastern llanos of Colombia during the period of "La Violencia," and which continued to operate until a few years ago (Maullin 1970). Do you expect a development similar to this activity in the ghetto? In other words, do you foresee the development of an indigenous vigilante or guerrilla police force emerging from the absence of formal authority?

Dr. Rainwater: You mean anti-police, or taking over from it? Well, we have movements in that direction now. I have a colleague at Harvard, Gary Marx, who is studying citizen involvement in police and has developed four types based on whether you are for or against them, and based on whether the police accept what you are doing or reject what you're doing. But, all of these groups turn out to not have much life or vitality, they kind of disappear very shortly. I would assume that as long as it's in the interest of the majority society to control those areas, at least to prevent them from becoming staging areas, then such groups won't, in fact, be able to survive for very long, even when they try to get started.

Dr. Weidner: Thank you very much for putting yourself on the grill for this evening and for the stimulation of the address.

An Overview

A careful reading of Professor Rainwater's paper reveals a thoughtful analysis of the urban social environment in the United States. His projections are provocative to the reader in 1971, but most certainly will be disconcerting to inhabitants of this world in 1985. His demographic dissection of population trends suggests that zero population growth can possibly evolve with the continued impact of effective contraceptive technology. The dominant sector of young adults can expect to experience rising affluence along with the rest of the population. However, Professor Rainwater interjects the caution that overall general affluence will still preserve its present unequal distribution for around 20 percent of the population. Not only will such relative social deprivation place this sector in a position "less equal than others," but, in fact, it will place them in a position of socio-economic inferiority to the mainstream of society in 1985. The critical importance of this type of status differentiation is concisely captured by the British sociologist, T. H. Marshall, "By social status, we mean a man's general standing vis-a-vis the other members of society or some section of it. . . . in such a comparison we are concerned not only with the objective facts, such as rights, wealth or education, but also with the way in which two people regard each other, that is to say, with reciprocal attitudes in reciprocal behavior." (1965:197) Professor Rainwater adds a most profound codicil to the phenomenon of social deprivation when he notes that, "In industrial society, people are positioned in the society principally by their relationship to the economy. We discover that when a group finds itself so removed from command over resources that it cannot participate in society in these terms, it adapts to its position by developing a lower class culture." Consequently, not only is inequality in a society culturally relative, but as stated by Professor Rainwater, this lower sector in, ". . . its accumulated wisdom tells its members that they are not a part of the society. . . ."

The ensuing audience-speaker interaction indicates that considerable discomfort is had with Professor Rainwater's observation that the principal problems of pollution control are technological. While a full reading of his text indicates a clear demarcation between the mechanical and social aspects of pollution control, it would appear that the primary disagreement centers on the interaction or symbiosis of social and technical dimensions of environmental problems. To assist the reader in an understanding of these disagreements, a brief explanation should help to place the differences of opinion in perspective and relate them to the other papers and discussions.

Professor Rainwater is relatively optimistic about the impact of population growth patterns in the United States. From previous papers, it is apparent that a difference of opinion exists between the quantitative dimension of his demographic projections and the projections of the biophysical demographers (Ehrlich 1968 and Ehrlich and Ehrlich 1970).

Professor Rainwater concludes his paper by stating that the problem is not to destroy, but manage affluence. In this respect his observations coincide with Dr. Brewer's concluding remarks in the first panel discussion. However, both of these gentlemen would find themselves in disagreement with the observations of some of their colleagues. First, some economists would argue that affluence is physically impossible at its present rate of consumption of resources, and environmentally devastating with the expected increment of population in the United States (on this point, see Kapp 1970, Mishan 1967, Mishan 1970). Second, the drive for prosperity and affluence in the United States and the "developed nations" exerts a "pied piper" influence on the third world nations, be they communist or capitalist (basically, the questions of difference would be in the distribution of economic rewards and the ideological placement and definition of the producers). Drives in the third world toward a parity in affluence would be physically unobtainable and merely serve to perpetuate or further exacerbate existing inequalities (a few works on this point would be Hetzler 1970, Illich 1969).

These arguments do not suggest that the problem is merely technical or constitutes a societal aspiration for technical legitimacy. There is a third dimension to the objection which is cultural; the ideological commitment of societies to specific types of technologies. An example of this dimension would be the use of the automobile as a method of transportation. The automobile is an uneconomic technologically inefficient mode of transporting human beings. The societal support costs for the automobile in present urban environments do considerable social and physical damage (Illich 1969). Yet the prevailing ideology associates affluence with some type of automobile ownership and argues that automobiles enhance individual freedom of mobility. The myth is most resilient, even though it is effectively negated in large urban areas (of course the commitment of large portions of the economy to automobile production further reinforces the ideological commitment to the automobile).

Another portion of the ideological attachment to technologies relates to the social cost of technical values. An example of this would be the treatment of buildings, people and now land as commodities (Barnes 1971). Commodities are items to be exploited for capital gain and then disposed of at the most auspicious moment. Preferably, the item is developed with a minimum investment and then sold high as an expendable resource. Social costs are conceptually irrelevant to transactions in this type of technological culture, but social costs do exist and are most dehumanizing. (An example of this would be the absence of moral responsibility for employment when a company shifts its base of operation. For those in the 50- to 65-age category, the ability to recoup their economic loss is virtually impossible even though the cause for the change might be the incompetence of the company.) The environmental costs are equally appalling, when it is apparent that some portions of the environment are ideologically irrelevant (air and water) and other portions may be bought and sold on the open market. It's not unlike discovering that one's vital organs are saleable and proceeding to treat them as an expendable commodity, irrespective of the ultimate effect.

Although these problems are both technological and social, what is considered to be more important is the manner in which society and its technology are wed (Kapp 1970). A prime example of this point would be Professor Murray's thesis on the first panel. The GNP is an ideological ledger which records hypothetical credits, but refuses environmental, social or individual debits. One contributing factor to the existence of social inequality may very well be the product of a society which rejects social inequality as a unit of measure. For scholars, this complexity contains nuances deserving examination. For the 20 percent, nuance is another term for the perversity of existence in an industrial society.

Professor Rainwater notes that the middle class and underclass will not tolerate a threat to their affluence. What some of these other gentlemen and members of the audience are saying is that the choice of tolerance may not be in their hands. The physical environment may not support their desire for infinite affluence, managed or unmanaged. (For additional reading on this view of the environmental problem, see Boulding 1964, 1970a, 1970b, Galbraith 1967, Heilbroner 1971, Mishan 1967, 1970.)

J.W.K.

PART 4

Institutional Response
To Technological Change

The Environmental Cleavage: Social Ecology Vs. Political Economy

Irving Louis Horowitz

Contrary to the customary view that the ecology movement is a response to dirt, filth, sex and sin, it is my belief that the ecology movement is basically a product of traditional social sentiments that lurk deeply in the minds of many Americans—especially those who still harbor faith in rural ideals and troglodyte values. Indeed, it is probable that these rural ideals are more firmly and fervently held by those who have never been on a farm and never encountered an honest-to-goodness farmer. The present mood was well summed up by the quasi-hero of Easy Rider, who says to the Arizona farmer with a wife and nine children, "You have quite a stake here—quite a spread—you have everything together, man, and if I had it, I would stay here too." The ecological movement is, in part at least, indicative of a fundamental retreat from the problems of technological development and urbanization.

It is an open secret that the ecology movement has as its core an essentially middle-class constituency. "Environmental politics" has rapidly become an electoral pressure group (DeBell 1970). It emerged as a "movement" out of the efforts in the early 60's to "keep America beautiful" and before that, from nature-loving conservation organizations such as the Sierra Club, that saw in the establishment of every factory, jetport or trailer court, an affront to the American myth of rurality (Swatek 1970). The middle class' swing from rural to urban styles between 1860 to 1920, and from 1920 to 1970, increasingly moved to suburban styles; but the problem at this point is that the lines of communication and transportation have become overextended. Lacking adequate mass transportation networks in the major urban centers, there is nowhere further to go out. Thus the move is back toward center cities, but with a new twist: having them cleaned up for proper bourgeois reentry—and that means urban relocation and industrial renovation.

So pronounced has been this trend of a middle-class suburbia which rings a working-class inner city, that the emergence of this new trend of returning to the inner city is perhaps not yet as noticeable as it might otherwise be. The culprits in this urban dramaturgy are both the indolent factory owners and the indifferent factory workers; in short, the keys to the industrial system itself. Further, as the middle classes increasingly are linked to service sector activities, rather than productive sector activities, the tempo and the tide of the assault upon economic development increases. As the middle classes were pushed out of urban sectors by the polarized expressions of wealth and poverty that have come to characterize our major cities, the resentment over environmental pollution seemed to quicken. Now that the reverse migration has begun, this resentment has become a veritable cascade of ideological assault.

We have come to identify Ludditism with the machine breakers of proletarian origin. In fact, it has become increasingly evident that the new enemies of industrial expansion are the middle sectors revealing the above characteristics. This bourgeois Ludditism, resting as it does on a wide network of ideologists, politicians, intellectuals, lawyers and people occupying middle ranges of power, has thrown up the challenge to the pollutists; but thus far, the challenge has taken a specifically middle-class twist: namely, consumerism (Shepard 1971). And what one finds is a linkage between consumer needs, clean products and a healthy environment. This very linkage to the consumer sector, however, reveals the essentially middle-class characteristics of the ecological movement.

The ecological movement is not only middle-class in character; more, it is a kind of Protestant drive toward hygiene and cleanliness, in which every home becomes a Howard Johnson's replica; and in which cleanliness is not only next to Godliness, but often indistinguishable. The religious variable and the class variable often overlap. This convergence of class and religion ought not to escape our attention. The working class is in large measure populated by ethnics and Roman Catholics. Therefore, the matter of life style, no less than work style, intersects to make the ecology movement something less than a universally regarded activity; in fact, for most people it scores far less in importance than unemployment in the factories and crime in the streets.

The ecology movement is also a suburban movement. The ideological explanation of a demand for cleanliness in the inner city lest the foul air waft its way into suburban American homes has become a central peripheral city concern. Of course the high costs of environmental reform often involve severe dislocation within the inner city and even the dismemberment of factory life in the inner city. The anomaly is that those who presumably suffer most from pollution are least involved in its reform while those least directly affected demand changes in the nature of factory management and factory control.

The most pronounced aspect of the literature on the ecology movement is that assaults from Left and Right are equally plausible and made with equal ferocity. Consider the following passages from a recent paper by Lee Thayer (1971:76-77), Professor of Communication and Director of the Center for the Advanced Study of Communication at the University of Iowa, on the subject of "Man's Ecology, Ecology's Man."

Our social policies move steadily in the direction of survival of the unfittest. We have confused freedom with self-indulgence. We have martyred the ill-formed, polarized mind. We have put mere existence before living to some end. We have enthroned tastelessness. We have mocked greatness and deified the put-on. We have made anything but shortsightedness appear "too philosophical." We have substituted the capacity to talk for the ability to say something worthwhile. We have made irresponsibility over into a state religion. We have outlawed success, made failure illegal. God is a piece of technology, like a light switch. Love is an illicit or novel orgasm. Mediocrity has become a socially-sanctioned and government-subsidized life's work. Perhaps most insidiously, our social ideologies and policies increasingly penalize competence and reward incompetence. We take from the capable and diligent student to give to the incapable or indifferent student. Our popular movies lionize the inept, the ignorant, the incapable, the purposeless (e.g., "The Graduate"). Competence and purposefulness are the butt of jokes; they are fit themes only for farce or satire. Excellence is rapidly becoming unconstitutional. "Security" is our social-policy answer to incompetence, incapacity and indolence. We have made a tacit choice between being exploited by competence and being exploited by incompetence, and have chosen the latter. Humanity will not expire in a noble fight against extinction by its natural environment. With but a whimper, humanity will simply grind to a halt, ignominiously, having ingenuously created and nurtured, in its man-made environment, the seeds of its ultimate irrelevance. That is the ecological crisis we must eventually face. The diminishing of man by his own hand is the greater cause, just as it is surer end.

It is quite obvious that social ecology for Mr. Thayer is but a stepping stone to biological eugenics and of course the history of eugenics movements in the twentieth century, particularly in its pristine Nazi variety, should caution anyone on this course of action. Now let us turn to a left wing critic writing on "The Ecological Crisis." Professor Barry Commoner (1971:174-175) of Washington University, one of the most distinguished biologists and physical scientists in the United States, writes as follows:

I believe that the system of science and technology, as practiced in the United States and in all other developed countries, is in many ways unsound and unfit as a guide to the nature of man and the world in which he lives. We live in nature; society operates in nature, and our ability to exist in the natural world depends on our knowledge of it. Science should provide that knowledge and technology guide our application of it. But we are failing in these aims. In New York harbor the sewage bacterial count has risen a hundredfold in the last decade, even though marked improvements in the extent of sewage treatment have been made. Apparently there is something wrong with the technology of sewage treatment, which after all was designed to get rid of bacteria. Increasing environmental pollution is evidence that our technology is, in important ways, incompetent. Behind this incompetence is an intrinsic weakness in science.

It is evident that Mr. Commoner believes the culprit to be science and not, as in the case of Mr. Thayer, society. But here a problem arises: if the problems are scientific in nature, shouldn't the resolutions be scientific in nature? The demands for social control many ecologists insist upon seem to blunt, rather than enhance, scientific efforts to resolve the problem of environmental and atmospheric pollution.

I am not suggesting that there is no ecological problem or that the environment is as clean as it should be, or that any of the many studies conducted showing the damage from water, air and soil pollution are in any way improperly worked or improperly diagnosed. Rather that the ideology that has come to be identified with this ecology movement has ignored the general context of economic development within which problems of pollution have been generated.

The ecology movement can be viewed as a coalition of economic conservatism and scientific narrowness that is often masked by radical slogans and by a secularized vision of the religious life. At every period economic progress reveals social chaos and negative consequences usually unforeseen. The more rapid the rate of change, the more monumental and even monstrous some of these developmental consequences appear to be. But if in fact the levels of pollution in the United States are much higher, so too are the comforts and life style superior to anything known in the past. It seems fruitless to enter into a philosophical debate over the nature of progress. For example, how does one measure the worth of automobile transportation to the urban-industrial complex, in contrast to the polluted atmosphere created by poorly designed engines and high lead fuels? While the answer may be theoretically ambiguous and open to discourse, from the practical point of view, there are few people who would give up a single jetport and fewer people still who would give up their family automobile for the sake of cleaning the atmosphere.

The fact that the ecology movement has spawned an enormous industry of scientific byproducts from clean detergents to clean gasoline to nontoxic soft beverages indicates that a kind of American shrewdness has taken hold of the ecological movement and has capitalized on its fears. That it has been able to do so is a consequence of a sophisticated awareness that any ecological improvement must take place within the framework of developmental ambitions and economic expectations. It is well known that no people will endure for long lower standards of income or a return to more primitive economic forms, in exchange for either a clean atmosphere or clean water. Cleanliness may be next to Godliness, but it is not next to industrialism.

The conflict between ecological and developmental modes is not simply a matter of ideology. It has been incorporated into the structure of legal relations affecting environmental pollution. Nearly every recent state statute claims, as does Missouri, that its intent and purpose is "to maintain purity of the air resources of the state, to protect the health, general welfare and physical property of the people, maximum employment and full industrial development of the state." A similar statute in the State of Illinois claims that the pollution law requires the board governing such matters "to consider technical feasibility and economic reasonableness" in making its rules and recommendations (Porter Jr. 1971). The law commands both an ecological solution and an unimpeded highly developmental economy. As a result, environmentalists claim that the laws as written have loopholes, while developmentalists claim that the laws enacted pave the way for court challenges of pollution control rules that they feel are too restrictive or severe.

State laws for fostering economic development have long been in the books, but with the challenge of environmentalists, officials of the state political network could make rules so harsh that they would put many companies out of business. Some corporate lawyers have argued that the environmentalists must be curbed, since otherwise they could ultimately argue for confiscation of industrial property and create the basis for riot and rebellion. Even the Federal government has taken an ambiguous tack on the relation of ecology to economy. President Nixon, in his new water quality legislation spoke of "taking into account the practicability of compliance." This phrase did not occur in the legislation as originally drafted in the Environmental Protection Agency. But by the time this measure was sent to Congress for approval, this Executive phrase had been inserted into the bill in three places. The modifying phrase indicates that the developmentalists are mustering considerable opposition to the environmentalists—and with great effect.

What people in this country want and feel entitled to is having their cake and eating it at the same time. That has always been a seminal genius of the American conscience and it has uniformly been the source of frustration of most protest movements, whatever their class origins. What the ecologists condemn, the economists celebrate. It may have taken a year, but calorie-free soft drinks are back on the market; and this time around without cyclamates. High test gasoline is now lead free, and plans for an electric automobile, noiseless jets, and other major technological innovations, have precisely as their starting points the existing levels of technology, and not a retreat from them.

It is hard to avoid sounding a celebrationist note on this matter. Quite the contrary. The problem with developmental programming is its utter disregard of social needs in its linear pursuit of technological goals. As Frank M. Coffin (1971) points out:

Aid has been administered as if there were only one objective—measurable economic gain in the foreseeable future. Projects were evaluated largely from a single-purposed point of view. Housing was financed in overcrowded areas. Sawmills were aided with no thought of the wisdom of cutting down the forest. Ports were exploited with no thought given to the ruin of nearby recreation areas. Steel mills were erected with no consideration given to the discharge of wastes or accumulation of slum areas. Fishing industries were promoted without asking whether overexploitation was being encouraged. Pesticides were made available for crops with no thought of their effect on insects, animals, birds, or humans. Highways were planned for the shortest route from here to there without considering what this would do to the pattern of life on the land in between. Dams were built to produce a certain power capacity on the strength of a cost-benefit analysis which left out the costs to fish in the river, human beings in the valley, communities in the area. To take the planning of the Aswan Dam as an example—and it could have happened to a U.S. project—the cost analysis was limited to the cost of a concrete dam. There was no study of the costs of a new fertilizer industry needed to desalinate the soil, of a massive medical program needed to combat the new diseases, of a soil reclamation program, of relocating displaced fishermen, or of fighting widespread community problems. In short, we have all too often wrongfully assumed that we could do merely one thing, without affecting a multitude of other things.

We should search out the contents of an ideology, especially when it is so easily embraced by many diverse sectors, which otherwise have very little in common with each other. Therefore, if the ecology movement is to have a positive payoff, it can no longer be perceived as a movement against the city or as a movement against technology, but rather as a protest against exaggerations, excesses and absurdities within urban living and technological society.

The essential need is not for an ecological movement, but rather a movement that once and for all recognizes the need for planning in an American society has a global need. And this means getting beyond the present consumerist stage, in which a box of low-enzyme soap suds is equated with ecological reform. The historic animosity for planning in America, the irrational linkage of any attempt at the regulation of people with a communist conspiracy, or at the very least, an affront on the free enterprise system has resulted in the special American problem of overdevelopment—which is often equated with the ecology crisis, but is rather a function of an economic system which still has not resolved the poles of wealth and poverty, overproduction and underconsumption, too little work for too many people.

The problems of American society are linked to issues of too much rather than too little. The issue of the quality of product, while real, is less significant by far than the problem of the distribution of already available goods in the society. And the careful delineation among environmentalists of the quality of life to read like a series of consumer reports, would indicate a failure of nerve on their part to face up to the heavy burdens of wealth in American society and the need to break the economic cleavages which still exist; and which, in some measure, account for the sharpened struggle of races, ethnic minorities, and outsiders for participation.

From a technical point of view, the distinct advantage of urging sound principles of planning and regulation is the restoration of confidence in the full development of American society. A development which accounts for an optimal ration of ecological and environmental conditions, but within the larger context of the quantity of available goods and not simply the quality of the environment. Unless it is possible to get beyond a piecemeal attack on problems of pollution, the environmental movement must fail in its noble goals, since solutions based on sentiment must yield to those based on economics; the demand for atmospheric and oceanic cleanliness must yield to the more urgent demands of full employment and maximum production. The laissez-faire approach encourages an almost irreconcilable contradiction between costs and prices, quantity production and quality control. As Lewis M. Branscomb pointed out in a recent (1971) article:

> Market forces are not satisfactory to allocate these secondary costs. We can't sell air, we don't sell frequencies, and we shouldn't sell the citizen's right to peace and quiet. Only recently have we begun to face this problem of the allocation and regulation of the environment through public stewardship. The individual wants good transportation and a clean environment. But when the benefit (clean air) only follows from everyone assuming the cost (a more expensive car), a collective market decision or a social decision is required. The individual's market behavior will not justify any manufacturer's effort to make a more expensive nonpolluting car. The chemical manufacturer is in the same boat. If he makes a unilateral effort to take care of the problem of wastes in the public interest, he has no protection from his less civic-minded competition. Thus, uniform standards are required.

The purpose of planning is both to assign a meaningful ordering of priorities, and also develop a two-pronged attack on social inequality and ecological destruction. Obviously, the physical environment cannot be ignored or abused in the distant expectation of a resolution of social inequality. But just as certainly, the physical improvement of the quality of life will mean precious little if it assists only the precious few. In short, the ecology movement, for its own survival, must become more linked to economic problems and less to ideological posturing. If it fails to recognize the general context in which ecological issues arise, and more specifically, if it fails to appreciate the primacy of industry over ideas, then it could well displace single-taxers, vegetarians, and snake-handlers, as the most impressive fossil of twentieth century social movements in the United States.

Common Property Resources And the Invisible Hand

Halvor J. Kolshus

I. The 18th century British economist Adam Smith—generally considered both the Adam and the Smith of economics—coined the phrase "invisible hand" when he described the efficiency of a free market in which the price system guided the allocation processes. Competition in a free market served as an invisible hand which, by appealing to the profit motivation of the individual, maximized the welfare of the individual and thereby the society without any central decision-making body or control.

The old hand is by now calloused and worn, and has lost its grip in certain quarters. Adherents of a socialist economy have treated it like the invisible suit in H. C. Andersen's delightful fairytale "The Emperor's New Clothes"—invisible because it never existed in the first place. Marxist societies have therefore institutionalized central planning and a command economy, with varying degrees of success. The Scandinavian countries are often called mixed economies, some segments of the economy are guided by the competitive market, some are publicly owned and operated and there are strong central controls. The rapid modernization of the U. S. has brought upon us a dilemma: The free competitive market had become an American institution, hallowed and revered, firmly and deeply rooted in social values. These values are now being modified and changed in some quarters, and at the same time more desperately clung to in others, while the economy is getting increasingly complex and requiring serious interventions into the market mechanism to attain equal opportunity, social and economic justice and other elusive goals. Welfare programs and Medicare provide excellent examples of actions growing out of social responsibility in strong conflict with the competitive market institution. The defenders of the traditional values can therefore build a strong case when they accuse such actions as being "un-American." Unlike the bald eagle which we can maintain as a national symbol after its eradication since we have made durable images in brass and cast iron, no manufactured substitute can be accepted for the invisible hand. The question that emerges is if it can coexist with the very visible hand of government.

II. After having explored the phenomenon of the competitive market as an institution in difficulty, let us turn to a specific complaint against it, being heard more and more frequently in this period of environmental awareness. Pollution has become a household word, and a popular viewpoint in these households is that industry is the villain, the greedy capitalist that destroys our environment while it grows fatter and fatter, aided by the competitive market.

Our viewpoint is that while industry certainly belongs in the group of exceptionally skilled and efficient polluters, this is not due to inherent evilness in the free enterprise system. Rather it is because the market economy is particularly inept at dealing with nonmarketable goods and the failure of our society to define certain resources as property resources.

Boulding defines the role of economics in the overall social system as that segment which deals primarily with exchange of goods and services (Boulding 1970:18). Let us take a closer look at what we mean by "goods." It is useful to separate free goods from economic goods (Crocker and Rogers 1971:411).

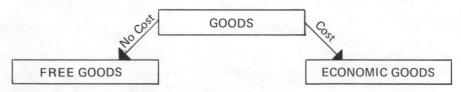

Economic goods are scarce, therefore they have a value. People establish property rights and transfer the property rights in the market place for a price. The use of economic goods thus involves a cost, either directly or indirectly as an opportunity cost (income foregone by not employing the resource in other ventures) (Samuelson 1967:443).

The free goods on the other hand are perceived as being so plentiful that no scarcity will develop. Without scarcity, there is no marketing value and no cost directly or indirectly involved in the use of that good. Therefore, there is no incentive to develop property rights over such goods. Thus the free goods category completely escapes the market since the competitive market can only deal with goods that have a market value. Unfortunately, prominent among these free goods are resources like air and water. Being free goods does not mean that they are without utility. Both air and water are used not only as inputs in most industrial processes, but these two resources also all too often serve as a convenient sewer for industrial waste. One interesting note in this connection is that when industries and households are charged for the use of water, they are not paying for the water per se, but for the services connected with supplying the water.

III. The fundamental question we will raise is the appropriateness of perceiving air and water as free goods. Our position is an emphatic negative response; in a spaceship earth economy (Boulding 1969:96-102) these resources are limited and scarce, a realization that is basic to the present environmental awareness.

Failure to include payment to these resources resulted in two major phenomena:

1. Pollution of air and water because:
   a. They are the cheapest sewers available (Dolan, 1971:36-37).
   b. No opportunity cost to the industry in the use of these resources.
   c. Without property rights in these resources there are few legal constraints on their use.
2. Consumers are not paying the full cost of items which production process results in a polluted environment.

IV. Blaming two institutions, the competitive market and our present definition of property rights, does not solve the problem of pollution. The functional value of this exposition lies in pointing to possible ways of reducing the present deterioration of the environment. Replacing the market economy with a command economy is presently not practical, and highly undesirable to the majority of this country. The other avenue is to expand the concept of property rights to include the free goods as common property resources, scarce resources which should therefore command a price in the market place. Gordon (1954) has shown the wastefulness of common property arrangements, as has Hardin (1969) in his excellent treatise on "The Tragedy of the Commons." The prohibitive cost of policing individual property rights in air is forcefully brought home by Crocker and Rogers (1971).

A different and imaginative approach has been suggested by the Canadian economist J. H. Dales (1968). He suggests the formation of pollution authorities in regional air and watersheds. These authorities should determine the maximum level of pollution that region would tolerate, and then market pollution rights, a certificate allowing a certain amount of pollution. The market would determine the price of these certificates which would be traded as stocks and bonds.

Industry would have the choice of developing abatement remedies or purchasing pollution rights. Special interest groups like conservation groups might purchase rights and destroy them, thus lowering the amount of pollution in that area.

There are a host of practical difficulties involved in the implementation of this and other schemes; they all bear out present dissatisfaction with the operation of the competitive market in connection with common property resources. Technological change is forcing a re-evaluation of this as well as other familiar institutions.

The cost of a car should include payments to water and air used in the manufacturing process, reflecting the degree of pollution. The benefactor of industrial pollution is in the short run the consumer who enjoys what economists call a consumer's surplus—he is getting more than he pays for, a gap between total utility and total market value. In the long run the situation is difficult—and it appears as if the long run has caught up with us—because the result of neglecting payment to the free goods is environmental decay, a condition shared by consumers and producers alike. The cost of cleaning up the environment as an afterthought is likely to prove considerably more expensive than had it been included in all facets of production.

The Environmental Issue: Basis For a New Genre of Revolution

Carol A. Pollis

The degree to which changes which occur in institutional structures are determined by technological developments continues to be debated. Many social scientists still use some form of technological determinism to explain social organization linking the appearance of new types of political, social and religious institutions to major shifts in methods of production or new methods of harnessing energy. Only more recently has a two-way model been advanced

wherein institutions are viewed as exerting independent effects upon technological developments. Unfortunately, since the one-way model dominates much of
both popular and academic environmental thinking, environmental problems are
often attributed to the fact that a cultural lag—the gap created as technology
outpaces adaptive changes by institutions—preempts man's effective control over
his technology. A common example of this line of thought, this one from Lewis
Moncrief in a recent issue of *Science,* contends that quick solution to
environmental problems is obviated by an inability on the part of our social
institutions to make adjustments to the stresses of democracy, technology,
urbanization, capitalistic mission and antagonism toward the natural environment (1970:510). What this amounts to is a cause-and-effect sequence in which
technology is viewed as controlling social institutions and quality of environment. Pessimists go one step further to conclude that technology is out of
control in "a runaway world (Leach, 1968)." A convenient remedy for
environmental problems then becomes one of taming technology (Branscomb,
1971) which translates as bringing about a reversal of the above sequence to give
man and his institutions rational regulation of technological capabilities.

It is the thesis of sociologist Robert Nisbet (1969) that such apparent
persistence and fixity of social forms takes precedence over change, at the
empirical level, and constitutes a natural, normal aspect of human affairs.
According to Nisbet, much of what appears to be change is really the mere
motion, activity, movement and interaction generated by day-to-day events. The
tendency to fixity is illustrated even in the institution of science which,
according to Professor Nisbet, is:

... actuated solely, as we like to think, by incessant desire to advance in
accretional, culmulative fashion. But, as some recent studies have re-
emphasized for us, the power of a single paradigm in the physical sciences
can often be as great as the power of dogma in religion. And the vast bulk
of the actual work of science is, in any event, mimetic, supportive,
concerned with additional demonstration of the already known. Not only
does science reveal infrequent changes of fundamental ideas or paradigms,
it reveals frequent hostility to such changes when they occur (Nisbet,
1969:274).

To put it another way, many so-called changes in science are little more
than motion, activity, movement, interaction.

I think that, in the same sense, a good deal of activity on the environmental
front, particularly of the sort alluded to in Professor Horowitz's paper, is not
change but the motion and activity Nisbet spoke of. It is still altogether limited,
self-interested, individualistic action and at one level is probably beneficial. But
as it takes the form of conflict between environmental issues and economic
growth, there is increasing potential for unanticipated and unintended negative
consequences to emerge which will produce change but perhaps not desirable
change and certainly not planned change. For if environmentalists ignore the
problems of production and distribution, they may well be increasing the
probability of future violence and revolution if Davies' J-curve theory of
revolutionary activity has some merit. Briefly put, Davies (1962) theory is that
revolutionary fervor is most likely to spring up when a long period of rising
expectations and gratifications, at the individual level, is followed by a period
when gratifications but not expectations are reduced. This produces a widening
gap between expectations and gratifications—a gap which stimulates revolution-

ary activity. Intense environmental activity resulting in several SST-type decisions, coinciding as it does with an economic slump, could easily have the effects of promoting this sort of gap among certain workers and exacerbating that gap which already exists among selected elements of minority populations. This hypothesis is speculative but points to the necessity of integrating environmental activity within a framework of economic and social problems if it is to result in real change accomplished through peaceful means.

What we need to do then is take a closer look at means by which peaceful but potentially effective change in institutional forms might be brought about. A strategy which has become increasingly important during the 1960's is collective action through social movements. Collective action can be not only a vehicle for change of institutions but a mechanism for unifying limited individualistic actions such as those mentioned above. Branscomb puts it this way:

> ... as the individual acquires from technology increasing independence, because of the diffusion of power throughout the world he loses his ability to influence that world except through collective action. However, once again, technology—through cheap transportation and good communications—makes that collective action possible and powerful (1971:974).

Collective action can and must be of the sort that will produce real change, rather than motion and activity, if we are to both survive and alleviate human suffering. Radical ecologists tend to view most of the current environmental movements as safety valves for established economic, political and social institutions. Professor Horowitz adopts the safety-valve approach in his interpretation of that environmental activity engaged in by a self interested middle class constituency seeking a return to "normalcy." The motivation is interpreted in some sort of relative deprivation model, the deprivation in this instance being the need to live and partake of leisure in a relatively clean environment consistent with the middle-class value on cleanliness. It is my feeling, as already indicated, that these activities produce too much in the way of motion, movement and activity and too little in the way of real change. Effective reform movements should act as tracer elements coursing through a social system, illuminating its deficiences and weaknesses and serving to identify points at which both radical and nonradical change in institutions is needed (Gerlach and Hine, 1970:217).

The sort of collective movement within the broader ecological movement that I think might be effective at this juncture in overcoming some of the superficiality of middle-class consumerist environmental activity is what I will call, for want of a better label, participatory evolution. The central thrust of a participatory evolution movement would be promotion of conscious participation in determining the future. While the ideology of this movement would overlap significantly with ecological ideologies, it would also have important differences from them. Ecological ideology as articulated by its more perceptive proponents probably does not pose a conflict between environment and development as much as between environment and certain ideologically-based modes of development—monopoly capitalism in particular. Like many of the political ideologies which emerged in the 1960's, including those in the new left and black liberation, the broader ecology movement is premised on an ideological stance which reorders fundamental value priorities so that values of community, quality of life and humanitarianism take precedence over those of individualism, materialism (quantity of life) and property rights. While many, if not most ecologists, envision the necessity of achieving rapid change in values and institutions, few, unlike those in new left and black power groups, advocate violent means to achieve it and thus are not revolutionary in the strictest sense of that term.

Participatory evolution in going beyond ecological ideologies would be framed around the goal of quality survival and would advocate institutional change appropriate to realization of the aforementioned values for the short run. But unlike many ecological ideologies it would not be based on assumptions about any ultimate values which must form the basis for a stable society. Neither would it be premised on assumptions concerning the basic nature of man, as so many political ideologies are, as being either competitive or cooperative, good or evil. A reordering of current values would be seen as expedient to resolving some current environmental problems but not necessarily as values which would provide persistent stability over the long run of things. The only enduring principles which would serve as a backdrop for the formation of values would be the broad ones of naturalism, the sense that man is a part of nature not apart from nature; holism, a sense of interdependence among things; and immanentism, a sense that processes are determined from within a system not from without, by a deity for example (Ferkiss, 1969:253).

A participatory evolution movement would seek to replace economic man with a type of man for whom economic activities would be shaped by a conscious participation in the process of social evolution but also a realization that conscious participation is not equitable with control of evolutionary process. This conscious participation would emphasize man's commitment to planning and surveillance by the people rather than by technocratic or ruling elites. And it would also yield man greater freedom. As Victor Ferkiss states:

Planning is the selfconsciousness of the human element in developing patterns of interrelation—a selfconsciousness that alone makes control and therefore freedom possible (1969:253).

Achieving this kind of conscious participation requires some basic reform in people's reaction to proposed changes in institutional spheres. It means that human beings must be socialized to see and accept continuing change as necessary to survival. Individual psychological frameworks would need to be organized around fluidity and order as providing the basis for psychological structure rather than stability and order as the basis for structure. This is akin to the sort of man Bennis and Slater (1968) envision as being necessary to the functioning of temporary or adaptive systems (ever-changing fluid units) or the kind of man needed to reach what Etzioni (1968) calls the active society, a macroscopic and permanent social movement.

Ecological actions pursued in the framework of a larger movement of participatory evolution need not and in many cases should not have as a focal point air, water, or noise pollution but also social problems such as poverty and inequality which are so inextricably linked with environmental issues. In this context, the ecological praxis would become much more than a single issue movement focused on environmentally conscious consumerism. It would provide a basis for accepting the necessity of planned change along with an image of the change process as partially accomplished through mass-based collective movements.

Panel Discussion

Dr. Posey (Dean, School of Professional Studies, UWGB): I have had the advantage of having these papers and having been able to read them and meditate about them. And I also have had the advantage of having been for many, many years a close and dear friend to Professor Horowitz. Therefore I think I can say a few things about his paper which I might have some trepidation about saying had we not been friends who mutually esteemed each other. Now it comes, Irv! You will recall he said that it is an open secret that the ecology movement has as its core an essentially middle class constituency and that environmental politics has rapidly become an electoral pressure group. It emerged as a movement out of the efforts in the early 1960's to Keep America Beautiful and so on and so on. Well, I don't buy that statement completely. First, because it seems to me that there were tragic events in the history of America that preceded this movement which I think had great bearing upon it. I am referring, for example, to the smog that took place in Donora, Pennsylvania, about fifteen to twenty years ago, as I recall, in which several dozen people in this small town, then of about only 8,000 persons, were killed as a result of a temperature inversion. I am referring also to another phenomenon that I have personally witnessed on numerous occasions and that is smog in the Los Angeles area. Smog affects lower classes, middle classes, and upper classes alike. It affects industry, it affects consumers, it affects government. And I believe that we can see the beginning of concern for environmental clean-up in the Los Angeles area on the Pacific coast. Therefore, although I agree that the ecology movement has been adopted by the middle class as its movement and that the middle class has been pushing it, nevertheless, I think its origins are much broader than that.

The next point that I would like to make is one that I think represents a different kind of projection than the one made by Professor Horowitz this morning or the one made by Professor Rainwater yesterday evening. I quote again from Irv's paper: "Lacking adequate mass transportation networks in the major urban centers, there is nowhere further out to go. Thus the move is back toward center cities, but with a new twist: having them cleaned up for proper bourgeois reentry—and that means urban relocation and industrial renovation."

I think if I may be pardoned for making a prediction myself that this is not going to happen nearly to the extent presumed in the statement by Professor Horowitz. I think instead that what is going to happen is that there is going to be a decentralization from suburban into rural areas. And I'd like to develop that thought for a few minutes so bear with me as I come to a favorite example of mine and that is the automobile in American society. We have had the automobile on a mass basis now for considerably more than half a century. Despite this length of time we have not yet in the United States begun to realize or take advantage of the full significance of the automobile. It was not until after the World War II, for example, and not until the slaughter of the highways reached unconscionable heights that we began to build a system of highways with limited access and with median strips between the two directions in which automobiles travel. I note, incidentally, that here in the State of Wisconsin the killing rate by automobiles has gone down in 1971 as compared with 1970 and 1970 was down as compared with 1969. This is extraordinary, and it is due in part to our increasing knowledge of how to build the highways upon which our automobiles travel so that the automobile will be less lethal as an instrument of transportation. But there are other aspects of the automobile. The automobile, of course, replaced the horse and carriage. And the middle class family in 1900 to 1910 had a stable at the back lot line and in this stable they kept the horse. It was as far from the house as possible because of the smell and flies in the summertime. Well, when the affluent middle class decided to give up the horse and carriage and get an automobile they had the stable and so, of course, they put the car in the stable. And so for decade after decade after decade as new houses were built we put the garage as far from the house as possible. Not because it should be there, but because that was where the horse had been housed. As a matter of fact, in a city in Massachusetts in the 1920's when an individual applied for a building permit to build a house and attached the garage to the house itself, the municipal council hastily met and passed an ordinance forbidding this. It was just too much of a break with tradition. Now even in 1971 we see houses being built with a separate garage and the garage placed far from the house. How long does it take us to realize all the ramifications of this particular technological invention—a long, long time obviously.

Now we are finding, at the present time, that it is possible to locate a factory way out in the country miles from any urban concentration. We are finding that it is perfectly possible for a person to live anywhere in the country and enjoy all of the advantages of urban life. And therefore my personal prediction is that we are going to have a spreading out of our civilization, not a movement back into the inner city, and a disappearance of the predominance of the metropolitan city particularly with its emphasis upon the center of the city. I think that is going to change in the United States and instead of having 80 per cent of our population living in 14 metropolitan centers, we are going to find that we will have metropolitan centers everywhere. This has several implications. One of them, and a very, very important one, is that it means our local governmental units are becoming obsolete and will become more obsolete in the future. Right here in Green Bay, for example, I personally look upon the separation of Green Bay from Allouez, from Ashwaubenon, from DePere and from Howard as being a relic dating almost to the oxcart age. I think that here in Brown County these local governmental units should disappear and be replaced by a Brown County metropolitan government. One of the impediments to our control of air pollution and water pollution is the fact that we have all of these little local governmental units, each with its jurisdiction over a very small geographical area. And yet we know that air pollution and water pollution do not respect these political boundaries. I think it was a Frenchman who spoke of political myths and economic realities. We constrain ourselves in the sense that we are a boxer meeting the demands of life by tying one hand behind our back politically as we try to cope with our changing environment. Now let me go on.

Professor Horowitz says that the ecological movement is not only middle class in character; moreover, it is a kind of Protestant drive toward hygiene and cleanliness. And then you had the lovely Howard Johnson simile there which I like very much indeed. Well, I don't think that's what it is at all. I think it is sort of a desperation movement as we see just what we are doing to ourselves. Therefore, I don't believe that the ecological movement is going to remain middle class in character; I think it's going to broaden. It seems to me that we need to conceive of the ecological movement as the beginning of a new set of data that economists and businessmen and governments must take into account as they control our lives and the development of civilization.

Professor Horowitz goes on to say, "I am not suggesting that there is no ecological problem or that the environment is as clean as it should be, or that any of the many studies conducted showing the damage from water, air and soil pollution are in any way improperly worked or improperly diagnosed. Rather that the ideology that has come to be identified with this ecology movement has ignored the general context of economic development within which problems of pollution have been generated." Now I think he's partly right here. I think the ideology in an emotional sense has indeed ignored the general context of economic development. But I do not believe that economists or businessmen have ignored this ideology at all. I am thinking, for example, of the work that is now taking place in the Accounting Principles Board, which is an unofficial organization made up of Certified Public Accountants and businessmen. It is an offshoot of the National Association of Certified Public Accountants. And what this board is doing at the present time is evolving a set of rules for CPA's so that when they report profits from income and expenses of industrial corporations, they will insist that these corporations include in their expenses the cost of polluting. Now this is not being done out of altruism; this is being done because what these CPA professionals see ahead is that there is going to be an insistence on the part of the public—led by persons in the environmental movement—that business include these costs in its operations. Now, if this is done and if it's going to be done by the CPA's as it will be, then it would not be possible for, let us say, DuPont to clean up and Monsanto not to clean up and therefore have a competitive advantage. The reason is very simple and it is that none of these corporations can operate without having an annual examination and certification as to the truth and reliability of its income and expense accounts and its balance sheets.

Now, I would like to underscore something that Professor Horowitz said. He said, "But if in fact the levels of pollution in the United States are much higher so too are the comforts and life style superior to anything known in the past." And I must say here that I agree with the predictions of Professor Rainwater in this respect that we are going to become more and more affluent and the affluence is going to become more and more widespread. In this, however, we are faced with a vexacious problem, a problem which Professor Rainwater belittled last night and that is the effectiveness of consumer action. All of us occupy at least two roles in life. One of the roles is the role of worker and the other is the role of consumer. As a worker we work at a single job; specialization of work is a phenomenon of the American economy and we identify our own welfare with how well the government or company for whom we work has been doing. It was, of course, perfectly logical for the workers of the Boeing Plant in Seattle to protest greatly against cutting down on development of the SST. Many of them were fired, and they cannot see the arguments against the SST—they simply cannot see them at all. But, on the other hand, when we look at ourselves as consumers, we have an utterly different situation. We are specialists in production but we are generalists par excellence in consumption. We buy foods of various kinds, we buy clothing, we buy automobiles, we buy shelter, we buy recreation and so on and so forth. And our interest in any one of these as an individual is very small. I've been trying to get my wife, when she opens a can, to take the label off and to open both ends, flatten the can and put it in a corrugated box which I have waiting in the garage so that we can take this down to one of the ecological collecting points. Furthermore, I've been trying to get my wife to stop buying milk in disposable containers and instead to buy it in glass bottles so that the glass bottles can be returned and used over and over again. And I must say—I can say this since she's not here—I've been encountering considerable resistance. And I think she is typical of the American housewife. It is extremely difficult to get us to do something for which our immediate personal benefit is very slight but which done collectively has great significance. In all phases of our life we find this sort of dilemma where we as individuals can benefit by going counter to what is the general good. I don't know what the resolution to this dilemma is except possibly legal restraints. And therefore (I'm now speaking as an editor, Irv) you were quoting a statute of the State of Illinois which said that the pollution law there requires the board governing such matters, "to consider technical feasibility and economic reasonableness in making its rules and regulations." Now, in December, 1970, the State of Illinois adopted a new constitution. In this new constitution we have the first article entitled "Environment" of any state constitution in the United States. It's article 11, if someone is interested. And in article 11 the extraordinary statement is made that any individual who feels that his health or welfare has been impaired by environmental pollution may sue the polluter, even if the polluter is the State of Illinois itself. It then goes on to say in the transition schedule that this particular requirement does not go into effect until January 1, 1972. The rest of the constitution goes into effect one year earlier. I think that is extraordinary, simply extraordinary, and it is a very heartening development.

These are all the observations I have at the moment with respect to Professor Horowitz's paper. I have some comments on Dr. Pollis' and Dr. Kolshus' papers, but how would it be to wait?

Dr. Clifton (Assistant Dean, UWGB): I think Irving is chafing at the bit here.

Dr. Posey: Fine, fine, you get back at me, Irv.

Dr. Horowitz: No! Actually, it's Rollin who's getting back at me. He will never forgive me for the contract I made him sign about seven years ago in which he had to give up half the holdings of Harper & Row to get my name on the line. It was a bitter moment in his life to lose. He's a hard loser, Rollin is. Yet on the other hand he is a good man, and you're very fortunate to have him. And as usual, he is very vigorous and very forthright and as usual, he's very telling—he's a very intelligent man indeed. I don't think there is that much disagreement between us, but let's see what there is and what there isn't. First, on the disaster in Pennsylvania. It's interesting, it seems to me, that in spite of the fact that these have been going on for many, many years throughout the 20th century, insofar as these were not disasters that uniquely affected poor working class people, it never led to a movement for environmental cleanliness. At the most, it led to a movement for trade unionization—it was the development of the mine smelting and ore workers union in the West. In other words, while it was true that there were terrible, terrible disasters, and certainly environmental pollution was nothing new, its solution or resolution in terms of working class ideology was toward unionization and the development of interest group attitudes and not toward a universalistic approach. So I think that the point you make is well taken, but on the other hand I don't think you can invalidate my own recounting of history in terms of ecology or environmentalism as a movement.

The second point has to do with decentralization. This is a very important point, and I admit to being quite conjectural at this level—whether the decentralization from suburbia will spread into rural areas or whether there will be any kind of return to the central city. This, I will grant, is a speculative point on my part. But I think that it has to be borne in mind that there is speculation on both sides. It has to be taken into account that social scientists have pointed out that one of the basic characteristics of an industrial society is the urban center. It provides more kinds of social spin-offs and educational byproducts that cannot be gotten in any other form. Whether the United States will have an enormous spread and whether you will have a megalopolis in which you will have a lower bed-city in any given area will hinge, I believe, as much on the environmental pollution problem as it will on the black-white problem. I think that the main question of whether we're going to have an urban civilization, a suburban civilization, or a kind of rural spread, a kind of megalopolis spread, will depend primarily on how the question of the black-white relationship gets resolved in the next 35 years. On this point I will certainly admit to being at least as conjectural as my colleague and I think the point that he raises is perfectly in order since I should have been much more tentative in its presentation. However, I nonetheless feel that there is in fact, among certain sectors of the intelligentsia, a return back to the inner city. In many cities like New York, Chicago, and San Francisco there is a high rate of return on the part of the intelligentsia and white collar stratum that prefers inner city living and is willing to run a great many risks to have that kind of life style and its cultural advantages such as they may be. There's still an awful lot of pulling, still an awful lot of magnetism left, I think, in urban life—so much so that people are willing to brave a great deal. A friend of mine has done a study, a very nice one too, on the working class poor in inner cities, in which he found that apparently there is much less discontent with inner city living than might be suspected. At least this is so in the city of Baltimore where this study was done. It was found that traditionalism, religiosity, and familism are very strong among many ethnic white Americans. They are reluctant to give these values up. They want better cities; they don't want rurality. So I think that this is a complex question. There are arguments to be made on both sides of it. My own feeling is that surrender of the city is going to be much more halting and slower than I think my colleague is prepared to admit.

The third point is not a disagreement as much as perhaps a temporal disagreement. I don't think that Rollin really believes that the ecological movement is not at present a middle class movement. He merely points out that he believes it will broaden. The difficulty with this belief that the ecological movement will broaden, and I have friends in the Environmental Protection Agency in New York who tend to bear this out, is that no one knows how to broaden it for the very same reason that no one quite knows how to reach people like Mrs. Posey. The kind of nuts and bolts response to environmental issues that you are talking about is very, very hard to get at. People won't even fasten safety belts in their cars unless you have veritable guns going off and alarms going off so that you can't drive the car. Imagine flattening cans and doing all the nice things that Mr. and Mrs. Posey want to do. So I am really not convinced that it will broaden out. I don't see why it should. It will broaden out when the ecological movement itself becomes a movement that identifies with other kinds of mass movements and that identifies more expressly and explicitly with inner city needs. It seems to me that if indeed this is where the center of the problem is, then this too will have to be where the solution is going to be. When you have a movement center based on morality and a problem center based in the urban center, it seems to me, you are going to have the same kind of continuing classisms which will prevent rather than enhance the possibility of the ecological movement broadening out. At the moment I just don't see any evidence that would support that kind of claim.

The fourth point is a very telling one and a very important one and again I'm not so sure that Professor Posey and I have a disagreement in substance as much as we do in temporality over when these things are going to happen. Esso, American Oil and Shell, for example, now have clean fuel oils—they sell for 42 cents a gallon. Hess Oil—it's a dirty fuel—still sells for 30 and 31 cents a gallon. It was reported in the Wall Street Journal several months ago that Standard Oil is in real trouble because of the competitive advantage of dirty fuels. And I can bear that out even for myself. I do not go into Esso; I don't go into many of the stations I used to frequent because I don't want to pay 42 cents a gallon. I don't want to pay more than 30 cents a gallon, and I'm willing to put dirty fuel in my car rather than pay 42 cents for clean fuel. Now maybe I'm alone, maybe it's just a certain quality on my part. Maybe I'm an impecunious misfit of sorts. Frankly, I just don't think that I'm an isolated case, and I think that unless you have a standardized planning network—and planning and legislation are the keys here—you're going to have these kinds of differentiation that are going to make the new state constitution of Illinois inoperable at the very level where it ought to be operational. The same thing is true about Monsanto and DuPont. Missouri told Monsanto to clean up. Illinois told Monsanto to clean up and to use clean coke in the burning process rather than employing the process that DuPont uses. But DuPont is in Delaware or really Delaware is in DuPont and nobody is telling DuPont anything about legislating and therefore DuPont has a competitive advantage and that competitive advantage is not going to be yielded without some kind of rational, across-the-board federal legislation. So it seems to me that the argument of more persuasion at this level with respect to American business practices, at least as far as I'm concerned, is a matter of the future and not a matter of the present. At the present, what is happening is that states like Wisconsin and Illinois are entering into this area with enormous vigor and vitality at community and state-wide levels and penalizing certain industries in their states. Those industries have been howling, they will continue to howl, and it's not an inconsequential factor. As long as the states cannot compensate for the cost of higher production, they cannot expect anything but an enormous kind of residual reaction both at the level of factory ownership and management and at the level of factory employees. As I pointed out, the SST situation is a very good indication of how the so-called environmentalist can score a victory and then lose the war in terms of the classes that they must affect and the kind of environment they want.

Now let me talk about the fifth point. I think this is a very profound point Rollin raises, and I can only concur with him. I think we are specialists in production and generalists in consumption, and I think this gap does exist. But I also believe that the problem in general with consumption is also a function of the lack of militancy for many, many years in this area of life. The most we ever got for it, and this took nigh on to 20 years, is the consumers union. The consumer report has had a very peculiar way of reporting products out, but it never reported bad products and it never told you what not to buy. It never performed an essentially necessary service for the poor. What it did was perform a very elite service for the middle class and the rich. It told one of a selection of possible products from a range of good and very good to excellent that one could choose from. But even at this point there is no consumer report for the poor that will tell one what to buy and what not to buy. Only with the rise of Naderism, whom I frankly consider to be one of the great Americans, only with this have we had the beginning of any real concern and understanding that what the American poor need is not a range of goods from good to very good to excellent, but rather what they need to be told is what to boycott and what to avoid buying. Unless we get that and build it into the planning network of American life, I don't think we are going to get very far with the ecological movement. Again, this is an area in which I hope we make much more concerted effort.

Finally, I want to remark on the question of the Illinois Constitution and its operational ability. I think that the point taken is well made. I think that the Illinois Constitution is a major step forward and by no means do I want to ignore or minimize the enormous leap forward which that represents, at least at the level of theory. The problem will be in those clauses that qualify the possibility of citizen protest or claims on the part of individuals against corporations or even against the State of Illinois proper. There is a growing fear on the part of some sectors that this movement could lead to some undesirable consequences. That is to say, environmentalism could be a half-way house to socialism and in point of fact, if we were to be really blunt about it and honest about it, if it does not turn into something like that, it will be less than successful. If it does turn into something like that, it will once again generate enormous class controversy and ideological polarization as the problems of socialism in fact always have. So if the possibility ever arises on genuine expropriational proceedings we will see then what the power of the Illinois Constitution will be. I tend to be very, very pessimistic at this level. On the other hand, needless to say, I share with Professor Posey the hope that this does become the norm. Thank you very much.

Mr. Kirk (student, UWGB): In his opening address, Dr. Khare emphasized the importance one must place on the norms and values of a technological society. The title of this panel, "Institutional Response to Technological Change," exemplifies our institutions' importance in not only reflecting values but also in influencing behavior. In this context I will briefly add my comments.

First, I must comment on Dr. Horowitz's interesting and controversial ideas. The economic and social parameters of which he spoke not only strongly determine environmental action but also influence larger social action. These middle class values in my opinion were all too present in this and previous panels. As the middle class dealt with its conscience during the Black Movement so the middle class deals with the environmental problems. Real solutions to our problems cannot be found in such a manner. We cannot satisfy ourselves with experiencing only the weekend racial sit-ins, police firehoses, and brotherhood speeches of the ecology movement; namely the eco-marches, occasional bicycle riding, and button wearing. The middle class, in past movements as well as in the ecology movement, has refused to take anything but superficial action. And this, from my perception as a student, is what you are doing.

My views are of passive humor as I watch the "concerned individuals" satisfy themselves with bicycle riding, occasional can collecting, and other eco-tactics while young men like myself are told to continue a war which destroys more resources than you'll ever save. To this point, Dr. Pollis has attempted to inform the people within the ecology movement of the enormity of its responsibility. None of us here can hope to find solutions but to ignore the massive social problems of our society is mania. We, as individuals, must begin to reshape our values with hard self-sacrificing labor and stop being contented with an ecology movement that saves trees, rivers, and our other resources while it allows them to be wasted in an undeclared war.

Dr. Clifton: Does anyone in the audience have a question they would like to address to Professor Horowitz?

Anonymous: I wondered if you would make a comment on whether you think governmental centralization is the answer to changing values to provide for a better environment?

Dr. Horowitz: The government has to plan much of this kind of legislation, otherwise, we're going to have differential responses and that means we're going to have very serious problems arising at the level of price structure and profit making, state by state, which will obviously be intolerable. It is not a matter of centralizing the government; it's a matter of central legislation rather than state and community legislation. I think the whole environmental movement will be of enormous national value for no other reason than that the American people may recognize that planning is an absolute prerequisite for their world. Without that, you're not going to get anything off the ground.

I'd like to address myself to Tom. I can sympathize with a lot of what he has said, and I know the problem is that we don't have any environmental involvement or participatory environmentalism. At the same time I raise the point that you raised about the war. You raised the war only in egotistical terms and how it affects you. You don't think of it as a war and how it affects the Vietnamese. You don't raise the war in terms of polluting Viet Nam. You don't raise the war in terms of napalming the country. I think if you want to have participatory environmentalism, so to speak, maybe you have to be content with the knowledge that you are going to go for the next three years or the nation itself is gone. Frankly, I think it's a timely snare to speak of environmental politics apart from international politics. If we can promote that kind of international politics and promote an understanding in those broad issues well and good. Now I think everyone who has said in recent weeks that the environmental issue is not going to go away is quite right. It's not going to go away for some special small sector of the population, but I don't think that the linkages between world problems and environmental problems are going to be made for the same reason that linkages aren't made between, let's say, labor policies and war policies. America is a land of interest group politics. It is important for us to recognize the contradiction in your remarks for on one hand you celebrate the idea of environmental politics and on the other hand you bemoan the fact that no attention is being paid by these many factions to world problems. You must face the fact that environmental politics is going to be mute on the war question, and I think that that is unfortunate but it is a fact of life. You ought not to expect anyone to promote environmental politics as an answer. That's the problem that seems to be in your thinking. If you want peace politics to link with environmental politics, it seems to me you're going to encounter the very problems of how you get a broad sector of people interested in those phenomena. This is an old problem that's been faced by many groups in the past. I think it's a very classic American pattern of interest groups and should be so seen. And not be criticized as if it were a new form of high political reality when I don't really think it is. And I don't really think, Carol, that the answer is resolved in your paper. But that's just a personal thing and I just want to give a response to that. I'd like to hear from you.

Dr. Pollis: I was primarily concerned with those people who are currently engaged in individual actions such as community members in Green Bay and students at UWGB. I am concerned with getting them to see the limitations of ecotactics and that perhaps they do not have much overall effect because of the lack of any sort of broader context within which they are taking place in terms of the individual and the level of individual consciousness. When I mentioned the idea of, well, if you want to call it environmental politics or participatory ecology or participatory environmentalism or participatory evolution, I am simply trying to present the idea that at the individual level the individual has a greater responsibility to prod himself, if you will, into putting these ecotactics that he is engaging in into a broader perspective. Perhaps it is through this that more meaningful action could take place rather than what I stated appears to me at the present as mere motion and activity of day-to-day events.

Dr. Horowitz: Why shouldn't it be possible for the ecological movement to remain a middle class movement? You know, it's quite possible that that's what could happen.

Dr. Pollis: I agree.

Dr. Horowitz: It just might be a movement involving a small part of the population, and it may not become a mass movement, isn't that possible?

Dr. Pollis: I think that particularly in its current form that's not only possible but highly probable. All I am talking about is one way in which the movement could be broadened. Still, at this level, I think it would appeal to a middle class constituency and this is a problem which would have to be overcome.

Anonymous: I don't think that it's going to remain a middle class movement and the reason that I don't think so is because steps are going to have to be taken in our economic system in order to reduce pollution and this is going to increase the cost of goods that we buy. Increasing the costs of goods we buy means that we're going to be paying more wages to the workers who produce these goods, and I think we're going to find the AFL-CIO and other unions getting in back of this particular movement.

Dr. Clifton: I'm very surprised to hear two sociologists characterize the American middle class as a small segment of the population. If in fact we can mobilize the American middle class, which covers quite a bit of terrain, we have mobilized a very significant, forceable and potentially effective segment of the population. How many major social movements in the past century have not been middle class movements?

Dr. Posey: I wanted to say a few words about the papers read by Professors Kolshus and Pollis. Mr. Kolshus spoke about the invisible hand and said it is calloused and worn and has lost its grip in certain quarters. I'd like to bend the invisible hand and say that it is viable under the present circumstances in the United States. I recall back in the early days of the Great Depression of the 1930's when in order to stay alive a number of competitive firms reduced their wage rates in order to reduce their costs, in order to reduce their selling prices, in order to stimulate their business, and as we know, when the New Deal came in minimum wages were established and the competition to lower wages began to disappear. It hasn't disappeared entirely in the United States. At the present time at any rate, to exert competition by means of lowering wages is no good and because of government intervention we are stopping that. I think the same thing is probably going to happen with respect to pollution of the environment by industrial concerns. We're going to stop it. Although in this respect let me say that I think among the major polluters in the United States are governmental units themselves. For example, the level and quality of sewage dumped into the Fox River by the city of Green Bay is nothing to be proud of, and we find in Wisconsin there are literally dozens of municipalities that dump untreated sewage into the rivers of this state. These are outfits that are supposed to be telling us not to pollute. The amount of governmental pollution is significant in this country, and it needs to be controlled. I strongly believe that the result of this is going to be an increasing focus on the pressure of competition in the operation of the invisible hand on such things as improving the quality of products and improving the variety of technological processes that will reduce the cost. And so, Halvor, I think the invisible hand is very much alive in the United States and I'm glad to have it so.

Now, in relation to Carol Pollis' paper I want to come back to this point of participatory evolution. I had the advantage of reading these papers beforehand: on page 139 I came to some points that alarmed me. She says participatory evolution, in going beyond present ecological ideologies, would be framed around the goal of quality survival and would advocate institutional change appropriate to the realization of certain values. But unlike many ecological ideologies it would not be based on assumptions about any ultimate values which must form the basis of a stable society, and that is why I got alarmed. If we're going to have a movement in participatory evolution and it's not going to be based upon any ultimate values which form the basis of a stable society then is this real evolution or is it just simply this activity of which you complain when you mention motion, activity, movement, interaction? At the bottom of that same page I came to another statement, and again I quote: "The only enduring principles that would serve as a backdrop for the formation of values would be the broad ones of naturalism, the sense that man is a part of nature; wholism, a sense of interdependence among things; and immanentism, a sense that processes are determined from within a system not from without." Well, let's say the goals, the ideals or the bases of naturalism, wholism and immanentism are of course extremely important but those are broad concepts indeed and they don't furnish to me the more immediate and more focused guidelines that I would like to see. One final point is that we are all members of various groups and if we think these groups are engaged in participatory evolution, they're not. We're members of many groups. Group behavior is a characteristic of our life and it's going to become more so. I take it when you talk about participatory evolution, you are speaking of turning our attention away from some groups and joining more actively in others, is that correct?

Mr. Kolshus: Of course the old hand is fine, but it's a question of perspective, I think. It's responsible for the present type of material welfare that we're enjoying and it's also responsible for the present trends. And my question is whether the competitive market in connection with a free goods concept leads us to certain types of action so that the invisible hand will result in what we don't want. If you are going to keep the free goods out of the competitive market then the hand doesn't have any weight to work with. The hand may be labeled, but there is no way that it can grip the free goods. So what I am suggesting in terms of pollution rights is that by making these free goods property resources, we are giving the hand a chance to work at and get through the market.

Dr. Posey: I think that the work of the Accounting Principles Board is requiring those goods once considered free to be accounted as economic goods with material value. So far as the capitalistic system is concerned, it was my good fortune a year ago to take a trip around the world as part of an educational seminar and we visited a number of countries behind the Iron Curtain as well as those beyond. I discovered the same pollution in air and water in Moscow, Russia, for example, as exists in the large cities of the United States. I don't think it's the system, although I do admit that our system has produced a lot of crud because it has produced a lot of affluence. The more affluence we have the more crud we're going to have as a result. I hope that the ecological movement is going to reduce the amount of crud and include this in the costs that we consumers have to pay.

Dr. Pollis: I was primarily trying to get at the idea that we take a longer run perspective and that the individual incorporate this longer run perspective which is so necessary in terms of the future, particularly if we are ever to find palatable any sort of planning. I think that all too often environmentalists, particularly the popular variety, ignore the long range perspective. We need a more open perspective. I am not advocating the absence of values but a certain sort of flexibility which the individual would incorporate into his framework of thinking in which he would see the relativity of his current values in terms of the long run of things. I also wanted to respond to Professor Posey's question of whether or not I envision individuals changing groups, for example. I don't think that is what I had in mind. Rather, I was thinking of the broadening of individual thinking not so that one would be changing groups or switching from one ingroup to another ingroup but so that one would be involved in lessening some of the rigidities of ingroup boundaries.

Dr. Khare: At this point of time in the conference I thought that I would take a few minutes and introduce a sense of perspective in what has been going on; particularly, it's a very good time to do this because there will be a different panel following this, and probably we can then have a chance to have more questions on or from that perspective.

What has happened is that after the first two panels and with our banquet yesterday evening, there came a diversification of opinions—a diversification in presentation and assessment. The first two panels started with the premise that the ecology movement was a foregone, well-established conclusion. Then appeared the address by Professor Rainwater which presented the nature and limitation of such a movement in the wider socioeconomic context, particularly with regard to more enduring social problems of social inequality, poverty and industrialization. This morning Professor Horowitz converged on the same general theme: the wider sociological context of environmentalism and its ephemeras. However, for the paucity of time, this important divergence in perspective could not be fully explored; I only wish we could have argued back and forth on this subject from the academic points of view to see whether we have reached a sound basis to develop a social science view of the ecological movement. The point is central to the theme and title of this symposium and the questions are how far and for what different reasons environmental quality is predicated upon social institutions and their values, for social responsibility emerges out of the latter base. That's where both the papers by Dr. Pollis and Mr. Kolshus became related. They, in turn, also relate to the point raised earlier in my comments on Professors Rainwater and Horowitz. Halvor's paper, as I understood it, enlarges upon a very central point that was made by Lee Rainwater. And he is incorporating that, he is enlarging upon it. Dr. Pollis views the question of individual participation and collective movement, ascertaining the nature and scope of environmentalism as a sociological phenomenon. In my opinion we have entered an invigorating phase in our discussions.

Anonymous: It may be of no concern, but it seemed to me a very significant political fact that two nations on the same continent with certain sociopolitical and demographic values have elected to demark their boundaries in a fashion which is, shall we say, questionable? The form that they're using is the worst one we've got. And it runs the entire breadth of the continent wherever it isn't already demarked by water. I'd like a response to that in regards to a political social conscience, if there is one, because without it I don't know how in the world social decisions can be made. What values are we talking about? If there is no reaction, forget it, but I thought it should be at least considered.

Dr. Kolka: I'll respond to it briefly. I'm not going to put your question off because I'm picking up this issue this afternoon and I'd rather not take away from the presentations. I agree it's serious and the height of national arrogance to demark a border which is essentially nothing more than a geographic area. I see a map, I see trees, and a physical composition. For a country to go through the process of showing its dotted lines, is ridiculous. I agree. I would hope that we could get over this sort of national ethnocentrism in the future, but at present it seems to be the same mind that we have among many in the country. I hope to analyze that more seriously and in more academic depth this afternoon so I'll hold off.

Anonymous: I just want to direct this question to anyone on the panel who feels like answering it. Isn't technology the real culprit in that it objectifies natural resources down to the level of materiality and is a demanding partner to the human species?

Dr. Posey: The answer is no. I think the answer is exactly the opposite. What technology does is make natural resources available to us for our utilization. The discoveries of technology are the reason why we have such an affluent society. I'll admit that sometimes we have used up or taken these natural resources in such a way that we have been very wasteful. I think that we are aware of the fact that we must be more careful in the utilization of natural resources. From a very, very long standpoint, I'll admit that in the United States we are using up natural resources at such a rate that if the rest of the world were to match it, we'd be running out of resources in not too long a time.

Dr. Clifton: I would say no and give an example to lay the blame on something although I doubt that it's possible to lay the blame at the foot of the great goddess of technology as if technology were separated neatly from everything else. If I might cite a glaring example, we American people have been engaging in massacres of defenseless native people since the very inception of this country, have we not, if you know your history a little bit. This kind of thing appeared long before we had the technological development in weaponry we presently have and, I abuse the word, enjoy. The technological destruction of the environment, therefore, is a set of misuses of tools in the hands of men with the wrong values.

Mr. Kolshus: I would also like to say no and very strongly so. It is society that develops and uses technology. It is also society that refines its natural resources. Therefore, it's not a technological solution to the problem. It's a social solution. Are you with me on that?

Anonymous: I just sort of took it for granted that society is a people who defend technology, but that technology is the thing that does the damage. Just a comment to Professor Posey. He said technology is what has made us so affluent. Well affluent from whose perspective? The middle class consumer or me who likes to enjoy my air and maybe is satisfied with my outdoor toilet?

Dr. Posey: That's a matter of individual choice. Each consumer chooses the way he wishes to consume, the way he wishes to enjoy life, and follows it to the best of his ability. I am reminded that when we talk about technology, people say we don't build cars to last very long and that we ought to build automobiles to last much longer. Well, I'm older than anybody else in this room and I can recall when it was an achievement if an automobile would run 15,000 miles before the engine was ready to be replaced. That was back in the 1920's. Also, I was horrified to learn yesterday that the average automobile lasts 5 years in the United States. I happen to have two five-year-old automobiles, and I think they're just well broken in right now. I think consumers oftentimes abuse the products rather than consume them and that we get once more to the point of individual guilt in prostituting our environment.

Dr. Pollis: I'd like to say something in response to that. I think you have to place your question in the framework of the remarks made by both Professors Rainwater and Horowitz who were talking about the necessity to integrate problems of affluence with other problems in this overdeveloped society. With problems of poverty and inequality there is less concern about how the air smells than with facts of life the poor and disadvantaged face on a day-to-day basis. And I think that the kind of comment you just made in respect to going out and enjoying your outdoor toilets and enjoying clean air has to be couched within this larger framework which has been brought out.

Student: Professor Kolshus, would you care to discuss more explicitly some examples of social or economic pollution control policies?

Mr. Kolshus: To stay within the competitive market, to be able to give that invisible hand something to work with, you set up a control board. For example, a board gets together and it is possible to get to the moon. It should also be possible to agree about the maximum amount of pollution put into the air or water. Let's assume we go into water. Let's assume that the maximum amount of pollutants that one wants to accept in a year are 400,000 units. You come up with a bill which gives a proprietor the right to pollute, let's say, ten units. If you are a manufacturer involved in some kind of process by which you are polluting the water, to be allowed to pollute the water you will have to purchase that amount of pollution rights. Either that or you have to quit producing. This is where the invisible hand comes in. You try other areas from which you will try to get this down. In other words, the competitive market will then force the person, because this is going to increase costs, to look at alternative ways of producing the same goods but with less pollution. So this takes place within the competitive market, but in this case the cost to the environment is built into it. I feel this is a very interesting thing to think about. To say whether it will work or not . . . .

Student: Do you think this is an advantage over other methods? Is industry going to accept these policies?

Mr. Kolshus: Technically, technically that meant . . . .

Student: That there will be an exodus of industry out of one region into another region?

Mr. Kolshus: Exactly.

Student: Or out of the country?

Mr. Kolshus: And also an influx of people who want to go to the airshed or watershed where they have less strict pollution rules, which means that the polluters can then live in the Chicago watershed area. People who prefer clean air and water will come up to Northeastern Wisconsin where the local people have said we don't want that much pollution here. It's going to be a reallocation process all across the board.

Student: Do most people follow, say clean air, or do they go where it's possible to make money?

Mr. Kolshus: What you are saying is that it is possible that Northeastern Wisconsin may be populated by very affluent persons who can afford to live in an area without having any pollution. Delightful, isn't it?

Anonymous: I don't really have a question, but I wanted to address myself to this question of income distribution and allocation of resources. Again and again, yesterday and today, the subject of the cost of things and distributional effects of different policies has come up as has the question of class distinctions within the ecological movement and the question of whether the ecological movement is a middle class phenomenon which can be defined, I think, in terms of family income. What's going to happen to the prices of goods if we force strict pollution rights is another question, for it seems to me that any effective means of enforcing pollution control is inevitably going to raise prices of goods and services. Dr. Posey suggested that that is going to happen and may lead to higher wages through a labor movement. I would like to see him expand on this a little bit. I didn't quite follow that for it seems to me it may well have the effect of pushing the "third world" element out of the consuming sector of the economy unless we have a very effective income transfer scheme of some sort. I don't think this economy is prepared to give people an income that way. The working people, yes, but they're not really the source of this revolution.

Dr. Posey: I agree that there must be some sort of system of transfer payments. We have a system of transfer payments in our present income tax, however imperfect it may be operated. What I was getting at was this. If we could say right now that an automobile costs $1,000 to produce, and that in order to equip it with anti-pollution devices will cost another $200 and that these devices are going to be required, then the increase in the cost of the automobile is $1,200. This means in all likelihood, of course, more labor will be employed in the manufacture of that automobile. We know that we have an unemployment rate in the United States at the present time of about 6 percent. This unemployment rate is a burden on society if we assume that at least half of these 6 percent are employable persons seeking work. This means we have 3 percent of the population that would like to be producing things and are not able to do so now. Perhaps we can put them to work on decreasing the amount of pollution—put them to work on recycling, for example. What I was referring to is that it seems to me, from a predictive standpoint, the labor movement would see rather clearly that to clean up our environment is not something that is going to reduce the amount of labor required and therefore reduce the effective size of the working force but will do exactly the opposite. Is that right, Arnold? Would you agree with that?

Dr. Zander (faculty, UWGB): I was happy to get to the question of individual attitudes. We have a little property out here and a cottage on it. I don't find any reduction in the amount of rubbish scattered there from one week to the next. I'm hoping that this movement will get some individual opinions and individual actions to ultimately make a difference in the number of bottles, cans and junk that are generally scattered at cottages and along the highways. We spend hundreds of thousands of dollars in Wisconsin per year picking up junk which is thrown out by people who don't want to do to others as we would like them to do unto us. It would make a very great difference. So much for individual attitudes and actions. Now another point. I was flying out of the city the other day and was out at the airport waiting for our flight when word came the flight was delayed for about an hour. Most people scattered about the place. I continued to sit there and engaged in a conversation with a woman. I learned from her that she was the mother of six children. I said something to her about the usual attitude toward families of that size thinking that she had passed her quota. She said, "Oh, don't talk to me about that sort of thing for as long as I go in the supermarket and find shelf after shelf of pet food, I'm not going to be convinced that we can't raise food for people. As long as we give untold acreage to raising tobacco, which is a totally useless thing, I am not going to be convinced that we can't find land to raise food for people." Once you think about that, it comes back to an individual situation again. To have an environmentalist smoking tobacco, it seems to me, is a totally erroneous contradiction. You go to an environmentalist meeting and sit in the room—this one is air-conditioned but some of them aren't—and it becomes absolutely stifling because of the people smoking. If we get some concept of personal responsibility in this connection we can change a lot of things in our environment by personal action. And one of them would be to not have wide advertising of tobacco smoking when it has no kind of value but harm as we all recognize now. We could make a contribution very directly if we change our attitude toward our health. I know the needle is piercing; I thought it might.

Housewife: Just a further comment about what he said. It's embarrassing to come to a meeting like this that would involve concerned people and have a man say his wife has problems crushing cans, a professor says he won't buy lead free gas, and then have a student yell at industry for not going out to clean up their own back yard before they go out to help other people. What are we doing here? Why aren't we starting with ourselves and our friends and our neighbors and doing every little thing that can be done as well as trying to educate other people?

Dr. Clifton: The answer to that is that it's not enough.

Housewife: If you can't start at home, where can you start?

Dr. Clifton: It's not nearly enough because even if you start at home you are fighting a losing battle with the packaging industry, for example. How many hours of the week do we spend disposing of the disposable things that products come in?

Housewife: Like saving our grocery bags and taking them back to the store or carrying string bags. It could make a difference to the market we shop in. We don't shop in markets where they sell eggs in styrofoam cartons anymore. We buy milk in returnable glass bottles.

Dr. Clifton: From the one dairy in town that sells them.

Housewife: Maybe others would start putting it in glass bottles if everyone would get involved.

Student: Has any true cost analysis been made of any industry and is it reported so that we can study the variables that have been considered in that industry? And the other question which I think is related to this is, do we think that the human mind is really capable of identifying and are technological tools capable of dealing with all the contingencies related to the various works that have been developed by man? That is, I'm wondering if these contingencies can be dealt with by the inner mind and with our tools.

Mr. Kolshus: As far as the cost analysis is concerned, I think Dr. Posey said earlier that CPA's have now started to do this.

Dr. Clifton: I want to thank you. I have to run along now to another meeting and I'd like Mr. Posey to take over. It looks like the discussion is going to go on for a while and unfortunately I have to leave.

Dr. Khare: I want to relate to your second question in regard to the capability of the human mind dealing with all sorts of problems that man has created. I'm of course talking in terms of reporting of researches on the human brain, particularly those in biological fields that have been done recently. But differences of opinion persist and there are no definitive indications. A section of experts say no, the human mind, as it is, cannot cope with all the implications of problems that have been already created by man—which means that he is on the losing ground. Biologically speaking, particularly in terms of the evolution of the mind over a long period of time, this seems to be a reasonable limitation to keep in sight. But, then, there are those who differ; they argue that we right now do not use the mind to its fullest capacity. Only then will we know whether we, the human beings, can cope with the problems we have created, opinions that are being met these days in discussions.

An Overview

Throughout the symposium there has been an emphasis on the complex interrelationships between man's institutions, values and environmental quality. In this panel on "Institutional Response to Technological Change," this emphasis becomes more focused and linkages made more explicit than has been the case in preceding panels.

The title of the panel should not be interpreted as naive in the sense that it implies a technological determinism of cultural life for if this were so, problems of environmental quality could presumably be solved by technological means alone. Yet it is clear that technology plays a significant part in shaping human institutions whether they be political, religious or familial, and popular analysts (as well as scholarly ones) are continually kept busy predicting cultural changes that will result from future technological innovations (see, for example, Simon Ramo's, "Likely Technological Developments of the Future Which May Significantly Affect Our Society," Annals, 1970). For the past couple of years a number of alarmists who feel that man has allowed technology to have too great an impact on shaping his values have been advocating that man must consciously alter his values radically, almost overnight, or vanish in his own filth. Such alarmists have been abetted by the mass media who have vigorously participated in the giving of verbal admonitions. But recently, more and more voices have begun to question the seriousness, so to speak, of the emotional outcries of environmentalism. At one end of the spectrum there are those who view environmentalism as a passing fad, an epiphenomenon. And there are more moderate voices, such as a recent editorial in *Science* (1971:518) who contend that the emotional, faddish aspects of the movement are passing and giving way to more rational assessments and judgments which will and can result in effective reform of values to promote a quality environment.

As Dr. Khare said in the panel discussion, this focus on sociological analysis of the movement and how it relates to societal institutions has given the symposium a new direction—a divergent perspective which does not question the facts of a deteriorating environment but questions the effectiveness of some popular outcries and current ecological activities. Professor Horowitz stresses the nature of conflicts between political economy and currently articulated social ecology, suggesting that unless the ecological movement addresses itself to problems of political economy it is bound to fail. Professor Pollis, in agreement with this thesis, discusses the necessity for individuals to incorporate a broader, less ethnocentric framework to facilitate significant change. And Professor Kolshus questions the suitability of the competitive market as an institution in light of our problems of environmental quality.

One of the most interesting aspects of the papers which is carried forth in the panel discussion is that of change as effected through individual actions versus that effected by collectivities working in a concerted manner, and power elites and social conscience versus convenience and limited self-interestedness as determiners of individual behavior. Many individual actions, even when simultaneously engaged in by millions of people, may be nothing but fads with no impact on societal institutions. An example might be the hula-hoop fad . . . or the wearing of environmental buttons. On the other hand, such actions may be crucial in triggering public awareness and change of institutions. Witness the rejection of the midi dress and its effects on the garment industry and economy! Or the potential rejection of throw-away cans and bottles. The context of these actions has much to do with their impact on social institutions but no social scientist would deny that individual actions enter into the equation of significant change. The question of how individuals and individual actions can acquire significance in change and be based on certain motivations is an intriguing one—one that will be explored in greater depth in the last panel on "Individual Versus Collective Good."

C.A.P.

PART 5

Individual Rights
Versus Collective Good

The Techno-Politics of Environmental Degradation: Twenty Propositions

Bertram M. Gross

It's a great pleasure coming from Manhattan to come to a part of the country where you can't see the air. I invite you to visit New York City sometime where we have a great variety of airs of all colors and weights and other descriptions.

I come here with a sense of modesty at this moment because the more I try to study what's happening in America and the world, the more I feel we are in a state of societal transformation, both here and in other parts of the world, which makes it extremely difficult to understand the confusions of perplexing change.

And so, while my comments might be for the purposes of drama and of debate stated rather emphatically as propositions, I really would like you to think there is a question mark behind each of them. In that spirit I am operating on the principle that underlies the famous statement by Sam Goldwyn of Hollywood who said, "For your information, let me ask you a question." I am really going a little bit further and trying to work myself out of my own puzzlement by asking twenty questions. For me, this is a new way to plan an address. I figure if I count my statements, you can always tell where I am! I have titled this paper "Twenty Propositions on the Techno-Politics of Environmental Degradation."

1. The progress of human civilization has been based largely on increased energy conversion and materials processing.

2. Each of these tends to deplete or disrupt natural resources and ecosystems and produce unused and polluting residuals.

3. The industrial revolution—with its high levels of production, consumption and concentrated urban population—accelerated these processes of environmental degradation.

4. The present transformation to a post-industrialism Service Society—with much greater increases in energy production, consumption of natural resources, population and urban concentrations—opens up grand new alternatives in human history.

5. These alternatives are techno-political; that is, they have both technological aspects (which some people concentrate on without looking at the political) and political aspects (which others concentrate on without looking at the technological).

6. On the technological side, the most dramatic sets of alternatives are (a) ecological catastrophe vs. ecological stabilization and (b) nuclear or bacteriological holocaust vs. comity among the nuclear powers.

7. The first set is usually regarded as having little or no relationship with the second. The theme of this paper is that the two sets may intersect in a disturbing manner.

8. Ecological catastrophe might come from the environmental degradation produced by the present linear methods of mounting economic growth. Most of the present anti-pollution efforts would do little to avoid this alternative. They are mainly ritualistic activities to move residuals from one part of the environment to another—air to water, water to air, both to ground, and solid waste to air, water, or another piece of ground.

9. Ecological stabilization could be obtained by broad central planning for slowing down energy production and materials processing, promoting product durability rather than product obsolescence, and developing new incentives, technological methods and institutions for the recycling and use of residuals. Taxes on energy conversion, processing and effluent discharge could be used to fund new institutions engaged in the capture and recycling of residuals.

10. The best way to develop the kind of program outlined above would be to create a Resource Recycling Trust Fund. This fund should be started with at least one third of the current income of the Highway Trust Fund, which now acts as a *perpetuum mobile* machine for expanding pollution (gasoline taxes to finance more highways to increase the number of cars that produce more

pollution by using more gas and paying more gasoline taxes to . . . *ad infinitum*, it seems). While the gasoline tax might be increased, similar taxes should be levied on other forms of petroleum usage (for electric power, heating, etc.). With many billions in the kitty, financial support could be given to at least seven Regional Residual Recycling Corporations. The first of these should be set up in New York to cover the Northeast Megalopolis, the most prolific source of large-scale residual (pollution) production in world history. In the Tennessee Valley, the T.V.A., which is already turning in this direction (although without adequate funding), might conceivably take on a similar operation. Still different arrangements might be contemplated in other regions.

11. Nuclear or bacteriological holocaust could come from the planned or accidental use—either small-scale or large-scale—of present stockpiles of advanced destructive weapons. Present arms control discussions—like most anti-pollution activities—are largely ritualistic, or else are aimed at maintaining the superiority of the strongest powers vis-a-vis other nations.

12. The destruction of populations and environments through modern warfare could be controlled, if not prevented, by comity among the great powers and the use of international armed power to confine minor wars.

13. There are many interesting connections between warfare and environmental degradation. The former, of course, has often been employed against the resources on which opposing forces depend; this use has been significant in the Indo-China War. Also, concern with the protection of trees, water bodies and wildlife has increasingly been used to divert attention from destructive actions against people. The most effective form of environmental protection, it might be added, would probably be a bacteriological world war that eliminated all human beings without injuring plant life, thereby returning the planet to its "natural state."

14. On the face of it, the prevention of nuclear or bacteriological holocaust is obviously much more than a technical problem. It is world politics on a grand scale, involving such matters as stronger international organization, the possible carving up of the world into stabilized spheres of influence, and changes in the internal regimes of the great powers.

15. The political aspects of environmental stabilization are not so obvious. Although ritualistic anti-pollution activity is political small potatoes, any serious program of environmental stabilization, particularly along lines suggested in 9 and 10, would be Big Politics. It would require entirely new dimensions of central economic planning and control, as well as powerful new institutions for residual recycling.

16. When fusion power becomes economically feasible (a situation which itself depends on political decisions now being made behind the scenes in Washington and Moscow), it will be possible to produce electrical energy without any pollution, with possible use of the "fusion torch" to assist in the recycling of residual materials (Gough and Eastland, 1971).

17. Either of the developments referred to in 15 and 16 would greatly accelerate present tendencies toward a technocratically managed society.

18. A major political possibility, indeed, is the growth of a manager society with unprecedented power in both foreign expansion and domestic repression. Such a regime could develop slowly as a natural outgrowth of historical trends

and with a slow but thorough-going restriction or destruction of constitutional restraints and personal liberties.

19. The most desirable alternative would be the evolution of a more humanistic, decentralized and more genuinely democratic social order. This would require radical shifts in the structure of societal power, human values and rationality and technology. Most of the constructive thinking in this area consists of little more than intimations and probings, seasoned with liberal amounts of rhetoric.

20. One of the great paradoxes of our new era is the probability that any serious action to enhance environmental quality might require the kind of managed society that would produce a repressive political environment.

What Collective-What Rights?

Richard M. Fontera

I'm not quite sure how what I have in mind here fits the shape of the panel as a whole. I will not take off from Professor Gross' remarks, and I apologize to him in advance if anything I say obscures the necessary discussion that ought to take place on his twenty questions propositions. I chose in advance to address myself to the overall topic of the panel by raising some, in my mind and I hope in yours, possibly irritating questions. In this sense I mean irritating to connote thought-provoking.

I see the problems that we are addressing ourselves to discussed at both the public-lay level and at the public-professional level as assuming ongoing mechanistic design, which seems to me ducks some fundamental issues. These fundamental issues have to do with the state of arts in social change itself and have to do with some lack of agreement on the nature of change, and where we are at in the social world (which affects our very thinking about political and social matters). The traditional assumption, in this country as well as elsewhere, is that man derives his individual rights as a function of birth itself, or immediately after birth as the guarantee of a good society. "We hold these truths to be self-evident, that all men are created equal." It seems clearer to me that individual rights do not truly derive in this manner, and this constitutes the basic underpinning of what I pose to you as the American folklore of individualism, that the individual rights of people in a society of this complexity do not come from birth, but come rather from the accidents of their accessibility to what the society has to provide. In fact, individual rights derive from that access and can be summarized as good health, a modicum of education, all of which is not a birth right in this or any other society so far constructed. Rather, access is something about which struggles have gone on for some time. The record of contemporary success is not particularly optimism-causing. We may, in fact, be going backwards, that is to say clearly that fewer people have access to the goods of society which are the underpinning of their individual freedoms. So that freedom, like right, derives from a social access and a social capacity which is unequally distributed at the present time.

The danger in this folklore of individualism is that it supports the idea that the economic and social standing of people derives directly from their own efforts; people are poor because they haven't tried enough! In other words, if the assumption is that man is created equal, then he can only become unequal by lack of his own efforts; the poor are poor because they don't work hard enough and the sick are sick for some other reason. Determining the collective good is a possible definition of what politics ought to be, and frequently has been about. In the United States, the process of defining the collective good now suffers from the fact that the problems perceived engage people belonging to areas unrecognized so far as our political structure is concerned. To whom or to what group does the problem of water quality in the Great Lakes belong? Wisconsin, all of it, or in part? Illinois, all of it, or in part? Michigan, all of it, or in part? Canada, all of it, or in part? The Western Hemisphere, all of it, or in part? The World, all of it, or in part? We needn't share hypotheses or nonhypotheses about human beings on other planets and take it to the next step. To whom politically does all of this belong? Are we organized, in short, to cope with these problems? I'm suggesting by asking the question "what collective" that we are not! Rather, we have some kind of attitudinal stake, some kind of traditional belief system that divides us now emotionally (not just legalistically) into states, towns, counties and countries more than any other subdivision one could name. These subdivisions are dysfunctional to get the job done. Consequently, the question of "what collective" is not something I'm trying to answer, but rather to raise.

The challenge of what is now being called environmental consciousness is that it attacks some of the most widely shared assumptions of the post-industrial revolution world, of which the dominant assumption discussed on this panel session seems to be that bigger is better. However, there are a whole set of other assumptions.

To be concerned with one's environment is to violate the basic attitudes with which one is raised. Attitudes are not changed, it seems to me, by tax mechanisms or by commission reports. I have in mind an illustration, an Indian prince I heard about, who in 1965 owned forty Rolls Royces at an estimated value of $560,000. He could drive his cars (presumably one at a time) on a total road system of 1.25 miles within his state at an estimated cost, that is the road cost, of $10,000. So to exercise his values, if you like, that "bigger is better" and his attitude concerning what constitutes wealth, he was investing a total of $620,000. Anthropologists might call this folklore a strange aberrant piece of behavior. How distant are we from my Indian prince? How far are we away from the point where we will own automobiles for the purpose of garaging them expensively and running them seldom? But, we would still want to own them. We would still want to own them because such ownership conforms to an accepted set of beliefs or values.

I think much that is said about environmental matters adopts the socially fallacious assumption that attitudes change as rapidly as models of cars or tastes in women's hemlines. That does not happen to be the case and that is not the way history records human behavior.

Let us return for a moment to the question of individual rights, which is the key to this panel's charge. We have not come very far from the biblical suggestion that man's individual rights include his dominance over the rest of the natural ecological system. Are there any limitations on those rights? None, unless Noah be taken as an example! Democracy can be defined as the tender balance between majority rule and minority right. Are we prepared to extend that balance to the environment as a whole, to seek some kind of a balance between man, the functional majority, and the rest of the natural environment, the functional minority? There are spokesmen for the functional minority, but nonetheless such minorities are not in control. If we begin to raise these sorts of questions and begin to take the notion of equality in this direction, I think we are again at a real problem, this has to do very interestingly with the language we use.

It struck me, in working on this paper, that we seem to be moving in the direction in which the word "environment" is substituted for the word "ecology." It would seem that it is not. Environment, it would seem, refers to a totality which may or may not be in balance and which may or may not be closed (a closed system). Whereas most of the writings on ecology, stemming initially from the biological sciences, seem to come with the extra baggage of a closed and more manipulatable system, this seems to me the base for our entering the kind of social engineering which talks in terms of manipulation.

Some have suggested we are entering a period of time when our capacity at social engineering will begin to match our previously proven capacity at technical growth, industrialization, and the applied science. Is fear the best motivation for change? It certainly is the most common. What we are now doing, it seems to me, is using media to suggest that for some abstract, collective good (perhaps just survival) the individual needs to be afraid of what is being done. He needs to be afraid and this fear will cause him to operate in a more environmentally conscious, that is conscious of the collective needs, manner. I only would throw into this great burst of optimism E. B. White's design in a novel, the title of which has slipped me, in which he talks about the earth under attack from another planet. Slowly through the novel you get the idea that it is not the outside attack, as many people had perceived in advance, which would bring the nations of the world together. Far from it. Civil war begins to substitute for previous conflict and the nations manage to fight each other over who has the right to protect the planet. Might something very similar happen in the area of environmental concern?

If the most industrialized nations begin to talk in terms of negative growth, are they not also talking about keeping the status, the relative status, of different nations at exactly the same level? Is this not possibly a re-run of the atomic control arguments of post-World War II which suggested that all was well as long as only the Soviet Union and the United States had atomic weapons. The task was to keep it out of other people's hands. There is one area in which this exercise is already operating and which relates to the local area. Population control in Brown County, Wisconsin, is nearly unthinkable. Population control is a national policy in the United States, a threat to free enterprise, individual rights, and motherhood. It certainly is the last. But, exporting a family planning program is all right. Our only answer suggests that an exported family planning program cuts down on brown and darker people, while pinker people, like ourselves, multiply at will. To assume both of these positions is to shrug our shoulders and say, "That's the way the world is."

Now many assume that man just doesn't know what he is doing when he kills off rivers and pollutes the air. If the people of Manhattan Island or other major centers had only realized what they were doing, they would have unplugged their coffee makers and proceeded to do a thousand other things to clean up the environment. That is pure nonsense and does not represent the direct line between education and activity. I realize that in an academy it is an act analogous to Luther's attitude toward the church to propose to the learned disciples of St. Dewey and St. Pestalozzi that education is not the answer to everything, but that is what I believe.

The availability of information only changes the message of the media. Just as running for office after making a fortune in a business turns the capitalist into an industrial statesman, giving money for environmental control from profits turns the capitalist into public benefactor. All that is changed is the language. The band-aids continue to be applied. What I am saying in brief is that this topic really implies a thorough-going, radical reconstruction of society as we know it, and the individual's role in society as we understand it. Knee-jerk, majority rule will not clean up the environment. The majority is not in favor of cleaning up the environment. The majority is in favor of having other people clean up the environment!

The state of Oregon recently reduced its tourist budget in order to cause a decline in the number of people marching into Oregon and throwing their gum wrappers under trees. That did not lead to a decline in the American population of one person. It may have spread the people out a little more differently. If Oregon does that and Colorado does not, and both programs are presumed to be effective, Colorado will have all the gum wrapper throwers discouraged by Oregon. I don't see that the environment will have gotten any better on the larger level where it is necessary. People do not disappear because Oregon decides not to have them. The collective good is, in fact, shaved into a lot of little pieces. The implications of most of this are rather ugly, as against our previous values.

I recently listened to what I think is a closely argued and well thought out paper comparing the family planning programs of Pakistan and India. To spare you my summary of the whole paper, I will merely tell you that the author assumed, and possibly rightly, that the Pakistani program is more effective than the Indian in terms of the distribution of contraceptive devices, specifically intrauterine loops. The "loop-before-you-leap" program, in other words, is doing better in Pakistan than in India and his reasons for it are simply that the Pakistani government is more authoritarian than the Indian government. A few people believe that they know what constitutes the collective good. They have been reading the writings of Paul Ehrlich and others and they are afraid. They have at hand the mechanism with which to socially exercise this fear without paying much attention to individual rights. Individual rights are postponed until after the world does not end. That is indeed a strong political engine.

The questions of choice are, in part, questions of where in a list of priorities one wants to place different sets of values. I think the argument is well taken that if the population increase is allowed to run wild, other problems won't arise. But, is it good enough to allow a government to order its people not to have children? Is it good enough to allow political structures to proceed to interfere in what has long been assumed to be one of the most profound matters of individual rights? I told you at the outset that the questions are many. I do not have a comparable set of answers to easily solve this dilemma. But, let me suggest a few ways that one might begin to look at this problem. One of them is to accept the interlocking of relationships, not only in terms of the physical environment and social activity (everybody now knows that water has some relationship to air, both some relationship to earth, and all some relationship to The University of Wisconsin—Green Bay), but to examine the interrelationship in our intellectual constructs. Let me throw out just one illustration. Assume that The University of Wisconsin—Green Bay, in its concentration programs, is infinitely successful. And that Environmental Control, to cite one, does a completely bang-up job and the environment is now beautifully controlled. Presumably, the success of this academic endeavor will be the product of interrelating disciplinary foci.

To the degree that such efforts are successful in diminishing attacks on human health, they will increase the problems dealt with by our concentration in Population Dynamics. In other words, our very constructs are interrelated in a somewhat systemic manner. Let me go back finally to an earlier point which I think I shouldn't let just slide by. That is the notion that the determination of the collective good may be the single most important political concern in the contemporary scene. It is not an activity which lends itself to traditional, democratic processes, local bridge referenda notwithstanding. The fact is that for this community to have voted on whether or not to have a bridge across the Fox River is to place before the voters of this community something about which the majority only by accident can decide rationally. We have, since World War II, faced up to this problem time and time again. Specifically, the democratic procedures in which we have high feelings and allegiances, particularly when our side wins, do not always face up to the issue. For example, it seems to me that the voters of Wisconsin, one way or another, are telling Illinois to clean up the Great Lakes, particularly Lake Michigan. The voters of Illinois are telling Wisconsin to do it and both can agree that Michigan ought to do it.

In this process individual rights are exercised, but collective good seems somewhere to disappear. I don't believe, essentially, that we are likely to get very far by arriving at the standard conclusion which says that education is the solution. I suspect, rather dismally, that a great deal of compulsion is the solution. I would suggest that Ralph Nader is one of the few people in America seriously talking about changing the compulsion system as it applies to one of our most important and cherished areas of individual rights, notably the rights of the corporation, defined as an individual able to do what any other individual does at law. This should provide us with a transition to Professor Kolka's remarks. Thank you.

Law and the Ecosystem: Does Nature Have a Legal Personality?

James W. Kolka

In his keynote address, Professor Gross directed his attention to "technical-political" dimensions of environmental degradation. This paper focuses on another phase of this panel's charge, namely, political-legal attempts to deal with

*The author gratefully acknowledges the stimulus of colleagues and students at University of Wisconsin—Green Bay and accepts the liability that the ideas and analysis set forth are his own.

environmental problems, and the resulting impact upon the individual and the individual in his role as a member of the collective called society. (This is not an attempt to debate Rousseau's "general will," "will of all" or dispute the reality of a group being greater than the sum of its parts, it merely distinguishes the individual in two of his configurations, alone and in the society.)

Obviously, the phrase "environmental quality" is value laden and subject to the ideological bias (conscious and/or subconscious) of the individual. If the proposition before us was to explore the meaning of a quality environment, arrive at a compromise and then discuss the virtues of different technical approaches compatible with our consensus, our task would be enormous, but identifiable. Unfortunately, any serious attempt to socially interact with environmental problems must also encompass those psychological, social, cultural, spatial, economic and political nuances which influence human behavior and consequently affect possible solutions. Too often these nuances are treated as irrelevant (the problem is technological) or resolved in an armchair fashion (if we pass this law we can assume that people will have to behave in the following manner). As a society we already suffer the consequences of insufficient data on human behavior and the uninformed speculation of decision makers. The only predictable element is that the society will probably precipitate its cultural mores and generate a variation on a cultural theme in solving its problems.

Among the more fascinating (both encouraging and depressing) dimensions of environmental problems is the formal declaration of social norms and values, namely, "the law." Two aspects of the legal world are especially deserving of our consideration. First, a law if it is enforced in some manner (this refers to law in action as opposed to law on the books, but inactive) can be visualized as a formal social rule around which some aspect of human behavior is entwined. Should this law be joined with others and form a constellation of social rules, it will generally define the maximum parameters for some phase of human behavior. While this statement might appear to be obvious, it is extremely subtle and insufficiently appreciated, especially when drafting legislation. (For an application of this principle to the influence of voting regulations on the development of politcal parties, see Duverger 1963, Key 1949, Crew 1968.)

Second, the application of law to the physical environment reveals perceptions of the physical world which are both anthropocentric to human beings as a species and endemic to particular human societies. (This point does not ignore differences in perception among the strata of a society, rather it is directed to the formal statements of the collectivity.) Since this second point contains two somewhat confusing dimensions, a clarification is in order. The statement that human beings are anthropocentric refers to the prevailing tendency of humans to view the universe as human centered and existent to satisfy human wants and needs. The result of this view is that laws are written to satisfy human aspirations, frequently ignoring ecological constraints (White 1967, Disch 1970, Potter 1971). In addition, certain human societies or nations interpret their interaction with nature from their own national or subnational bias. (For general reference, see Murphy 1967, 1971, Davies 1970, Ridgeway 1970, and for subnational variations in riparian water use, see Meyers and Tarlock 1971.) The first order dimension refers to the bias of the human species and the second order dimension refers to the bias of social subsets of the species.

Although this preliminary analysis details some of the facets to the legal-political problem, it would be remiss to turn directly to the contemporary legal scene without a brief examination of the venerable tradition of natural law and see whether it suggests some legal remedies for the clash between "modern man" and his physical surroundings. Historically, natural law describes a search for the "law of nature," a moral absolute which would reveal the essence of human existence and comportment. While this quest for the essence of the human community contained the word "nature" in its title, it should be noted that, " . . . notwithstanding the similar words which are used to denote them, the notion of natural law which has played so prominent a part in ethics and politics is something intrinsically different from the notion of the law of nature which is elaborated by the scientist." (d'Entreves 1965:10)

While the stoic exposition of the doctrine of natural law and its subsequent Christian modifications may have sought a divine source for law, the doctrine of natural law never appears to have been logically dependent upon that premise (Hart 1961:183). Instead, the doctrine demonstrated a remarkable ability to evolve with changing circumstances and demands (Hart 1961:181-195, Pollock 1961:124-168). The contemporary quest for the ultimate source of natural law has had to contend with the inevitable progressions of human societies hypothesized by Karl Marx (the law of nature re-postulated, if you will), and the existential uncertainties of Kierkegaard in the last century, and more recently Sartre and Camus.

If to this attempt to describe existence as preceding essence we add the observable behavioral regularities of aggregate human communities, we emerge with a morally uncertain but behaviorally intelligible socio-political world. However, up to this point we have only described a world of human organisms who demonstrate some regularities in their patterns of behavior and who suffer moral quandaries, but who exist in a spatial vacuum. In other words, we have human societies (like the grasshopper) to which the world owes a living. If we place these floating communities in a physical setting by using the explanatory paradigm of the ecosystem and suggest that human societies are interdependent on other organisms for biological survival, it might be possible to push natural law a bit closer to the scientific law of nature.

With this general introduction, it is appropriate to turn to some current legal applications and observe how the legal world is presently responding to environmental questions. When confronted with the harsh reality of court decisions, one is tempted to begin his analysis by using the tried and true, "once upon a time," or pirate an eloquent phrase from Charles Dickens, "It was the best of times, it was the worst of times, it was the age of wisdom, it was the age of foolishness . . . " Given the title of the paper, it might be easier to escape into the archives of legal prose, "Now comes the plaintiff before us who alleges that . . . "

Fortunately, I was spared reliance on such synthetic devices by a decision handed down by the Supreme Court of the United States on March 23, 1971. In a case entitled *Ohio v. Wyandotte Chemicals*, 401 U.S. 493 (1971), the state of Ohio brought an action against some chemical corporations to abate the discharge of mercury into streams comprising the watershed of Lake Erie. Because the dumping actions occurred in states other than just Ohio, and because the governmental entities surrounding Lake Erie are the states of Michigan, Ohio, Pennsylvania, New York, and the Canadian Province of Ontario, the Supreme Court was asked to invoke its original jurisdiction. In the words of that tribunal, the justification for such an extraordinary action is as follows.

"Original jurisdiction is said to be conferred on this court by Article III of the federal Constitution. Section 2, Clause 1, of that Article, provides: 'The judicial power shall extend to controversies between a state and citizens of another state and between a state and foreign citizens or subjects.' Section 2, Clause 2, provides: 'In all cases in which a state shall be a party, the Supreme Court shall have original jurisdiction.' Finally, 28 U.S.C. 1251 (b) (3) provides: 'The Supreme Court shall have original but not exclusive jurisdiction of all actions or proceedings against the citizens of another state or against aliens.' " 401 U.S. 493, 495 (1971)

While the court acknowledged that the Ohio complaint stated a cause of action within the compass of its original jurisdiction, the court declined to adjudicate the matter. Mr. Justice Harlan, speaking for the majority, observed that the court's history had not been impressive with environmental issues. In declining to act on the case, the majority opinion observed that; (1) the major responsibility of the court lies primarily with matters of federal law, (2) the matter would consume too much of the court's time, (3) the case was technically too complex for consideration by the court. 401 U.S. 493, 501-505 (1971) The only instance in which the court might consider violating these points would have to be in matters "justified only by the strictest necessity." 401 U.S. 493, 505 (1971) Although Mr. Justice Douglas contested that such cases could be considered by the court and in point of fact have been considered by the court, he stood rather isolated as the lone dissenter in an eight to one decision. 401 U.S. 493, 505-512 (1971)

The effect of this finding is to hand the case back to the state of Ohio and its respective court system with the notation that the Supreme Court accepts Ohio's final determination in this matter. Further, the court looks to interstate agencies and international treaties to resolve these types of problems, although the court also observed that these devices have not always met with success.

While the decision of the court seems crisp and in full possession of judicial logic, it also points to one of the legal dilemmas of Western man. And that quite simply is: legally, Lake Erie does not exist. Of all the courts in this country, only the Supreme Court was broad enough to consider Lake Erie, or at least the larger portion of it, within its grasp. It declined to do so.

Any reasonably well-educated child should be able to spatially locate Lake Erie on a map of North America. When that child progresses to high school he will hopefully begin to understand the rudiments of lakes and streams and how they possess the biogeological character of aging. Should this young man or woman enter a university, he or she will learn that a lake is an ecosystem, a fragile state of biological equilibrium which responds when tickled and experiences convulsions when assaulted. Finally, should this same person enter an extraordinarily unusual social science course in college, he would discover that human beings and their daily activities comprise a component of an ecosystem, and their human ability to interact favorably with this ecological entity will ultimately determine the system's survival and the extent and quality of their own survival. (A few social scientists have directed their energies in this direction, most notably Kenneth Boulding 1965.)

If this same hypothetical student had examined several maps he would discover dotted lines delineating political units. Were the student to enlarge any portion of this map he would discover an ever increasing number of political units. Should this same person convert the dotted lines of a plat map into a house and lot, he would discover that interaction with the appropriate political unit and its designated legal authority would be essential to the successful occupation of a piece of ground.

Let us examine this piece of ground in another context, namely property rights. The popular conception of property is that it is a thing which can be occupied and subordinated to one's individual desires, future inhabitants be damned. For a moment let us assume that the property in question is a lake shore lot from which the owner wishes to extend a pier and on which he wishes to perform all manner of miraculous feats by means of a bulldozer. Our owner would quickly discover that his dotted lines owed allegiance to a superior authority, namely the state or sovereign, the originator of those dotted lines. This authority would quickly inform the owner that without the state, he would possess no dotted lines. Therefore, the authority can and will exact conformity to such zoning laws and sanitary codes which it deems beneficial to the society at large. A striking example of this point is the comprehensive shoreland zoning act passed by the Wisconsin legislature, administered by the counties, and in general supervised by the Department of Natural Resources. (1969 Wisconsin Statutes 59.97, 59.971. For more detail on this point see Yanggen and Kusler 1968, Kusler 1970, Wood 1970.)

We have now learned that the individual's world view may be at odds with society's world view, and that it is society in its judicial-political role which will ultimately decide the acceptable view. Note very carefully one point: it is toward man that these lines are focused, either as an individual or as a participant in a society. Lakes exist only as they relate to man's desires and ambitions.

Stepping back from this analysis, we have witnessed the transition from ecological awareness to social reality. The origin of the social universe revolves around dotted lines, not around ecosystems even though the latter will ultimately determine human survival. As a social scientist, it is fascinating to observe the perceptual complexity of this human drama. One begins to dimly grasp the enormity of the frustration experienced by Copernicus when he observed that the earth was not the center of the universe, but, in fact, the earth revolved around the sun. The suspicion that ecology or Earth Day is an alien plot pales when compared to the ignorant derision Copernicus received for his discovery. Nevertheless, the prevailing cultural belief that nature can be callously subjugated to human will grants man the rare opportunity to relive a more pathetic portion of his past. (This specific point was probably stated most vividly by Leopold 1968:203.)

An additional example might serve to clarify this point. For a moment let us return to the student and his struggle to visualize a particular lake and the adjoining watershed as an ecosystem. Recall again that the shore of this lake is composed of lots owned by the human occupants (note the ecological arrogance of this assertion). Assume that the lake has at one end a marsh through which flows a stream. As with several inland lakes, this marsh is a product of a centuries old gradual evolution and acts as a biological filter trapping nutrients which might otherwise enter the lake accelerating the aging process. Now let us return to the social world and discover that someone has purchased the marsh and is carving new channels through it with the objective of diverting the stream through a subdivision of his creation. While these physical activities may increase this person's wealth and accord him the status of entrepreneur in his culture, he has also unloosed the accumulated nutrients of his marsh upon his neighbors in the lake.

In the social world, this newfound fertilized wealth will probably accrue to the detriment of his neighbors in declining property values and recreational degradation. In the legal world, battle lines will be drawn with neighbor vs. neighbor, county vs. wrongdoer, state vs. wrongdoer or agency vs. wrongdoer. Note very carefully, though, the lines are drawn between human rights, societal rights or some legal creature of the society which is empowered to protect the public good. At no point do we observe that the lake is an ecosystem and the human inhabitants are interdependent organisms operating within that system. Social and legal sanity (anthropocentric and culturally endemic) are assaults upon our life support systems and serve to endanger all species, ourselves included.

Let us review this sequence of events. A man purchases a lot and that lot is a biological filter. By gouging the marsh, he disrupts the orderly processes of the ecosystem and proceeds to commission the filter to restabilize in a new location. By so doing, he threatens the economic livelihood of his neighbors.

It is the opinion of this author that until this individual is compelled to directly face the ecosystem at law, legally review his role in the system and the consequences of his activity, he will continue to repeat his pattern of behavior in accordance with the formal norms of his society, quite simply because lakes do not exist or relate effectively to laws in the socio-legal world. One must face directly the consequences of his behavior and the liabilities must be clearly laid in front of the potential wrongdoer. Damages are inadequate, as only humans receive legal damages, lakes are incapable of benefiting from irreparable damage. Such legal hindsight will guarantee in the future that society will have virtually no lakes to enjoy. Potential consequences must be assessed before action, and behavior linked to the broad consequences of that behavior. By making individuals and society responsible for the consequences of their respective actions, it might be possible to move natural law a bit closer to the law of nature.

Let us return to our earlier considerations and raise some basic questions. In the Wyandotte case discussed earlier, the Supreme Court observed that the state of Ohio shared the same legal base as the court for adjudicating the controversy at issue, the common law of nuisance. 401 U.S. 493, 501 (1971) Nuisance for whom? Human beings, of course. The possibility that humans constituted a nuisance to Lake Erie or a threat to the ecosystem or biosphere never arose. While this is legal common sense, in translation it means that nature, in fact, does not have a legal personality.

It is now appropriate to move to another facet of this malignant dilemma; what is a legal personality? Fortunately, we are spared much pain on this problem. A legal personality is man and those artificial entities which he has created in his own image, such as corporations, cities, states, townships, school boards, cooperatives, etc. All these contrived creatures possess legal personalities; they can sue and be sued, and are frequently called individuals at law. Any forthright citizen with good and sufficient cause is entitled to his day in court with these products of his creation. Should this same citizen wish to play a more passive role, he can sit as a spectator in the judicial arena and watch gargantuan legal battles being waged between these creatures of his invention.

While man and his organizational Frankensteins is amusing to watch, this brings us to the next phase of our dilemma. Perhaps this point was best captured by a friend, who, when confronted with some of the ideas in this paper, responded, "Why that's ridiculous, you're treating Lake Erie as a person; that just can't be done!" Rather than escape with the philosophical "why not," a few of my more pragmatic friends simply observed that treating Lake Erie as a legal personality would be pantheistic. Ignoring the cultural relativity of that response, this brief scenario highlights the dilemma of our human myopia.

It is patently absurd to demand that a child learn the meaning of lakes, rivers, and other portions of the biosphere only to discover in adulthood that the Mississippi River, Lake Erie, and Lake Michigan do not legally exist, except as they are touched by human hands. Perhaps it is necessary to grant such natural phenomena the ability to sue and be sued. After all, we permit every other will-o'-the-wisp to stalk our courtrooms. Why not grant entry to a lake in the sweet simple logic of Sir Edmund Hillary, "Because it's there!"

Lest this lighthearted statement be taken as the interjection of whimsy, rest assured that it is most serious. The treatment of certain geographical entities as legal personalities might provide a mechanism which would compel a serious appreciation of the biosphere and man's reliance on it for the survival of his species. Given the present state of the legal art, we would probably need either a guardian or court-appointed representative. With some legislative modification, an Ombudsman could be appointed on behalf of a lake, river, or certain designated watersheds. This would bring us North Americans around full circle back to the trial-and-error wisdom of our Indian ancestors. Through environmental natural selection, these ancestors evolved a crude ecological conception of their natural universe. They appreciated that their survival was dependent upon a favorable interaction with their natural environment. It is just possible that we could follow their example.

(In effect, this suggestion is equivalent to compelling legal recognition of "The Land Ethic" described in *A Sand County Almanac* by Aldo Leopold 1968:201-236.)

Panel Discussion

Dr. Armstrong (Chairman, Urban Analysis Concentration, UWGB): We will begin the panel discussion with comments from our representative from industry, our student representative and from the moderator of this session. Our next speaker is Mr. James Barhydt, who is the Assistant for Environmental Affairs of the DuPont Company. If you recall the comment this morning that Delaware is in DuPont, we have our own representative from DuPont to give industry's view at this point.

Mr. Barhydt (Assistant for Environmental Affairs, DuPont Company). I must say it gets a little tiring living in Delaware, everybody you meet works at the DuPont Co. I am going to ramble a bit here, because in my role as a commentator I haven't prepared any particular position paper to express ideas and offer solutions. I would like to begin by offering a critique on this meeting. First, I would like to note that there are far too few meetings between representatives of industry and the academic world. I would like to see this type of symposium expanded to include a segment of the political world and those people in government and regulatory agencies. I know the reason why there is no one here from the Environmental Protection Agency and I also know why there are no politicians here. Perhaps the main reason is that it is Earth Week and they are all busy. But I think it would be well to have more meetings such as this in the future for citizens, students, faculty, politicians, bureaucrats and industry to get together and listen to each other. There is a tendency in industry to go to meetings and meet no one there but other representatives of industry. You sympathize with one another, but you really don't get anywhere in dealing with some of the real problems of the day, except in your own particular activity. I was in college work for three years, and unless things have changed, you also periodically are just talking to each other. So I am recommending and suggesting, not only here but everywhere else, that there be more meetings among citizens and groups such as this.

From the papers presented earlier in this symposium, it is apparent that we will have a large labor force to contend with when discussing solutions to environmental problems. The labor force for the next twenty years is already born. Unless there are some drastic changes in our economy, I don't think there is any question that by 1980 our production will be 50 percent more than it is today. I believe that in the period from 1937-1970 there was as much growth in our economy as there was from the last Pilgrim days up to that time. We are growing very rapidly. The big danger, as I see it, is whether we can cope with this growth so that any progress we make from today to 1975 (which is the magic year everything is supposed to be cleaned up) isn't wiped out by 1980 by our progress and pollution abatement problems.

I think there is a changing of values taking place in business and industry today. In our own state of Delaware, which I'm most familiar with, the governor of Delaware is a former DuPont chemist. I would like to call to your attention that the governor of Delaware has come out strongly against an oil refinery in Delaware, and an island someone would build in the Delaware Bay to transship coal. The Chamber of Commerce supports him on these positions. I hope the Delaware governor wins, because I don't like to see wetlands destroyed along our coastline. I think this is not only confined to Delaware but the entire east coast. Also in Delaware, the Hercules Company is building a ten million dollar treatment plant for wastes. This process hopefully will segregate various elements of waste into useable products. What probably will happen is they won't plan a market for these products. So the recycling idea may not always work. At least today it hasn't started to work effectively on a broad scale. This doesn't mean we stop and say it's not going to work.

I would also like to comment on standards and laws for pollution abatement. I think my company would support uniform standards throughout the nation. There are many many different agencies you must deal with in pollution abatement, and they all seem to have their own idea of what a corporation ought to be doing. I think the creation of the Environmental Protection Agency is certainly a step in the right direction. If this agency can exert the authority, I think it will go a long way towards cleaning up the present mess. I also noted an element of consumerism in these discussions. This is a growing movement, thanks in part to Mr. Nader, for whom I have a lot of respect. I also believe that the consumer should exert a choice. As one lady indicated today, she buys her milk from a particular company because she can get it in a glass bottle. But the consumer is also looking for the most economical way to spend his dollar. This has had its effect on business and it certainly has had its effect on the DuPont Company. Very recently we announced that we were no longer going to make corfan, which we consider a superior product. Unfortunately, it was more expensive than other cheaper leather substitutes. So this argument for quality is fine, but the problem is, how much quality do people want? Will they exert pressure when they have to pay a few more dollars for an item? The same thing is true in the textile industry. American textile manufacturers, I believe, make a pretty good product. However, there are many mills closing in the South. The reason is that textiles produced in the South are competing, competing to the extent that a lot of people are out of business and a lot of people are being put out of work.

I'm throwing out problems and I'm not offering many solutions. I'd like to say how industry is responding to environmental problems. I am aware there are responsible industries and irresponsible industries. I believe I represent a responsible company. Recycling offers some hope for recovery of resources and this is a very grave problem, and, as we have discussed earlier in this symposium, another way we can conserve resources is through process change. It would be less wasteful as there is actual value in waste. The other obvious way is terminal treatment. One problem which disturbs me somewhat is, even if large companies such as DuPont can pay the price (and they are paying the price of pollution abatement), middle-sized companies faced with rising fuel costs and higher raw material costs are being put on the squeeze. I'd like to suggest that this question be pondered in greater detail in light of the social ferment presently taking place in the country. Due to the fact that we are faced with rising affluence, a rising population, and rising productivity, the environmental crisis is upon us. Problems of company size and cost will have to be seriously evaluated.

I really don't have much more to say, except that I was hoping I'd be asked more questions. I even prepared information on women's lib in case anybody asked me about that. As a representative of DuPont, I was looking forward to an opportunity to talking with more students, because our company wants to know what students think. Maybe I shouldn't have had lunch with Dean Posey yesterday, which I thoroughly enjoyed, but instead lunched with students. Incidentally, Dean Posey, I don't agree with you on your statement that the labor unions will be getting into this environmental movement, but getting out of it instead. A year ago Walter Reuther of the United Auto Workers made a remark at a meeting I attended, that the environment was going to be an issue in bargaining this past fall. In fact, it was not an issue in bargaining. I think the labor unions are backing off from this concern and I think it is a very touchy subject with the labor leaders.

Dr. Armstrong: Our next commentator is the student member of our panel, Mr. Desmond McCullagh. I think it only fair to note that Mr. McCullagh has an extraordinarily broad and diverse background. He was born in Ireland, raised in England and served with the U.S. Army, Marines and the Peace Corps. He has served from Scandinavia to South and Southeast Asia. I would take from all this that, regardless of any antecedents or any territorial loyalties which he might have had, he has chosen UWGB for what we have to offer, and I would like to give him this opportunity to comment at this conference. Mr. McCullagh.

Mr. McCullagh (student, UWGB): It's rather difficult for a student to comment at a particular forum such as this. On this panel, I have just a brief comment that I would like to make on the student's perspective concerning how many of the students (including myself) have approached the environmental problem. I think by looking at this problem during the last two years, we can see where many of our problems have been. The problem that I am basically concerned with is the method by which we have attacked the problem of ecology. As a student attending an environmentally focused university, the subject of ecology has a tendency to infiltrate most discussions, whether they are formal or informal. And in the majority of cases, the question of tokenism arises. It is to this question that I will direct my comments.

A good question to ask ourselves is, "How do we attack the problems of ecology?" A summary of the various answers would probably go something like this: I have collected cans and glass for recycling; I am buying anti-pollution products; I have joined an environmental action group; I bought several buttons that are helping support ecology movements; or, I'm going to stop having children. Are these fragmentary efforts enough, and will they result in enough collective action to solve the overall problem in time? My contention is that they will not. I am not here this afternoon to criticize the many efforts of thousands of ecology minded citizens, but what does disturb me is the end result of their fragmentary efforts. Much of my concern has been generated as a student at UWGB. As I mentioned previously, ecology is a theme that is integrated nearly into every subject. Thus, students are always undertaking some form of ecological project to better the world in which we live. In the last year we have had a number of different groups involved in ecological projects, or promoting basically the same goal or pursuing it in different directions. What these group efforts have amounted to is only solving a minor portion of the overall problem. I have yet to see these organizations together attack a problem as a whole. They are content with merely cutting a tentacle from here and there. What UWGB efforts represent is a microcosm of the world outside the university community.

The way the student groups have attacked the problem of ecology is an excellent example of the way thousands of individual groups around the country have attacked this problem. We have in this country, for the last 100 years, wrestled with the problems of race, poverty and war. We have, for the most part, attacked these problems in piecemeal fashion and looked at the end result. They are still with us. But there is one distinct difference from these problems and the problems of ecology. And that is, we can't hide from them! We can't hide from destroying our environment! We can't put it on the other side of town or deny it entry into the country club. We can't take it to another land to fight it. What we need in attacking the problem of ecology is a collective effort. We have seen an attack at the grass roots and have witnessed its progress. We must now pursue it at the federal government level. We must attack this problem on a mass scale, and not in a piecemeal fashion. The federal government is the only agency to possess the necessary jurisdiction and finances to undertake this massive project. How do we get the federal government to do it? I'm not sure that I have the answer. But I think if we place much of our energies into working to get the federal government involved, as we do in the present ecological movement, I think we will see some changes. Some of the results might be a little harsh, some might infringe on our personal liberties, and we can rest assured that there'll be an increase in taxes.

In closing, I would like to add that I do not wish to criticize the thousands of concerned people, including the students of UWGB, who have started to attack the many ecological problems that are facing this nation. They are to be commended for their efforts. But, we are running out of time. The problem we are dealing with is far too large and complex to be attacked in a fragmentary way. We need a collective effort, and that leadership must come from the top if we are to leave a habitable world for our children. Thank you.

Dr. Armstrong: As I was driving home last night, it suddenly struck me how I felt I could make a brief comment to tie things together for this panel. I was so excited by the sudden dawning of an inspiration that I pulled over in front of some well-lighted institution, I think it was a nursing home, and began to madly scribble notes on the only thing I could find on my floor board, namely a map. I got up early in the morning, finished off my thoughts, arrived at the symposium and proceeded to hear the speakers entirely vitiate my comments. I'm left with only one thing, and you all are therefore spared and should be grateful. I'd like simply to add a codicil to the remarks made today.

Concerning Individual Rights vs. The Collective Good: Professor Kolka's paper indicates the evident necessity for granting certain environmental forms with a legal personality through the same fiction that allows us to create fictional entities—corporations—and endow them with some human rights, to sue and be sued.

But the statements of Mr. Carmouche yesterday afternoon led me to think that we place undue emphasis on the "rights" possessed by such fictional constructs and would do well to consider their responsibilities as well. The linkage between rights and responsibilities is certainly not original with me, but I think it is well worth mentioning in the context of our overall conference theme and the theme for today's panel.

That such legal constructs do have responsibilities along with rights is at least implied by the fact that they can be sued—presumably for acts which in some sense are irresponsible. But the thrust of Mr. Carmouche's remarks seemed to me to take a different tack, which is relevant here. Although I shall doubtless fail to do justice to the power and sophistication of his argument, I would synopsize it thusly:

After stating that the vast majority of his corporation's 40,000 employees shared his and our deep concern for the quality of the environment, he suggested that we were in need of forming national priorities to direct our collective efforts. This in turn would be predicated on the achievement of a consensus—difficult, but nonetheless possible. And, he stressed, this consensus should be used to pass stringent legislation to control the quality of the environment. Such legislation must be universal, he said, because corporations will naturally move to any locale which provides them an incentive in the form of lax regulations. Governor Lucey's recent message to the legislature on the environment, wherein he proposed tough legislation in this area, also reflected the opinion that such action, if taken unilaterally by the state of Wisconsin, would result in a real blow to the economy of the state.

At the time, I asked the gentleman why those ecologically concerned individuals who make policy decisions for his firm required laws to restrain them from socially counter-productive acts. Why might they not simply follow their natural individual orientations and, as a result, yield a corporation whose acts would show a social conscience?

He responded by saying that a corporation's goals are (1) to show a profit and (2) to satiate product demand and thereby serve the people whose desire for goods and services caused its formation in the first place.

I am forced to conclude from these remarks that not only does a corporation predicate its actions on a basis which at best is a moral, but that it feels it has no responsibility to the society which created it; that those otherwise principled and concerned individuals who comprise such a corporation—and society—somehow are brought to divest themselves of their own ethical baggage when they go to work and pick it up again at quitting time. It is almost as though by choosing to engage in this form of collective enterprise they have assumed a right to corporate irresponsibility. How extraordinary!

The rejoinder might well be made that the corporate manager's responsibility is to his stockholders. Insofar as he is their fiduciary agent, I would agree to the proposition. But I have not been disabused of the notion that society demands more of the creatures it endows with legal rights than merely being great mindless organs, satiating demands, no small portion of which may be due to planned obsolescence and manufactured demand.

I would think that society, of which such corporate managers are a part, both as individuals and as those who guide a creature of the society, demands that each organization it charters—suffers to exist—must necessarily act in the best interests of the whole society. For society to do otherwise is for it to commit a form of suicide. . . .

An individual who refused to look after his own interests and endangered his life as a result would not infrequently be judged incompetent and relegated to a mental institution!

I cannot believe that society intends to commit suicide by chartering legal personalities which it expects to act irresponsibly. Mr. Carmouche said that if we wish to control their actions—and I do—then we must regulate them—and I would—most stringently. But I would go one step further and suggest that it is nowhere written in the stars that society must continue to allow organizations to possess rights without also acknowledging and fully executing their societal responsibilities as well. In such instances of continued irresponsibility, I would not tax or fine such malefactors, I would revoke their articles of incorporation and put them out of business for having shown themselves unworthy of public trust.

The transformation of such corporations into moral, socially responsible beings should not be difficult. While it would be exceedingly hard to achieve consensus among an electorate of almost 80 million people, it should not, in practical terms, be difficult to achieve consensus among the mere handful of persons on each corporate board of directors—most of whom, if I remember Mr. Carmouche's remarks correctly, are like-minded individuals highly concerned with the preservation of our environment. It is within their power to do something, and I would expect them to do it.

I do not mean to imply that corporations are the only cause of pollution, for they are not. And I would accept the premise that ultimately society bears the responsibility for shaping its creations as it sees fit. But I am calling into question the assumption that when men enter into a corporate unit and thereby achieve limited personal liability for such things as financial reverses, they also enter a position of limited social responsibility. The men themselves are society and the corporation is a construct of it. That they work for a corporation should in no way bar them from pursuing their own ethical goals, nor those of society.

If we do not come to this view, we will soon have neither individual nor collective good; all individuals (even corporate managers) are part of a collective known as inhabitants of this orb, which is presently bounded and finite in its capacity to absorb environmental insult and still sustain human life.

At this point in this session, I will turn the panel over to the audience for questions or comments on the panel topic, Individual Rights vs. The Collective Good.

Mr. Janquart (student, UWGB): I'd like to stick my neck out just a little bit here this afternoon and express a little bit of what I've gotten out of this two-day symposium. I feel that it has been pretty much implied throughout the discussions that what we need in order to efficiently handle the ecological problem is a revision, an extreme revision, or a change, if you will, in not only our market system but our political system as well. I have thought this over—because to me it does seem extreme, indeed; however, in my courses in the university, it certainly seems to point to the fact that this change will definitely be needed. Certainly any chaos which I feel would follow, any changes in either our market or political systems, would only add pollution to our environment. How much, I don't know, it's merely speculative. However, I'd like to use Dr. Taylor's phrase which he used yesterday, which I think is ideal not only in reference to population but to the entire pollution problem: "We're damned if we do, we're damned if we don't and we're damned all the while we're trying!" I think what we have to settle upon is the extent to which we wish to be damned, the extent to which we wish to pollute or not to pollute. I feel, if I may use my own traditional ideology, the best way in which we can handle this problem, the only way I can see, is that we rationally decide to what extent we wish to pollute. We should decide to what extent we wish to be damned by using the pluralism of our existing political institutions. I don't feel that any authoritarian mode of government or any other form of government will handle this or will be able to pulse this country's opinion any better than the system of organization that we have operating in our political structure and in our market economy today. That was just a statement, not a question. Thank you.

Mr. Lingelbach (student, UWGB): There seems to be another question underlying some of the assertions that have been made in this symposium. Dr. Horowitz earlier talked about the Protestant ethic of cleanliness. There is another Protestant ethic we should be concerned with, and that's the moral attitude towards work, whether work is necessary and whether 3 percent unemployment is good, or total employment or unemployment is good. I'd like to have a comment from the gentleman from DuPont. How does industry feel about this; is full employment good for the country or should we have a minimum income or something like that to solve the problem?

Mr. Barhydt: I'm not a labor expert, but I would opt for full employment. I think almost everyone would agree on that. The thing that disturbs me, and I wish Mr. Carmouche were here to respond to your remarks, is that we are faced with this growing labor force and yet our economy is in not too good a shape at this moment. I realize you don't want to be bored by figures of losses, but in the DuPont Company we have had to lay off roughly 7,000 people throughout the country. This is not good. In my own area there have been a few people who have lost positions, and I was sweating it out a little bit myself. We all want to work and we all want to be productive at something. I don't think anyone does not want to work. There may be some people who are not seeking annual full employment among the 3 percent unemployable such as transitory workers, students looking for work in the summer, housewives and so forth, but I think full employment is something we have to strive for. Our economic condition today is difficult, and I personally don't see how we can achieve full employment this year. This is a personal view, but I think the people in my company would probably be in agreement.

Mr. Lingelbach: You state that you have a lot of people employed in your company, and in your earlier comments you stated that the labor force of the next twenty years is here. What do you do with the people if there isn't work? I don't want to put the responsibility on industry to create the jobs, or necessarily on government in sort of a WPA project, but maybe we should realize that we simply can't employ people or just limit unemployment 3 percent. Perhaps we will have to say that 6 percent or eventually 10 percent of the population will have to be unemployed!

Mr. Barhydt: Well, I think you're going to have to pay for it in the end one way or another. I think industry, at some point in time in the future, is going to have to deal with a non-expanding economy, a stable economy. I don't think industry has looked at this yet. It may be too early to look at it, but if you ever have a stable population, you're going to have a stable economy. Keep in mind, though, that we're only one part of this planet. In the United States we can make all kinds of moves toward pollution abatement, population control and solving economic problems, but this is just the United States. Many different problems are confronting Japan and other countries in the world.

The question of taxation was raised and I'd like to throw out this idea just to ponder. Should we have taxes on affluence; and should we pay for the use of water and air, which is a form of taxation? The proposal has been made in Japan, which is probably the most polluted nation in the world, that everyone is responsible for pollution and everyone should therefore pay for it and be taxed, not just industry. In other words, the price of pollution abatement is not going to be built into a Japanese product. Everyone's going to be taxed and the money distributed to clean up their pollution problem. This is not the approach that is being taken in this country, and I don't think it's the approach that should be taken in this country. I think if we are polluting we should pay for it. And I also think we should keep our prices as low as possible, so we can compete. Obviously, there will have to be tradeoffs, and I'm not so sure that prices of our products are necessarily going to go up that much. I think we are going to find ways to conserve our resources. Hopefully, the price is not going to be that enormous.

You have heard, mostly from the automobile companies, that the problem here is of the other companies, the other industries in the United States who have not spoken up, or if they have spoken up, they haven't been heard. The issue of lead in gasoline was created by the automobile companies because they don't have a catalyst which will work with nonleaded gasoline. To raise another issue, if you take the lead out of gasoline, at present, the only way you can raise the octane ratings is add aromatics. Aromatics have been shown to be carcinogenic. What happens if everybody is driving around with unleaded gasoline? This is a matter of a tradeoff. We have to look for some other means of transportation, but people aren't riding buses. In Delaware, there's a Chrysler assembly plant about fifteen miles from Wilmington. The Chrysler Company was running a free bus from Wilmington to the Chrysler plant. They discontinued the service because only five people were riding the bus.

Dr. Fontera (Special Assistant to the Vice Chancellor, UWGB): I think the matter being discussed is exactly at the point that we hear it come to so often. This is the underlying assumption that somehow somebody will discover a way in which you cannot only choose from a plate of delicious pastries, but you don't have to suffer the implications of your choices. This is to say that somehow everybody is going to get the full platter of goodies even though you are only allowed one platter with the dinner. Now we know we are six inches away, it seems to me, or six seconds away from somebody getting up and saying, "Let's hear it for full employment! Let's hear it for more cars! Let's hear it for onward and upward!" However, we are not at that point, it seems to me, dramatically not at that point. We are at the point where we have one platter, a person chooses, and that's the only choice he's got. Then it's a choice of which of those you really wish to choose. I do not believe, even if it were technologically possible to continue the present rate of growth in the United States through the twenty-second century, that there would be anybody around to enjoy the fruits of that growth. That is rather serious, and it can't be swept under the rug by discussing it as if we faced the same universe people confronted when they got off the Mayflower and ruined the neighborhood.

In light of that, I'd like to reflect on both of these statements and the questions which have been raised. I really believe that one cannot have the old values and an old system at the same time—some of these values have to flex and give. One of the first values to give may very well be a cardinal plank of the liberal to radical political view in the United States, and that is our traditional opposition against monopolies. It might become necessary to encourage monopolies on the grounds that by the continuation of competition in some areas, we are inviting greater environmental degradation. Now I grant that I know the litany of things that are wrong with monopolies, but again we are up against the pastry tray. You can have one of these two things, but you can't have them both. And I think that is really where it's at, my impressions of the first statement are that of a plea, "Please, can't we progress the way we always have in this country?" I think the answer is no!

Mr. Gorder (faculty, UWGB): I would like to address myself to the issue of taxes and subsidies which has been kicked around quite a bit. I don't think the issue is taxes or subsidies. I think what we have got to do is make polluting unprofitable. Professor Kolshus' earlier discussion of the invisible hand points to the nature of our problem. The invisible hand is directed toward polluting because, indeed, it is profitable to pollute. Whatever we talk about, taxes, write-offs, subsidies or whatever, what needs to be done is to make polluting unprofitable. We wouldn't need a bureaucracy or anything else, it would stop! For example, in 1946 there were very few junk yards around that I can recall. The reason there were very few junk yards around was that the price of scrap was high enough to make it profitable to get rid of these crummy things. If someone wanted to get rid of junk yards in the United States, all they would have to do is subsidize scrap or do something whereby the steel mills would find it more profitable to utilize this scrap than utilize low grade ore converted into taconite. That's all they would have to do, it's as simple as that! In other words, make non-pollution profitable.

Another point we talk about is overproduction. Maybe we're going to have to have a guaranteed annual income. I look at it from the standpoint of underproduction. I think we are producing much too little. Our problem is priorities and a reallocation of resources. At present it is better to produce something new. What we are going to have to buy and produce is better air, better water, more and better recreational facilities, and less junk! We are going to have to grow less tobacco, perhaps produce less dog and cat food, lipstick containers and what have you. Recently I got back from the South, the Blue Ridge Parkway, the Smokies and Mammoth Cave. On Easter Day, believe it or not, I could not find a campground in the Mammoth Cave National Park. Mind you, this is Easter, about the tenth of April. What is it going to be like in July? There was a notorious lack of personnel and guides in the park. They took 200 people at a time through Mammoth Cave. They should have taken only twenty. The whole park operation was understaffed. We need, in this day and age, more park rangers, electrostatic precipitators and qualified staff. It would appear that we need both fantastic production and better sewage disposal plants to maintain some equilibrium. I don't look at this problem as one of overproduction, rather I view the problem as one of underproduction.

Dr. Thompson (faculty, UWGB): I'd like to give my colleague, Dr. Fontera, a little trouble, if I might. It seems to me that you are advocating a controlling agency which would by-pass the sort of referendum thing we see going on here in Green Bay in respect to the bridge. I think you are advocating an agency composed of environmentally conscious and sophisticated elite individuals who will determine environmental policy. I think you are proposing an agency that is, in point of fact, very close to the second model I showed the audience yesterday and very close to an agency which we have been studying with some interest of late. I won't be uncharitable enough to name it yet. I would like to challenge your model simply because I don't think it will work. Do you want to respond?

Dr. Fontera: What I attempted to do was to say that there ought not to be a more dictatorial or elite form of political rule. It has been my experience that elite is a word which trips lightly from the lips of the elite. I would like to see us apply our social science skills, given the present state of the arts or science, to social, economic and political matters.

In terms of our old values, it appears to me that we have to face up to the increasing crunch of finding that, in areas of environmental concern, where these matters such as referenda are shortcutted, you get effective and timely action. Let us use the recent bridge referendum in Green Bay as an example. I hear tell, though it may be a fairy tale, that bridges were necessary in this community before this past spring, that a long struggle has existed over the bridges in this community. Presumably the bad effect of not having bridges has affected a large number of people for a long period of time. Yet, apparently the society here was capable of tolerating that situation until now. What I'm really trying to reiterate, if you like, is a portion of Paul Ehrlich's point, from which he recently appears to have retreated. The point is if we don't get a high degree of volunteerism, in which voluntarily we give up some of those aspects we considered to be individual rights, then we entertain quite briskly the kind of specialized controlling agencies which will be necessary to handle the problem by force. Consider one of many paradoxes we presently have in this country. If you filled out your income tax this year, you discovered that you get an increased bonus for children. It's not much, but it's going up a little bit the next few years—the dependency allowance. This is being done by a government which states that population is a national problem. Now one of those two goals is going to have to give. When the French thought population was a national problem, e.g., they didn't have enough people, they gave free railroad passes to any woman who could prove that she gave birth to four or more children. They claim it worked, that is, they produced more kids. Perhaps some of the things that are being said here is that the reverse might work, if we have the time. And if we don't have the time, it seems to me that we will then have to press into the authoritarian Pakistani model, rather than the relative consentual Indian model as I discussed in my paper. That's really what I'm saying. I'm not saying that in my ideal universe an intelligent and smart person determines the future for the rest of us.

Mr. Alvorson (environmental resource teacher, St. Louis, Missouri): I was not here yesterday so I don't know whether this was discussed, but I just want to give a couple of points of information: one to Mr. McCullagh and the other to Mr. Barhydt. Mr. Nader's name has come up a couple of times today. In February I attended a junior college conference in Washington, D.C., where Mr. Nader made an unexpected presentation. One of the things I remember him saying was that in a number of industries, the unions are not cooperating on environmental problems. However, he did cite the oil and gas line workers as showing an active interest in environmental concerns. Now, they may have done this because they saw more opportunity for jobs in inspection, nevertheless he did cite their interest as active.

The other comment is directed to Mr. McCullagh. I'm not too sure how many people know this, but I know it has been circulated in the newspapers as well as from Mr. Nader in February when he made his announcement. There are some colleges in the country, Oregon, California, and Minnesota among them, which are asking their state legislators to let them assess the students in state universities a certain number of dollars, I think the fee is $3 in Oregon, to build up a reservoir of money so that the student senate could use the money to hire a lawyer to work for them on what they see as a collective problem in their community or area. I don't know if that's what Mr. McCullagh was referring to in his comments, but I would like to just throw it out for consideration. Mr. Nader has two young lawyers working with him in Washington trying to respond to university needs along legal lines.

Finally, I would like to ask just one question, if I could. This question is directed to Professor Gross. I don't quite understand how it is that a managed society is necessarily going to be a repressive society. I'd simply like to ask, if an unmanaged society has produced many of the problems we believe we see about us today, won't we have to move toward a managed society to attack this problem?

Dr. Gross: I think that most of the discussions here have pointed in the direction of some more effective methods of managing our affluence, to pick up a term used by Professor Rainwater yesterday. I happen, as a technician and an analyst, to believe that there is nothing whatsoever in the ecological movement but ritualistic tokenism, unless the basic orientation is toward national planning and management for the use of the residuals created by an increasing highly affluent society. Professor Rainwater happened to mention as he left that if he was wrong in his prediction, there would be no basic change in the distribution of income and wealth, and if there was a disproportionate increase in the income and wealth of the lower part of the population, a leveling up of a more egalitarian nature, this would make the problem of pollution and environmental degradation much greater. So, I ended my statement on a paradox, which is part of what I believe to be the grand alternative—part of the grand alternatives confronting the modern world. Namely, the prevention of either ecocide or other forms of nuclear or bacteriological types of biocide will necessitate a larger degree of societal management to prevent these evils. It may mean moving from the managed economy to the managed society. At the same time, it is entirely possible for such management to be increasingly elitist and technocratic and increasingly repressive. In my judgment, we have moved into significant forms of economic planning and economic and social management during the twenty-five years since the end of World War II in both our capitalistic and socialistic societies. In different ways, this movement has been increasingly repressive.

Thinking mainly about the problems of America, I see the potentialities of subtle and effective changes as well as the more terroristic forms of repression in any movement toward central management and control in this country. However, one can also start to consider the possibilities for democratic, humanitarian, decentralized, participatory planning—terms of this type have been used also. I said in my paper, with a note of great sorrow but also of candor, that while this has been the basic thrust of my own intellectual efforts, I have little that I can be proud of either. I believe that the potentialities for a widely participatory democracy with less elitist planning, are inherent in our society. They are inherent in some of the developments of post industrial science, but these potentialities have not been developed either by our political leaders, our corporate leaders or our social scientists. So I'm saying there is a real internal danger here. I would feel much more confident if those of us who were aware of this danger could set forth institutional programs of fundamental reconstruction or transformation of values and of modes of rationality and of power, which would lead us to have less fear. It's quite possible that the road to enlightened management is the road to a new science-based serfdom. I believe there are other roads; and I think one of the great contributions of conferences of this type and of colleges of this type is to try to explore these other roads and recognize that the new science/technology-based road to serfdom is a genuine possibility. This is something that can only be avoided by conceiving of more democratic, humanist and decentralized forms of planning and management!

Dr. Kolka: I would like to respond to the question too. I don't wish to take issue with Professor Gross because that isn't my intent. I would like to examine another portion of the question. The dilemma is a rather large one containing many facets. I am encouraged that we have organizations to manage our forests. I am discouraged that internally they can manage and control forests and not be bothered by outside opinion. The arrogance of the U. S. Forest Service and the Department of the Navy independently contracting for Project Sanguine is a glowing illustration! One wonders whether the Latin root of the project's title is a reference to bleeding the public forests? This is precisely the point being made by Ralph Nader. These types of organizations tend to be somewhat independent of human control. Once they are large and settle, and once they forge forward, they don't want to experience the little irritants, the pinpricks from the outside. This behavioral characteristic tends to be one of the habits of public corporations or public associations, if you will.

To point to places where I see things to be feared, I would examine the present direction of the FCC. Their statement that they want to protect free speech carries with it the intonation that they would like to hear the kind of speech with which they agree and that things with which they disagree or find distasteful ought to be inspected and perhaps cut off the air. This will give us good American speech. The CBS documentary *"The Selling of the Pentagon"* offers an illustration of this potentially heavy-handed censorship by a public agency. I see this sort of activity as being a terrorist type of tactic and potentially the sort of control that Pravda or Izvestia do well, but something I would hate to see in our society. Maybe Nader is correct, that we need his type of irritant to provoke these people and keep them humane and alive. After all, he took on the Federal Trade Commission rather effectively.

Perhaps we need to move toward the type of solution suggested by Peter Bachrach in the final chapter of his book, *A Theory of Democratic Elitism* (1967). By virtue of size and market domination, our largest private corporations are allocating values for our society—in other words, making public decisions. Traditionally, we consider this activity to be reserved to the duly elected members of our democratic processes. Bachrach's suggestion is that we ought to then allow greater public participation in the management of such corporations by forcing them to accept public membership on their boards of directors. To illustrate this point I would note the failure of the Penn Central Railroad in the eastern United States. In congressional debate, Congressman Pattman argued, with considerable justification, that if a corporation is badly managed and is going to die, let it die. The response in Congress was that Penn Central was a vital transportation artery which critically affected the lives of sixty million persons. If the corporation died, these people went with it. If this is true, then it is not a private corporation, rather it is a public corporation making public decisions by virtue of its size and existence. Perhaps we should allow more public participation on the board of directors, such as the recent appointment of a black representative by General Motors of its own accord. Maybe we need to have more public appointments to boards of corporations which enjoy a public monopoly or oligopoly.

I would like to move into another area to illustrate another dimension of the managerial problem, specifically the urban crises or urban problems. Living near greater Kansas City for a few years I was able to watch in excess of fifty governmental units duplicate several of their services. This type of political multiplication is the sort of thing which we have ideologically accepted in our society. We permit each of these units to politically make their own decisions, even though economically these units may be spending five times as much money getting to the same point. This has brought me to two conclusions which I have toyed with a great deal and would like to thrash out in print when I have a bit more concrete data. Maybe the economic base of political units needs to be larger in order to gain economies of scale by buying on a mass basis. It is possible to demand greater durability in goods and achieve this result with more effect.

However, I would hate to see political units reach the same point which would maximize economic efficiency. I'm rather fond of the types of problems which arose in New York City when the Ford Foundation funded the Oceanside-Brownsville school district. You divide large units into small units. The unit or school system can be large for economic reasons, but small for political or representative reasons. It was assumed, in this experiment, that a unit of fifty thousand people would be beneficial because the parents would be closer to their own elected school board and wouldn't fear walking in and pounding on desks concerned about their child's education. In fact, the parents did demonstrate a greater interest in their children's welfare and began to show a greater degree of political responsibility. It is possible that we maximize political participation by utilizing these smaller units.

Contrary to a statement made earlier, I don't see pluralism now, I see the loss of pluralism and I would like to see it re-established, but I would also like us to handle our societal problems. Maybe national planning in one area is the most efficient economic solution. But at the same time I would like to give a human being in New York City an opportunity to feel that he is a human being rather than forcing him to pick up a phone along with several other people, say 7,000 a day, and state that his child is being abused in school. They reply, "Yes, sir, we'll see to that right away!"—while a bank of twenty people handling forty telephones throws it into the bureaucratic hopper where it accumulates with the other complaints of the day. That's not humanism and that's not humane!

So I can see two types of solutions emerging: economic planning in one area operating on a large based economic unit, and political planning in another area operating with smaller political units. As Dr. Fontera mentioned earlier in this panel, "bigger is better" doesn't necessarily solve the problem. At present in this state we are watching the movement to merge our two large university systems. While I would like to see us economically improve our educational systems, I would hate to see us establish a ratio of seventy-to-one as the optimum student-teacher ratio for all classrooms. With a "bigger is better" mentality, somebody might say, "Man, that's going to be all right, because now we're going to get more bang for the buck! For $12,000 we put a guy in the classroom and he always teaches at least seventy students." All the while the students sit there saying, qualitatively, this is horrible. Even with our own situation in this university, it's necessary to take two slices at the problem. One slice is to economically prune our operation to achieve greater efficiency. The second slice is to get better teachers, improve the quality of teaching and permit student-teacher interaction which will qualitatively provide both parties with the most rewarding learning situation. I'm not saying all large classes are bad, rather I think a mix is more effective.

Anonymous (question from a community participant in the audience): I'm wondering whether or not DuPont is working with the government agencies that have been set up to protect the environment, and if not, why not? Because as I see it, part of the problem involved is that you have government agencies set up with industry working on opposite poles. Usually you come up with the same goals, but you are working against each other. Are you working together with the government?

Mr. Barhydt: Yes, let me explain a couple of things that are happening. I'm dying to say something about Mr. Armstrong's remarks about Dow Chemical Company—I won't say it now, but save them for later. The Environmental Protection Agency was formed to bring together the Air Office, which was under the Department of Health, Education, and Welfare, the Federal Water Quality Administration which was under the Department of the Interior, the Bureau of Solid Waste Management, and several others. The objective was to treat pollution as not being only an air problem, a water problem or a solid waste problem, but being just one single problem. I believe Dr. Gross mentioned that if you can take things out of air, they go into water, if you take it out of water, you create solid waste, and so forth. This is the most horrendous problem we've got. The Environmental Protection Agency recently released contracts to industry to set effluent standards for water quality. Some of DuPont's engineers are on these committees. They are working with people in EPA on the problems of setting effluent limits. These limits will be policed. Each industry in this country will have to have a permit to discharge effluent into any navigable waterway. Under this interpretation, if the stream floats a canoe, you will need a permit to discharge. This is only industry, it doesn't apply to municipalities. Oddly enough, this is based on an 1899 act which was originally written to make sure that the waters were kept navigable and open. It was interpreted by the Supreme Court as an anti-pollution law, so you can't put anything into a river without a permit from the Corps of Engineers without being liable for suit. Several companies, including DuPont, have been sued under this act.

The states will grant industries original certification. Then if the industry gets state certification, this will be passed on to the Corps of Engineers and the Corps of Engineers will then take it up with the Environmental Protection Agency, and a permit or a temporary permit will be issued for discharges. This whole procedure is based on the criteria that is being developed now by the Environmental Protection Agency. This sounds very complicated and it's perhaps too complicated, but it is what is happening and it is a horrendous undertaking. EPA estimates there are 40,000 pipes discharging effluents into rivers in the U. S. I've heard people say there are at least 100,000, if not triple that many. So, if you have to have a permit for each pipe, it's going to take two or three years before you have this thing policed. Perhaps that's not the way to go at the problem.

There is legislation now being considered in Washington which will take up the basin concept. In other words, an entire river basin will be an environmental area in much the same way as there are presently air regions. On the whole subject of legislation, I don't think there is anything wrong with legislation. I think that is the only way you are going to get people to comply with the laws, set uniform standards and get people to stop polluting. If it is necessary to hit them with heavy fines, and it has to be done I think, it will have to be done on a federal level so there are uniform standards throughout the nation. Otherwise you will have the case of one little town which would love to have industry and would ease its regulations so that it can attract industrial development. These are the facts of life, and we will have to deal with them until we start restructuring our thinking. I see evidence that some people would like to see this happen but aren't quite sure how we are going to bring it about. We have to live with what we have now. There certainly has been progress made in racial equality through legislation, and I can't see why there can't be the same type of progress made, however imperfect, in the legislation of pollution abatement.

Dr. Zander (faculty, UWGB): I would like to write a scenario of about three minutes, if I may. I would like to set the stage by suggesting that one of you here put himself to work to find a solution for the automobile pollution problem. You have succeeded! You came up with a device which you found by your own testing would reduce smog, would increase mileage, would increase power output, would give you a cleaner engine, your oil would last longer, and a few other things of that sort. You were jubilant about it. You said, "Now I've got something the whole world needs; I will now see what I can do with it, I'm sure industry will grab it, the government will approve it and I will be on my way."

So you sent it to Washington for the purpose of having it patented. Your patent comes back in short order because at the present time the patent office has been advised to give special and quick consideration to this kind of device. Now you have a patent on your device. You then say, "How will I proceed with this thing? Who will be most likely to grab it and run with it," and you think the government. So you write your senators and you say to them, "Will you please see what can be done about this device; it has been patented by Washington and you are in Washington, see what can be done." Senator Nelson writes back to you and says, "It's a proprietary device, privately patented and therefore I don't think the government would be interested in it." Well, you thought there was an emergency in this connection. So you write to Senator Proxmire, and he responds quickly, as he does, and he says, "I will write to the Air Pollution Control Administration and give you some help at that end; I'm sure they will be interested!" He does that and sends you a copy and you write to them; and after some considerable correspondence a date is arranged when you can go over to the laboratory at Ypsilanti, Michigan, and have your device tested. So you take it and go over there and you spend two very pleasant hours with two gentlemen in charge of the laboratory. They are lovely men—they take you through the laboratory and show you it standing there idle. The staff is there, not working, and you say, "Will you please test my device?" And they say, "No, we don't have budget for that." And you say, "Well, we thought you got a three million dollar appropriation for this institution over here." They say, "Well, we don't have budget to test your device." So, you go back home.

Then you think, "Well, I'll go to the automobile companies." You go to each of them in turn. There are only four, and you do not get your device tested. They are pleasant, you talk with them, and in the course of these conversations one of them says to you, "You know, there's an awful lot of talk about this business of pollution. The country can't get along without the internal engine—internal combustion engine—and we just are not so terribly concerned." And another one of the officials of the companies will say to you, "There are only four companies, and if you don't like the car you've got you will buy one from the other company, and after that you will buy it from the other, and after awhile you will come back to us in due time and we will get our fair share." And then you think, "Well, something else has to happen." You've just got to get through. So you write again to the senator and he writes back and says it's proprietary, so you say, "Well, I'll give it away!" You say, "I'll take it down to the Wisconsin Alumni Research Foundation and give it to them." So you travel down there. You make a couple of trips and you have some conversations and they decide that it's too risky to take a patent that has not been invented by someone in a university laboratory, and you can't blame them for it because that's the law. They may lose their Foundation privileges if they exploit a patent not originating in a university laboratory, not a state university laboratory, a University of Wisconsin laboratory.

And so, you write to Mr. Nader, and you don't get a response. You try everything conceivable and you are finally totally frustrated. You can't even get it tested! You go to your friends in the Esso Research Laboratory. They say, "Why, yes, I know the people in the Esso Research Laboratory very well, I'll contact them for you." They do, and Esso Research sends a man out to look at the thing. He takes a lot of notes, goes back and then they write a letter back and say, "We must concern ourselves with matters that flow through pipes. We can't be interested in this. If you want it tested, you can go to a laboratory down in Texas." Finally, you throw up your hands and quit. Now, this is not just a scenario, it is based on my personal experience. If it opens up any doors to the situation in which we find ourselves, I would appreciate your assistance. So far we have found corporate lack of interest, government lack of action, private research foundations hemmed in by legal restrictions on what they can do—try the tune on your piano.

Mr. Schneider (student, UWGB): I would like to direct this to Mr. Barhydt, and more specifically to corporations in this country. I think people today are becoming very aware of the ecological problem and situation we are faced with. They fear this as consumers that they are the ones who are going to have to foot the bill. I don't think that corporations are truly footing the bill and doing their share, especially when they can spend millions of dollars a year on advertising, on lobbying in Washington and on outrageous salaries for their top executives. As a sidenote, I think a lot of the lobbying that is going on is probably against legislation which would restrict them and probably, in the end, cost them some money. If this money were put to the proper use, I'm sure they could come up with many means to fight and combat pollution. Therefore, take many of the people who are employed in corporations and put them to work to combat the pollution problem. Why not reallocate these funds from which the consumer ultimately doesn't gain any benefit?

Mr. Barhydt: Was that a statement or a question? I'll try to take these things one at a time, if I can, and I may not give you a satisfactory answer. High salaries: I believe that I would like to get a high salary myself and I think that if I was in a high position I would deserve it. These are incentives to get highly capable people. I would like to turn the question back to you and ask you, what do you consider to be a high salary?

Mr. Schneider: I think $500,000 a year is a high salary.

Mr. Barhydt: $500,000 a year, I don't know of anybody who is making that.

Mr. Schneider: Well then, I consider from $150,000 to $500,000 to be a high salary.

Mr. Alvorson: The president of General Motors Company two years ago, a year before this year, had a salary of $550,000. It was reported in the paper the other day that he opted to take a salary of $250,000 this year. A voluntary cut of $300,000 commensurate with the losses in General Motors' overall operations. The young man is absolutely right about a salary of $500,000! I used to work for National Distillers Corporation years ago, and the president of our company at one time made $450,000, it was either 1953 or 1954, so even though those salaries sound unconscionable, they exist.

Dr. Armstrong: Mr. Barhydt, the ball is back in your court.

Mr. Barhydt: Well, being an industrialist, or rather a representative of industry, I think $500,000 is rather high. I don't think $150,000 for a president of a major corporation is high with the responsibility he has to assume and the odds against any of us ever making it. I think the salary structure in the corporation itself cannot be considered high. It might be slightly higher than in universities. Although some of you laugh, I would be happy to get together privately with somebody and tell them how much money I make. I'm not even sure that if I were a full professor here I'd be making a little more. As to your question on advertising, I would rather not get into that at this time.

Dr. Gross: Do full professors get stock options?

Mr. Barhydt: I don't get stock options either.

Dr. Gross: Do full professors come into capital gains outside of their regular income?

Dr. Fontera: OK folks, let's hear it for $150,000!

Mr. Barhydt: I think if we consider advertising, and let's confine ourselves not to this ecology area, environmental area, we can open the whole bag of consumerism of whether you are creating demands by advertising or whether you are creating false demands. I noticed in the paper this morning that cigarette sales are up 2 percent over a year ago. Yet, on December 31, 1970, all cigarette advertising went off television. Whether it means something or not, I don't know, but it's an indication that advertising has not accounted for the fact that cigarette sales went up 2 percent. Maybe there are just more people smoking. Maybe this labor force is smoking, that we have been talking about.

Lobbying: DuPont is not a lobbyer per se. We have offered testimony before senate committees and house committees. We have lent our expertise to governmental agencies. We have twenty full-time environmental engineers at DuPont, very bright and dedicated people, and hopefully we can hire somebody from this university sometime. Again, these are people concerned with environmental issues and they have offered their expertise to governmental agencies and control authorities. Many times their advice has been accepted. Many times industry is in a better position to make evaluations than government. The Environmental Protection Agency, I understand, is looking for about 2,000 people. They are very short of technically oriented people. They need them now, and if there is anybody here interested in this type of work I'd start looking around the Environmental Protection Agency. I'm sure this answers your question, but you expressed an opinion and I expressed an opinion.

Dr. Armstrong: Professor Fontera would like to make a comment.

Dr. Fontera: Let's try to clarify for a moment what we're talking about when we talk about regulatory agencies at the present state of the art. We are referring to agencies which usually begin because of a public outcry. In one case I can think of a novel which drew public attention to what seemed to be a sad situation, such as throwing dog and horse carcasses into a sausage machine. That's where it starts, and public concern lasts or has lasted historically right through the founding of the agency, at which point we move to a new kick, from hula hoops to frisbees. Then the agency very slowly, but much too fast really, grows closer and closer to the industry it is supposed to regulate. Where people at various corporations used to have to send people to back rooms, they now send experts and consultants. For example, in the area of the Internal Revenue Service, which is supposed to collect revenue, we have large corporations (at taxpayers' expense) having full-time staffs from the IRS showing them how to do, what they wish to do, without doing anything wrong! In the food and drug area we have the same picture.

Now, if we are going to talk in terms of a new environmental control agency, just founding the agency and bringing a lot of little things together is not going to improve the environment or get the public interest represented. I think Ralph Nader is right about this and the question really is related to complex human organization itself. I think this backs up the statement that if you put black people on a board of directors because you have a concern for racial balance, you have to put people on regulatory agencies and boards to represent a community interest. I would like to hear the gentleman's response to a proposal of Nader's to force the DuPont Corporation to indicate one of its individuals who can be sued by an offended citizen on his personal liability. The basis for such an action would be to force DuPont to appoint one of its socially conscious executives to a position where corporate misbehavior would result in the person seeing his own ox gored. Because as it now stands, when a corporation misbehaves as GE did a number of years ago, nobody knows why it happened. The corporation is sued but the individuals who make the decisions are sentenced lightly or not at all, something which does not happen to the rest of us legal individuals when we do something wrong. I think the plea for new regulatory agencies as the victory at the end of the rainbow ought to also be a plea for real regulatory agencies, and not what has happened historically in this country with the agencies we have created. Professor Kolka mentioned the FCC. The same case in point can be made with the FAA which has evidenced a tie between the agency that regulates airlines and the airline executives. They have a lot in common; they both like airplanes!

Dr. Pollis (faculty, UWGB): I don't want to detour the serious line of discussion that we have going, but my curiosity has overcome me and so I will pose this frivolous question to Mr. Barhydt. You said you came prepared to answer questions on women's lib and I want you to just briefly tie in women's lib, DuPont chemical, environmental quality and social responsibility.

Mr. Barhydt: I don't really know how to answer that, and I'm not trying to duck the question. I really have to have time to think about that; I can give you statistics on the number of women employed at DuPont and it really doesn't mean anything. There are not enough women in responsible positions as yet, but we consider it important to appoint more women to such positions. At present, we have several women scientists. We don't have enough women in managerial positions. I will admit this, but how it ties in with the environmental issue, I think you and I would have to ponder that one.

I would also like to answer the question here, if I may, about who you are going to sue. There's a saying now among persons angry with corporations on environmental issues, "Sue the bastards." Now you want to know who you are going to send to jail. Under the permit system set up by the Environmental Protection Agency, which will operate under the 1899 act, the chief executive officer of a corporation or an officer of a corporation, I don't think this has been thrashed out yet, has to certify that what he is saying on his permit application is indeed true. If he is caught polluting and can be convicted under the criminal portion of the 1899 act, he is subject to a fine of, I believe, $2,500 for each violation, or a year in jail. So the corporation executive is putting himself on the line when he makes application for this permit to discharge.

Dr. Posey (Dean, School of Professional Studies, UWGB): I've been somewhat saddened by the thrust of the discussion lately. A minor point, Dr. Fontera, executives of General Electric, Westinghouse, and a number of corporations were jailed in the electrical equipment case. It apparently gives us a feeling of comfort that we have accomplished something worthwhile if we can point to the other fellow and all of his defects, all of his shortcomings and all of his failures. I think that it is fine for us to attack corporations. I also think that many of these attacks stem from complete ignorance, but whether that is true or not, corporations are made up of people. Most of the students here are going to be working for corporations. When they start working for corporations, I hope that they will bring some of their idealism into their operations. But so far as a corporation is concerned, if it doesn't take in as much money as it pays out, it's going to disappear. It is not in the position of a university or a governmental unit, where taxes can be raised in response to the pressure for a better job. A corporation has to live on the gate. I would like to get back to one of the themes that came up yesterday and to some extent this morning and simply say, I think we should all realize that we ourselves are partially responsible for pollution. I think that Walt Kelly is right when he said, "We have met the enemy and the enemy is us."

Dr. Armstrong: For a final question today, I will call upon Professor Gross.

Dr. Gross: Mr. Barhydt was in trouble because not enough questions were being asked, and I wanted to ask him a question which is not anti-corporation in form. Recently, as some of you may know, the Tennessee Valley Authority was the subject of a court action because the TVA had failed to conform with the new federal law requiring all government agencies to file an environmental impact statement ninety days before certain kinds of actions. The TVA had just not been aware of the fact that this law was on the books. They pleaded guilty, and they are now faced with the question of filing a complete statement on the effects of their purchase of coal from strip mining operations on the hillsides that are denuded nearby. Now it seems to me that the new provision of law requiring government agencies to do this was a very wise use of a very restricted form of legislation which merely requires that some facts be presented. The question I wanted to raise, in the spirit of what we have heard about the new work of the cost accountants, deals with the recommendation of some of the cost accountants that we have periodic social audits of corporations in which objective statements will be made concerning all sorts of secondary consequences of corporate activity. It seems to me that there is a discriminatory flavor about legislation which requires federal agencies to file statements ninety days in advance. Why shouldn't major corporations be required to file statements days in advance, considering the fact that they are engaged in longer range planning than most federal agencies? After all, corporations are the major planning instrumentalities in modern society. Why shouldn't they be required to file an environmental impact statement a year ahead of time as a basis of their going ahead with their operations in the following year? The particular environmental statement that I have in mind is not a fancy pants statement concerning social indicators or anything like that, although I have been very much involved with the development of social indicators, just a simple statement of emissions. This would include emissions from energy conversion, fuel, heating and also the residuals corporations are throwing into the society in the form of the very large residual problem created by two-ton automobiles produced in the Detroit area.

The question I want to put to Mr. Barhydt is not to react immediately to what is, I think, a challenging and perhaps disturbing proposal—namely, extending to the corporations the new requirements that have been placed upon certain government agencies, but a very simple question. What is the residual production of DuPont? What are the tons? What are the quantities of effluents and other residuals being produced through DuPont's far-flung operations? Has the amount of such effluents risen considerably, or has it fallen? I would assume that while your company's recorded profits have probably fallen in the last two years, the quantity, the physical quantity of emissions and effluents has probably risen very significantly. Maybe I'm wrong. It's a factual question. I would like to ask Mr. Barhydt whether he has any, speaking for the corporation, facts or impressions concerning the effluents or residual emission output of the DuPont Corporation into the American environment?

Mr. Barhydt: Again, I may not answer your question completely. However, before we can open a plant these days we must have permits from several agencies, hopefully in the future it will be from only one. We are opening a plant in North Carolina which will make the plastic interliner used in making windshields. We have had to obtain permits from the state of North Carolina and from the Corps of Engineers; we have also been checked out on any air effluents. Before we even began construction of the plant, and this isn't the first time that we have done it, we had a study made of the stream by the Philadelphia Academy of Natural Sciences. There is a limnologist there, a very prominent person by the name of Dr. Ruth Patrick, who looked at the condition of the stream. Based on her stream study, we designed our plant. Now, keep in mind, you can put something at the end of the production line and take out the pollutants, but you are much better off if you make a process change or design your process so you don't pollute in the first place.

I'll interject here that by 1975 every industry in the country should have, by law, the equivalent of secondary sewage treatment. This is not going to be the case for municipalities. Insofar as an environmental impact statement, the states and the federal government are getting this information, at least from the DuPont Company and from several other companies. We cannot operate unless we can demonstrate that we are not going to upset the ecological system of a river and we are not going to pollute the air. I think that the government is even going to move further and ask you what raw materials you're using, how much is coming out of the production line, and subtract the difference to find how much waste you've got. The big problem is waste. It is a problem which gets into deep well injection in some industries, it gets into barging, it gets into landfill and it gets into incineration. It is going to take an awful lot of work to solve the waste problem.

Dr. Armstrong: I want to thank our panelists this afternoon and throughout the conference. Five o'clock is a popular time for departing our fair city of Green Bay. I would like to thank all those who helped make this conference a success. And in closing, I would simply like to recall to you some of the aims of this conference. It is to draw attention toward the social counterpart of the problem of environmental deterioration. It is to indicate that man, technology, and the environment are mutually interdependent variables, and technology alone cannot resolve the problems to which it has given rise. Society, with its norms and values, provides us with a fundamental dimension which should be considered essential to any lasting solution devised in the biological, physical, and technological sciences. If education is the process of raising and answering questions, I hope we have made some inroads on that. I hope we have been able to make a contribution which does not end when we leave this symposium, but will be diffused among us and come back in succeeding waves, hopefully when we have a cleaner environment. Thank you for your participation, good day!

An Overview

The title of the final panel "Individual Rights Versus Collective Good" rhetorically places the question of environmental quality in a combative arena to highlight a major dimension of the problem. Because a human being is a complex biological creature who is socialized into the interactive dynamics of a larger social system and subsets of that system, the separation of the individual from the collective is set forth here only as an object of study. Although the individual and the collective are intertwined, political philosophers will recognize the title of the panel as containing a question which has occupied their attention for centuries. (For a general study of socialization, see Child 1954, and for a theoretical application, see Warriner 1970. For an application of this approach to political science, the two most ambitious studies are Hess and Torney 1967 and Easton and Dennis 1969. For a classical analysis of political philosophy, see Sabine 1961.)

The panelists are confronted with a series of basic questions to be dealt with by any society; what do we mean by environmental quality and what type of quality do we desire? Who decides questions of quality and why should they decide? How does a society implement its desires? What implications does implementation have for the quality of life in a society? While the list is not exhaustive, it does suggest the range of problems to be dealt with by societies attempting to define questions of environmental quality.

Professor Gross' paper is especially interesting as he examines some of the subtleties of attempting to achieve ecological stabilization while at the same time attempting to avert ecological catastrophe. That ecological solutions could yield a managed society is morbidly apparent for those who cherish some degree of individual freedom. The residue of these attempts at a managed ecosystem could leave us with what Professor Gross has labeled "friendly fascism." (Gross 1969) What is even more distressing is the implication that a conscious failure to consider these questions at the present time could leave a society a captive of values capriciously adopted or randomly assimilated by the dominant political culture. The consequence of behavior characterized by political drifting could very well yield societies captive of environmental crises where human survival or annihilation would dictate extreme measures. The timetable for such political measures would depend upon the size and capability of the human population, the size and quality of its natural resources (including the capacity of agricultural production vis-a-vis the human population) and the gross nutritional proximity of the society to its physical base of support. While food support could come from the outside, its ideological dependence upon the concept of the nation state renders reliance upon this base, tenuous at best.

Professor Fontera's paper is directed to a classic concern in the realm of individual rights. He notes that, " . . . the individual rights of people in a society of this complexity do not come from birth, but rather come from the accidents of their accessibility to what society has to provide." His concern is basic and finds an Anglo-Saxon derivation from mid-nineteenth century English liberalism. The philosopher T. H. Green observed that the liberalism of John Stuart Mill marked a shift from **negative freedom** (a person is free except when he would infringe on the political rights of his fellows) to **positive freedom** (a person is free only when he has the real capacity to share in the fruits of that society). (Sabine 1961:729) Attempts to translate positive freedom into day-to-day human behavior and individual rights occupied the interests of the English intellectual community and in particular the Fabian society. Some of the earliest activity for this definition of freedom supported Mill's concern that an individual could not truly participate in a society unless he had some minimal education. His campaign for public education reflected the degree of his concern.

Later in the nineteenth and early twentieth century the Fabian society and the heir to many of its ideas, the Labour Party, argued that unless a man were physically healthy, he would be unable to effectively participate in a society. Health, too, became a basic right. Among the earliest attempts to extend this range of ideas into the American academic community were the analyses of John Dewey (1927, 1929, 1939). Writing during the Depression, he observed that liberty was an evolving phenomenon relative to forces at a given time and place. Although liberty at one time signified a release from chattel slavery or serfdom, "today it signifies liberation from the coercions and repressions that prevent multitudes from participation in the vast cultural resources that are at hand." (Dewey 1963:48) He suggested that society should extend assistance to each individual in order to eliminate these coercions and repressions or, put in reverse form, society should guarantee each individual those rights which would allow him to participate in the society.

To leave the reader with the impression that a concern with "positive freedom" was the sole province of the Anglo-American intellectual world would do an incredible injustice to the writings of G. W. F. Hegel and Karl Marx. Many of the previously described gentlemen have been labeled as neo-Hegelian. All of them were acquainted with the writings of Marx and his revolutionary and evolutionary contemporaries.

With this thumbnail historical sketch in mind, we will now return to the central point. "Positive freedom" or the actual ability to participate in the deliberations of a society necessitates a capable mind, physical health and all of the other socio-physiological and socio-economic accouterments which each collective must provide its individual participants if it expects them to have access to the deliberations of that society. A few societies have attempted to legislate political, social and economic rights in hopes of guaranteeing them to their citizenry. (See the constitution of the United States of Mexico.)

This brings us to another point; access is an ambiguous term. Left by itself and without qualification, access suggests that if people have an equal right to actually participate in decision making they will have a meaningful existence. However, access to participate and actual participation are not the same thing. In fact, a simple individual right to access could constitute a severe limitation on meaningful participation in a society. One contemporary political scientist suggests that only when participation extends to each person will, ". . . the majority of individuals stand to gain in self-esteem and growth toward a fuller affirmation of their personalities by participating more actively in meaningful community decisions." (Bachrach 1967:101)

It is apparent from the preceding analysis that access alone is both an ancient concern of political theorists and an inadequate statement of individual rights in contemporary political societies. It is also necessary to again observe that these discussions of individual rights, collective good, decision making and social behavior have occurred in a spatial vacuum. That this is an organic universe is a point well made in this symposium. Failure to recognize that we are an interdependent organic species living in a biosphere could very well realize Professor Gross' fears of a managed society discussed earlier in this overview.

Because the author of this overview also wrote the final presentation for this panel, comment on the paper would be inappropriate. We will now turn to an analysis of the panel discussion.

Although the panel discussion raises several issues of individual rights and the collective good, one theme appears which has surfaced unchallenged in virtually every discussion in this symposium. It has been frequently called to our attention that a corporation is a mindless social organ which pursues profit and does not possess a soul unless Congress should legislate a moral transplant by means of fining certain liquid effluent discharges or by taxing air polluters. In his opening comments, Professor Armstrong challenges the notion that corporations have no moral obligations to society. While it is not our intent to suggest that corporations are malevolent "pinocchios" of the parent society, it is also untenable to accept the statement that corporations are simply made up of average folk like you and me. A corporation is a complex social organization which develops procedures and behavior patterns. Organizational goals, formal and informal rules, role patterns and evolving traditions exert an overriding influence on the behavior of the organization. Granted that corporations are composed of "average folk," but that has little to do with the behavior of the organization. The same can be said of universities.

Two points deserve a brief consideration in this regard. First, it is true, as observed in the panel discussion, that corporate violators are punished for wrongdoing. However, any student of anti-trust laws in the United States would quickly observe that penalties for corporate crimes are less severe than those applied to a man who empties the cash register of a ghetto liquor store. The latter act is considered a despicable crime, while the former act is generally treated as an unfortunate instance where the miscreant was apprehended. Corporate crimes like congressional wrongdoings are social misdeeds but are not treated as social evils, even though they are both classified as crimes. The penalties meted out for corporate misbehavior are mild compared to penalties which will befall their poorer brethren. (For a specific and detailed analysis of this point in the application of anti-trust laws, see Sutherland 1949.)

The second point relates to the obligation owed by corporate management to the stockholders. The assumption that a bad profit performance would automatically bring on the wrath of the stockholders and occasion the selection of new corporate managers is appealing, but inaccurate. In the words of the late Adolph Berle, "We have seen that the holdings of common stock are gradually—or perhaps rather rapidly—beginning to be concentrated in the professional managers of the pension trust funds and mutual funds. To a somewhat lesser extent, the same is true of the great insurance companies." (1959:52) Even though the real owners of this voting stock are pension holders, owners of mutual funds and owners of insurance policies, these people exercise virtually no power over their property. The probability that the directors of these pools of stock would enter a proxy fight for new corporate management is both remote and raises interesting legal questions of legitimacy. For all intents and purposes, the stock will remain unvoted, corporate decisions unchallenged, and corporate management becomes self-perpetuating. While not all corporations mirror the preceding analysis, the majority of large corporations, in fact, enjoy the protection of this legal moat. (Perhaps the nonresponsive, managed society feared by Professor Gross is already at hand!)

Another dimension to the problem can be added by applying the "iron law of oligarchy" first enunciated by sociologist Robert Michels in 1915

(1959:377-392). In brief, the law observes that as an organization grows in size it will demand a greater degree of skill from its leaders. For a democracy (or republic), the result of this process will be a specialized head with managerial skills (the leaders) which will become remote from the body politic which it serves. This will give us political parties, ". . . which are increasingly based on the competence of the few." (Michels 1959:407) If we apply this rule to the corporate world and add the market mechanisms described in the preceding paragraph, we have the head (corporate management) owing little or no obligation to its body (the property owners—shareholders).

In conclusion, it becomes apparent that a part of the difficulty inherent in examining social factors affecting environmental problems is the popular conception of how the social world operates. The mythologies are exceptionally strong and tend to cloud meaningful analyses of environmental quality and social responsibility. Hopefully, this symposium will have assisted in identifying, some of the problems, discussing some of the social ramifications, and nudging decisions of environmental quality toward the level of choice rather than chance.

J.W.K.

A Selected Bibliography

Abelson, Philip H., 1971, "Changing Attitudes Toward Environmental Problems." *Science,* 172:577.

Asimov, Isaac, 1971, "Can Man Survive the Year 2000," *True Magazine*, January, 1971:31.

Bachrach, Peter, 1967, *The Theory of Democratic Elitism.* Boston: Little, Brown and Company.

Bajema, Carl Jay, 1971, "The Genetic Implications of Population Control," *BioScience,* 21:71-75.

Barnes, Peter, 1971a, "Land Reform in America II: The Vanishing Small Farmer," *The New Republic,* 164,24:21-24.

Barnes, Peter, 1971b, "Land Reform in America III: The Case for Redistribution," *The New Republic,* 164,25:13-17.

Bennis, Warren G. and Philip E. Slater, 1968, *The Temporary Society.* New York: Harper.

Berelson, Bernard, 1969, "Beyond Family Planning," *Science,* 163:533-543.

Berle, Adolf A., 1954, *The 20th Century Capitalist Revolution.* New York: Harcourt, Brace & World, Inc.

Berle, Adolf A., 1956, *Power Without Property.* New York: Harcourt, Brace & World, Inc.

Berle, Adolf A. Jr., 1959, *Power Without Property.* A Harvest Book. New York: Harcourt, Brace & World, Inc.

Boulding, Kenneth E., 1965, *The Meaning of the 20th Century.* Harper Colophon Books. New York: Harper & Row, Publishers.

Boulding, Kenneth, 1969, "Economics of the Coming Space Ship Earth," in *Environmental Handbook,* New York: Ballantine Books.

Boulding, Kenneth E., 1970a, *A Primer on Social Dynamics.* New York: The Free Press.

Boulding, Kenneth E., 1970b, *Economics as a Science.* New York: McGraw-Hill, Inc.

Branscomb, Lewis M., 1971, "Taming Technology," *Science,* 171:972-977.

Burton, Ian, 1968, "The Quality of the Environment, a Review," *Geographical Review,* 58:472-481.

Child, Irvin L., 1954, "Socialization," in *Handbook of Social Psychology.* Edited by Gardiner Lindzey. Vol. II. Boston: Addison-Wesley.

Coale, Ansley G., 1970, "Man and His Environment," *Science,* 170:132-136.

Coffin, Frank M., 1971, *Moment of Totality* (Development in the Decade of Ecology), Development Paper IV, Washington, D.C.: Overseas Development Council.

Comfort, Alex, 1967, *The Nature of Human Nature.* Pelican paperback, New York: Harper & Row.

Commission on Population Growth and the American Future, 1971, *Interim Report to the President of the United States*, March, Washington, D.C.: Superintendent of Documents.

Commoner, Barry, 1971, "The Ecological Crisis," in *Social Responsibility of the Scientist,* edited by Martin Brown. New York: The Free Press.

Crew, Robert E. Jr., ed., 1968, *State Politics.* Belmont, California: Wadsworth Publishing Company, Inc.

Crile, George J., 1969, *A Naturalistic View of Man.* World Publishing Company.

Crocker, Thomas and Rogers, A. J., 1971, *Environmental Economics.* Hinsdale, Illinois: Dryden Press Inc.

Curtin, Paul, 1970, "Social Deprivation and Disease," Proceedings, Annual Meeting, AAAS—Chicago, December, 1970 (Broadcast on Wisconsin State FM Network, 28 March, 1971).

d'Entrieves, A.p., 1965, *Natural Law.* Harper Torch books. New York: Harper & Row, Publishers.

Dales, J. H., 1968, *Pollution, Property and Prices.* Toronto: University of Toronto Press.

Dasman, Raymond F., 1968, "The U.S. Environment—A Time to Decide," PRB Selection No. 25, December. Washington, D.C.: Population Reference Bureau.

Davies, J. Clarence III, 1970, *The Politics of Pollution.* Pegasus. New York: Western Publishing Company, Inc.

Davies, James C., 1962, "Toward a Theory of Revolution," *American Sociological Review,* 6, 1:5-19.

DeBell, Garrett, 1970, *The Voter's Guide to Environmental Politics: Before, During, and After the Election.* New York: Ballantine Books.

Dewey, John, 1927, *The Public and Its Problems.* New York: Henry Holt and Company, Inc.

Dewey, John, 1929, *Individualism Old and New.* New York: Minto Balch and Company.

Dewey, John, 1939, *Freedom and Culture.* New York: Henry Holt and Company.

Dewey, John, 1963, *Liberalism and Social Action.* Capicorn Books. New York: G. P. Putnam's Sons.

Disch, Robert, ed., 1970, *The Ecological Conscience.* A Spectrum Book. Englewood Cliffs, New Jersey: Prentice-Hall, Inc.

Dolan, Edwin G., 1971, *Tanstaafl,* New York: Holt, Rinehart and Winston, Inc.

Dubos, Rene, 1968, *Man, Medicine, and Environment.* New York: Praeger.

Dubos, Rene, 1970, "Will Man Adapt to Megalopolis," *The Ecologist,* 1:12-15.

Duverger, Maurice, 1963, *Political Parties.* Science Editions. New York: John Wiley & Sons, Inc.

Easton, David and Dennis, Jack, 1969, *Children in the Political System: Origins of Political Legitimacy.* New York: McGraw-Hill Book Company.

Ehrlich, Paul R., 1968, *The Population Bomb.* New York: Ballantine Books.

Ehrlich, Paul R. and Ehrlich, Anne H., 1970, *Population/Resources/ Environment.* San Francisco: W. H. Freeman and Company.

Ellis, Harold H.; Beuscher, J. H.; Howard, Cletus D.; DeBraal, J. Peter, 1970, *Water-use Law and Administration in Wisconsin.* Madison, Wisconsin: Department of Law, University Extension, The University of Wisconsin.

Etzioni, Amitai, 1968, *The Active Society.* New York: The Free Press.

Falk, Jacqueline, 1971, "Some Unanticipated Results of Unconscious Family Planning During the Present Century," Lecture—The University of Wisconsin-Green Bay, 5 May 1971.

Ferkiss, Victor C., 1969, *Technological Man.* New York: George Braziller.

Frazer, Franklin E., 1939, *The Negro Family in the United States.* Chicago: University of Chicago Press.

Frejka, Tomas, 1970, "United States: The Implications of Zero Population Growth," *Structures in Family Planning,* New York: The Population Council.

Galbraith, John Kenneth, 1958, *The Affluent Society.* Boston: Houghton-Mifflin Company.

Galbraith, John Kenneth, 1967, *The New Industrial State.* Boston: Houghton-Mifflin Company.

Gerlach, Luther P., and Hine, Virginia H., 1970, *People, Power, Change: Movements of Social Transformation.* New York: Bobbs-Merrill.

Glass, David C., 1968, *Biology and Behavior: Environmental Influences.* New York: Rockefeller University Press and Russell Sage Foundation.

Glazer, Nathan, 1966, "Introduction," *The Negro Family in the United States.* Edited by E. F. Frazier. Chicago: The University of Chicago Press.

Goffman, Erving, 1959, *The Presentation of Self in Everyday Life.* Doubleday Anchor Books. Garden City, New York: Doubleday & Company, Inc.

Goldman, Marshall, ed., 1967, *Controlling Pollution: The Economics of a Cleaner America.* Englewood Cliffs, New Jersey: Prentice-Hall.

Gordon, H. S., 1954, "The Economics of a Common—Property Resource: The Fishery," *Journal of Political Economy,* April, Vol. 62, pp. 124-142.

Griffin, John Howard, 1960, *Black Like Me.* Boston: Houghton-Mifflin Company.

Gross, Bertram M., 1969, *Social Intelligence for America's Future.* Boston: Allyn and Bacon, Inc.

Hardin, Garrett, 1968, "The Tragedy of the Commons," *Science,* 162:1243-1248.

Hardin, Garrett, 1969, "The Economics of Wilderness," *Natural History,* Vol. 78, pp. 20-27.

Hardin, Garrett, 1969, "The Tragedy of the Commons," in *Environmental Handbook,* New York: Ballantine Books.

Hare, F. Kenneth, 1970, "How Should We Treat Environment?" *Science,* 167:352-355.

Hart, H. L. A., 1961, *The Concept of Law.* London: Oxford University Press.

Hauser, Philip, 1970, "Crisis in the Man-Made Environment" Proceedings, Annual Meeting AAAS, Chicago, December 1970 (Broadcast Wisconsin State FM Network 28, March 1971).

Heilbroner, Robert L., 1970, *Between Capitalism and Socialism.* A Vintage Book. New York: Random House, Inc.

Hess, Robert D. and Torney, Judith V., 1967, *The Development of Political Attitudes in Children.* Chicago: Aldine Publishing Company.

Hetzler, Stanley A., 1969, *Technological Growth and Social Change.* New York: Praeger Publishers.

Illich, Ivan, 1969, "Outwitting the 'Developed' Countries," *New York Review of Books,* 13 (November 6, 1969), 20-24.

Iltis, Hugh H., Loucks, O. L. and Andrews, P., 1970, "Criteria for an Optimum Human Environment," *Bulletin of the Atomic Scientists,* 26:2-6.

Jarrett, Henry, ed., 1966, *Environmental Quality in a Growing Economy.* Baltimore: Johns Hopkins Press for Resources for the Future.

Juenger, Friederich G., 1956, *The Failure of Technology.* Chicago: Henry Regnery, 1956.

Kahler, Erich, 1968, "Culture and Evolution," *Culture,* edited by M. F. A. Montagu. New York: Oxford University Press.

Kapp, William K., 1971, *The Social Costs of Private Enterprise.* New York: Schocken Books.

Key, V. O. Jr., 1949, *Southern Politics.* New York: Alfred A. Knopf, Inc.

Keynes, J. M., 1964, *The General Theory of Employment Interest and Money.* A Harbinger Book. New York: Harcourt, Brace & World, Inc.

Kusler, Jon A., 1970, "Water Quality Protection for Inland Lakes in Wisconsin: A Comprehensive Approach to Water Pollution," 1970 Wis. L. Rev. 35.

Laski, Harold J., 1938, *A Grammar of Politics.* London: George Allen and Unwin Ltd.

Lave, Lester B. and Seskin, Eugene P., 1970, "Air Pollution and Human Health," *Science,* 169:723-733.

Leach, Edmund, 1968, *A Runaway World,* New York: Oxford.

Lee, Richard B., 1968, "What Hunters Do for a Living, or, How to Make Out on Scarce Resources," *Man the Hunter,* edited by R. B. Lee and I. DeVore. Chicago: Aldine Publishing Company.

Leopold, Aldo, 1968, *A Sand County Almanac.* Oxford University Press paperback. London: Oxford University Press.

Linder, Stephan, 1970, *The Harried Leisure Class.* New York: Columbia University Press.

Marine, Gene, 1969, *America the Raped,* New York: Simon and Schuster.

Marshall, T. H., 1965, *Class, Citizenship, and Social Democracy.* Doubleday Anchor Books. Garden City, New York: Doubleday & Company, Inc.

Maullin, Richard L., 1970, "The Private War of a Guerrilla," *Trans-action,* 7,6:16 54.

McKinley, Daniel, 1969, "Ethics, Technics, and Biology," *The Yale Review,* 58:617-620.

Mead, Margaret, 1970, "Fractional Life Style and Urban Planning" Proceedings of Annual Meeting, AAAS—Chicago December 1970 (Broadcast Wisconsin State FM Network, 28 March 1971).

Means, Richard L., 1969, *The Ethical Imperative.* Garden City, New York: Doubleday & Company.

Meyers, Charles J. and Tarlock, A. Dan, 1971, *Water Resources Management.* Mineola, New York: The Foundation Press, Inc.

Michels, Robert, 1959, *Political Parties.* New York: Dover Publications, Inc.

Michener, James, 1971, "The Quality of Life," Interview on Wisconsin State FM Network, February 1971.

Miles, Rufus E. J., 1970, "The Population Challenge of the '70s," *Population Bulletin,* 26:1-36.

Miles, Rufus E., 1971, "The Future Population of the United States," *Population Bulletin,* 27:4-31.

Miller, Herman P., "The Credential Society," *Trans-action,* 5,2:2.

Miller, Herman P., 1971, "Population, Pollution and Affluence," *Population Reference Bureau Selection No. 36,* Washington, D. C.: Population Reference Bureau.

Milton, John P., 1968, "Resources in America—The Coming Crisis," PRB Selection No. 23, May. Washington, D. C.: Population Reference Bureau.

Mishan, E. J., 1970, *Technology and Growth.* New York: Praeger Publishers.

Mishan, E. J., 1967, *The Costs of Economic Growth,* New York: Praeger Publishers.

Moncrief, Lewis W., 1970, "The Cultural Basis for our Environmental Crisis," *Science,* 170:508-512.

Murphy, Earl Finbar, 1967, *Governing Nature.* Chicago: Quadrangle Books.

Murphy, Earl Finbar, 1971, *Man and His Environment.* New York: Harper & Row Publishers.

Nisbet, Robert A., 1968, *Social Change and History.* New York: Oxford University Press.

Odum, Howart T., 1970, *Environment, Power and Society.* New York: Wiley-Interscience.

Ohio v. Wyandotte Chemicals, 401 U.S. 495 (1971).

Ornati, Oscar A., 1966, *Poverty Amid Affluence.* New York: Twentieth Century Fund.

Ornati, Oscar A., 1969, *Transportation Needs of the Poor.* New York: Praeger Publishers.

Pollock, Sir Frederick, 1961, *Jurisprudence and Legal Essays.* Edited by A. L. Goodhart. New York: St. Martin's Press Inc.

Porter, E. F. Jr., 1971, "Built-in Loopholes for Pollution Laws," *St. Louis Post Dispatch,* (March 7, 1971).

Potter, Van Rensselaer, 1971, *Bioethics.* Englewood Cliffs, New Jersey: Prentice-Hall, Inc.

Rainwater, Lee, 1960, *And the Poor Get Children.* Chicago: Quadrangle Books.

Rainwater, Lee, 1965, *Family Design: Marital Sexuality, Family Size and Contraception.* Chicago: Aldine Publishing Company.

Rainwater, Lee, 1970, *Behind Ghetto Walls: Black Families in a Federal Slum.* Chicago: Aldine Publishing Company.

Rainwater, Lee and William Yancy, 1967, *The Moynihan Report and the Politics of Controversy.* Cambridge: MIT Press, 1967.

Ramo, Simon, 1970, "Likely Technological Developments of the Future Which May Significantly Affect our Society." *Harmonizing Technological Developments and Social Policy in America,* December:62.

Rickover, Hyman G., 1965, "A Humanistic Technology," *Nature,* 208:721-726.

Ridgeway, James, 1970, *The Politics of Ecology.* New York: E. P. Dutton & Co., Inc.

Rienow, Robert and Rienow, Leona, 1967, *Moment in the Sun,* New York: Ballantine Books.

Rohlich, Gerard, 1971, "Environmental Problems and Policies," in *Environmental Quality and Social Responsibility,* edited by Ravindra S. Khare, James W. Kolka and Carol A. Pollis, Green Bay, Wisconsin: The University of Wisconsin-Green Bay.

Russell, W. M. S., 1970, *Man, Nature and History: Controlling the Environment.* Garden City, New York: Natural History Press.

Sabine, George H., 1961, *A History of Political Theory,* 3rd ed. New York: Holt, Rinehart & Winston, Inc.

Samuelson, Paul A., 1967, *Economics,* 7th ed. New York: McGraw-Hill.

Shepard, Thomas R. Jr., 1971, "We're Going Too Far on Consumerism," *The Reader's Digest,* 50 (February).147-150.

Slater, Phillip E., 1970, *The Pursuit of Loneliness.* Boston: Beacon Press.

Starr, Roger and James Carlson, 1968, "Pollution and Poverty: The Strategy of Cross-Commitment," *The Public Interest* (Winter, 1968), 104-131.

Sutherland, Edwin Hardin, 1949, *White Collar Crime.* New York: Dryden Press.

Swatek, Paul, 1970, *The User's Guide to the Protection of the Environment.* New York: Ballantine Books.

Thayer, Lee, 1971, "Man's Ecology, Ecology's Man," *Main Currents in Modern Thought,* 27:3.

Thompson, Laura, 1949, "The Relations of Men, Animals, and Plants in an Island Community (Fiji)," *American Anthropologist,* 51:253-267.

Wagar, J. Alan, 1970, "Growth Versus the Quality of Life," *Science,* 168:1179-1184.

Warriner, Charles K., 1970, *The Emergence of Society.* Homewood, Illinois: The Dorsey Press.

Watson, R. R., and P. J. Watson, 1969, *Man and Nature, An Anthropological Essay in Human Ecology.* New York: Harcourt, Brace & World.

Wheeler, Reuben, 1968, *Man, Nature and Art.* London: Pergamon Press.

Wissler, Clark, 1926, *The Relation of Nature to Man in Aboriginal America*. New York: Oxford University Press.

Wood, Donald F., 1970, "Wisconsin's Requirements for Shoreland and Flood Plain Protection," *Natural Resources Journal,* 10:327.

Yanggen, Douglas A. and Kusler, Jon A., 1968, "Natural Resource Protection through Shoreland Regulation: Wisconsin," *Land Economics,* 44,1:73.

1969 Wisconsin Statutes

Notes on the Contributors

JAMES D. BARHYDT is assistant for environmental affairs with the Du Pont Company in Wilmington, Delaware.

MICHAEL F. BREWER is vice president of Resources for the Future, Inc., in Washington, D.C.

LOUIS CARMOUCHE is manager of Functional Products and Systems Department with Dow Chemical Company in Midland, Michigan.

RICHARD M. FONTERA was associate professor of Community Sciences at
the University of Wisconsin—Green Bay. He is currently Dean of the
Faculty and professor of political science at Southeastern Massachusetts
University.

BERTRAM M. GROSS is distinguished professor of urban affairs and planning at
Hunter College, City University of New York.

IRVING LOUIS HOROWITZ is chairman and professor of sociology and
director of Studies in Comparative International Development at Rutgers
University.

R. S. KHARE was associate professor and chairman of modernization processes
at The University of Wisconsin—Green Bay. He is now professor of
anthropology at The University of Virginia.

HALVOR J. KOLSHUS is instructor in modernization processes at The
University of Wisconsin—Green Bay.

JAMES W. KOLKA is assistant professor of modernization processes at The
University of Wisconsin—Green Bay.

JAMES M. MURRAY is associate professor of regional analysis at The University
of Wisconsin—Green Bay.

CAROL A. POLLIS is assistant professor of modernization processes at The
University of Wisconsin—Green Bay.

LEE RAINWATER is professor of sociology in the Department of Social
Relations and the John F. Kennedy School of Government at Harvard
University.

GERARD A. ROHLICH is professor of civil engineering and vice chairman of
the Natural Resources Board at the University of Wisconsin—Madison.

JAMES SHIPMAN is vice president and member of the board of directors at
Kimberly—Clark Corporation in Neenah—Menasha, Wisconsin.

LARRY J. SMITH is instructor in modernization processes at The University of
Wisconsin—Green Bay.

N. B. G. TAYLOR is chairman of population dynamics at The University of
Wisconsin—Green Bay.

THOMAS W. THOMPSON is assistant professor of ecosystems analysis at The
University of Wisconsin—Green Bay.